My Oxford Reading Tree Dictionary

Series created by **Roderick Hunt & Alex Brychta**

OXFORD
UNIVERSITY PRESS

OXFORD
UNIVERSITY PRESS

Great Clarendon Street, Oxford, OX2 6DP, United Kingdom

Oxford University Press is a department of the University
of Oxford. It furthers the University's objective of excellence
in research, scholarship, and education by publishing
worldwide. Oxford is a registered trade mark of Oxford
University Press in the UK and in certain other countries

Illustrations © Alex Brychta 2019

Dictionary text copyright Oxford University Press 2019

Headwords chosen from *Oxford Reading Tree* stories. The
characters in this work are the original creation of Roderick
Hunt and Alex Brychta who retain copyright in the characters.

Lexicographer Jenny Watson

British Library Cataloguing in Publication Data
Data available

ISBN: 978-0-19-276964-0

10 9 8 7 6 5 4 3 2 1

Paper used in the production of this book is a natural,
recyclable product made from wood grown in sustainable forests.
The manufacturing process conforms to the environmental
regulations of the country of origin.

Printed in China

You can trust this dictionary
to be up to date, relevant
and engaging because
it is powered by the
Oxford Corpus, a unique
living database of children's
and adults' language.

contents

Meet the family and their friends

Biff and Chip are twins. Kipper is their little brother. Floppy is their dog. Gran is Mum's mother.

Biff

Chip

Floppy

Kipper

Dad

Mum

Gran

Introduction

This dictionary helps children to understand the meanings of words and phrases in the **Oxford Reading Tree** stories. It is perfect for using alongside the stories from Level 1 to 9. It helps children to learn how to use a dictionary using alphabetical order and to discover the meanings of unfamiliar words.

The pictures of Biff, Chip and Kipper and their family and friends help children to remember the meanings, and the example sentences show how the words are used.

The words in this dictionary have been carefully chosen to support and develop children's reading, writing and speaking ability. At the back of the book you can find phrases, people, places and funny vocabulary from the stories.

Wilma and Wilf

Anneena

Nadim

Lin and Lee

Mrs May

Mrs May is a teacher at the children's school.

Button

How to use this dictionary

The words in this dictionary are in alphabetical order. This makes it easy to find the words you are looking for.

- When you want to look up a word, you look at the letter the word begins with.

- Then you use the alphabet on the side of every page to find that letter.

- Now look at the second letter in your word and match it to the catch words at the top of the page. These will guide you to the page where your word will be.

- When you find your word, you will discover lots of information about it. On this page you can see the types of information that you can find.

If a word has more than one meaning, each one is numbered.

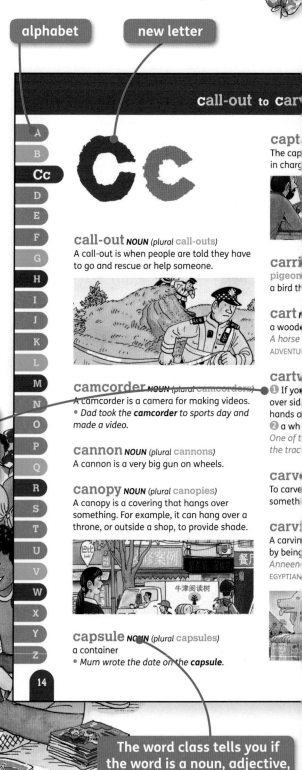

alphabet

new letter

call-out to car

Cc

call-out NOUN (plural call-outs)
A call-out is when people are told they have to go and rescue or help someone.

camcorder NOUN (plural camcorders)
A camcorder is a camera for making videos.
• Dad took the **camcorder** to sports day and made a video.

cannon NOUN (plural cannons)
A cannon is a very big gun on wheels.

canopy NOUN (plural canopies)
A canopy is a covering that hangs over something. For example, it can hang over a throne, or outside a shop, to provide shade.

capsule NOUN (plural capsules)
a container
• Mum wrote the date on the **capsule**.

capt
The cap in charg

carri
pigeon
a bird th

cart
a wood
A horse
ADVENTU

cartw
❶ If yo
over sid
hands o
❷ a wh
One of t
the trac

carve
To carve
someth

carvi
A carvin
by being
Anneen
EGYPTIAN

14

The word class tells you if the word is a noun, adjective, verb, adverb or exclamation.

Catch words tell you the first and last word on the page.

word

plurals

verb forms

meaning or definition

(plural **captains**)

ip or aircraft is the person

cascade *NOUN (plural* **cascades**)
A cascade of something is a large amount that suddenly drops down.
Suddenly a cascade of snow fell on Chip's head.—LEVEL 7, SURVIVAL IN THE ARCTIC

cascade *VERB* cascades, cascading, cascaded
If something cascades down, a large amount suddenly drops down.
A gush of water cascaded down.—LEVEL 9, SCULPTURES FOR THE EMPEROR

cellar *NOUN (plural* **cellars**)
A cellar is a room under a house.

charger *NOUN (plural* **chargers**)
A charger for a phone, console or computer is the thing you plug into it to put power into the battery.
• *Chip wanted to borrow Biff's* **charger** *for his game.*

chariot *NOUN (plural* **chariots**)
A chariot was a cart with two wheels that was pulled by horses.
• *Biff pretended to be a* **chariot** *driver in a race.*

cheese *NOUN (plural* **cheeses**)
a whole round piece of cheese, in its rind
Dad bought four cheeses.—LEVEL 9, DUTCH ADVENTURE

➤ **Say cheese!**
Smile for the photograph!

cheesed off *ADJECTIVE*
If someone is cheesed off, they are upset about something.

chest *NOUN (plural* **chests**)
a big strong box
It was a treasure chest and it was full of gold.—LEVEL 6, THE TREASURE CHEST

chewing gum *NOUN*
Chewing gum is a sticky substance that people chew.

chopsticks *NOUN*
A pair of chopsticks is a pair of small thin sticks that you use for eating.

chrysalis *(say kriss-a-liss) NOUN (plural* **chrysalises**)
A chrysalis is a caterpillar that will soon turn into a butterfly or moth. The hard cover around it is also called a *chrysalis*.
• *Soon, Kipper's caterpillar was a* **chrysalis**, *then it was a butterfly.*

on *NOUN (plural* **carrier**

note or letter to someone

carts)

me along.—LEVEL 9, DUTCH

OUN *(plural* **cartwheels**)
wheel, you flip yourself
ting your
nd.
t
els got stuck in
, THE STEAM TRAIN

ves, carving, carved
one is to make
by cutting it.

(plural **carvings**)
ect that has been made

the carving.—LEVEL 8,

a
b
Cc
d
e
f
g
h
i
j
k
l
m
n
o
p
q
r
s
t
u
v
w
x
y
z

15

Examples in blue are from the *Oxford Reading Tree* stories.

example sentence

This will help you to say the word.

page number

Aa

adviser *NOUN (plural* advisers*)*
An adviser has the job of telling someone what to do.
• *The Queen's **adviser** told the Queen to read the letter.*

afar *ADVERB*
far away
I come from lands afar.—LEVEL 9, THE TRAVELLING PLAYERS

aisle *(rhymes with* **mile***) NOUN (plural* aisles*)*
The aisle is the passage between rows of seats.
• *Mum sat with the children. Dad sat on the other side of the **aisle**.*

alarm clock *NOUN (plural* alarm clocks*)*
An alarm clock is a clock that makes a noise to wake you up.

almond *(say* ah-**mund***) NOUN (plural* almonds*)*
Almonds are a kind of big seed. They are eaten like nuts, and are often called nuts.

ancient *(say* ane-**shunt***) ADJECTIVE*
Ancient places and things belong to a time that was long, long ago.
• *The children found an **ancient** pot with gold coins inside.*

apatosaurus *NOUN (plural* apatosauruses*)*
An apatosaurus was a dinosaur with a long neck and a long tail.
• *The children saw an **apatosaurus** in the museum.*

armour *NOUN*
In the past, armour was metal clothing worn by soldiers.
• *The children heard the clanking of the knight's **armour**.*

arrest *VERB* arrests, arresting, arrested
To arrest someone is to take them prisoner because they have done something wrong.
• *The guards tried to **arrest** Wilma and Biff.*

artefact *NOUN* (plural artefacts)
Artefacts are objects made by humans. Artefacts that are very old can help us to learn about the past.

astound *VERB* astounds, astounding, astounded
If you are astounded, you feel very surprised and impressed.
• *Biff and Chip* **astounded** *the audience with their magic tricks.*

attendant *NOUN* (plural attendants)
Someone's attendant is their assistant.
Then, two of the Emperor's attendants ran up.—LEVEL 9, SCULPTURES FOR THE EMPEROR

auto-pilot *NOUN*
When a plane is on auto-pilot, it flies without the pilot's help.

backflip *NOUN* (plural backflips)
A backflip is a backwards somersault.

bad-tempered *ADJECTIVE*
A bad-tempered person often gets angry or grumpy.

bagpipes *NOUN*
a kind of musical instrument. To play them, you squeeze air from a bag into pipes.

ball *NOUN* (plural balls)
A ball of something is a round object made of it.
The light in the dark sky looked like a ball of fire.—LEVEL 9, FIREBALL IN THE SKY

ball pit *NOUN* (plural ball pits)
A ball pit is a play area with lots of coloured balls in it.
• *Anna lost her glasses in the* **ball pit**.

Aa
Bb
c
d
e
f
g
h
i
j
k
l
m
n
o
p
q
r
s
t
u
v
w
x
y
z

ballroom NOUN *(plural* ballrooms*)*
A ballroom is a large room for dancing.

bamboo NOUN
a tall plant. Its dry stems are used to build things or to support other plants.

barbecue NOUN *(plural* barbecues*)*
❶ a thing with a metal rack over a fire, for cooking food outdoors
Dad set up the barbecue.—LEVEL 5, THE ADVENTURE PARK
❷ a meal with a barbecue

beanbag NOUN *(plural* beanbags*)*
Beanbags are used in games. They are small bags filled with dried beans.
• *The children had a **beanbag**-throwing competition.*

beauty NOUN *(plural* beauties*)*
❶ If there is beauty in a place, it is beautiful.
All the beauty had gone from the land.
—LEVEL 9, THE QUEST
❷ a beautiful or really good person or thing
• *The blue marble was a **beauty**.*

bed NOUN *(plural* beds*)*
❶ a piece of furniture that you sleep on
❷ a piece of ground that you grow plants in
Gran had a bed of strawberries.—LEVEL 6, SEEING IN THE DARK
❸ the bottom of the sea
• *Wilf said the submarine could explore the sea **bed**.*

beehive NOUN *(plural* beehives*)*
A beehive is a special box that bees live in. It is often just called a *hive*.

beekeeper NOUN *(plural* beekeepers*)*
A beekeeper is someone who owns bees and collects their honey.
• *Anneena's dad had a **beekeeper**'s suit.*

bee suit NOUN *(plural* bee suits*)*
This is special clothing that protects a beekeeper from bee stings.
Biff put on her bee suit.—LEVEL 8, THE BEEHIVE FENCE

bellow VERB bellows, bellowing, bellowed
If someone bellows, they shout loudly.
• *A rude man in the audience **bellowed** at the children on the stage.*

bellows NOUN
Bellows are an object that blows air through a fire to help it burn.
• *The children pumped the **bellows** until the fire glowed hot.*

bench NOUN *(plural* benches*)*
❶ a long seat for more than one person
• *Dad and the children had a picnic on a **bench**.*
❷ a long work surface
• *In the workshop, the children saw a **bench** with clay heads on it.*

betray VERB betrays, betraying, betrayed
to harm someone, instead of helping them

billow VERB billows, billowing, billowed
If cloth billows, air fills it or pushes it sideways.
• *Mum's scarf **billowed** in the wind.*

bin man NOUN (plural bin men)
The bin men do the job of emptying dustbins into a big truck.

binoculars NOUN
Binoculars are an object that you look through with both eyes to see something that is far away.

bi-plane NOUN (plural bi-planes)
A bi-plane is an old-fashioned aeroplane with two sets of wings.

blacksmith NOUN (plural blacksmiths)
someone who fits metal shoes on horses

board game NOUN (plural board games)
a game played on a board, with pieces that you move around

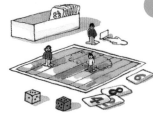

bodyboard NOUN (plural bodyboards)
a kind of board used for bodyboarding in the sea
"Wow!"called Biff as she rode in on her bodyboard. "This is fun!"—LEVEL 5, QUEEN OF THE WAVES

bodyboarding NOUN
playing in the sea by lying face-down on a special board and riding towards the beach on a wave

bongo drums NOUN
Bongo drums are a set of two drums that you play with your hands.

bony ADJECTIVE bonier, boniest
❶ If someone is bony, they are so thin that you can see the shape of their bones.
• *The strange creature had **bony** hands.*
❷ made of bone, or like bone
• *These creatures had **bony** shells.*

a
Bb
c
d
e
f
g
h
i
j
k
l
m
n
o
p
q
r
s
t
u
v
w
x
y
z

11

boom VERB booms, booming, boomed

❶ to say something in a very loud deep voice
• *"I'm going to battle the dragon," boomed Percy.*

❷ to make a very loud deep sound
• *The earthquake made a booming noise.*

boomerang NOUN (plural boomerangs)

A boomerang is a curved stick which comes back to you when you throw it. Boomerangs were first used for hunting.

botanist NOUN (plural botanists)

A botanist is someone who studies plants.
• *The man was not the flower thief — he was a botanist.*

bowling NOUN

Bowling is the game of knocking down bottle-shaped objects called *skittles* with a heavy ball.

breath NOUN (plural breaths)

A breath of air or wind is a small movement of air or wind.
A whisper ran along the crowd like a breath of wind.—LEVEL 9, SCULPTURES FOR THE EMPEROR

➤ **hold your breath**

to try not to breathe in or out
The children held their breath and waited.
—LEVEL 9, TURTLE BEACH

➤ **out of breath**

gasping for air
Teddy was still out of breath from running.
—LEVEL 8, THE SECRET POP STAR

➤ **under your breath**

speaking very quietly, in a way that is hard to hear
• *The prince muttered under his breath.*

brightly ADVERB

cheerfully
"Good morning," Chip said brightly.
—LEVEL 9, WAKE UP!

broadly ADVERB

If someone smiles broadly, their smile is wide.
Mendax smiled broadly, showing his sharp little teeth.—LEVEL 9, FIREBALL IN THE SKY

budge VERB budges, budging, budged

If something does not budge, it does not move at all.
• *Chip tried to lift the rock, but it didn't budge.*

buggy NOUN (plural buggies)

❶ a pushchair
• *Jo needed a buggy for the baby.*

❷ a small car with an open top or sides

bulldozer *NOUN* (plural **bulldozers**)
A bulldozer is a big machine with a scoop for moving soil, and metal tracks over its wheels.
The bulldozers began to dig.—LEVEL 7, THE MOTORWAY

bull's-eye *NOUN* (plural **bull's-eyes**)
the centre of a target

burglar *NOUN* (plural **burglars**)
someone who goes into buildings and steals things

burglary *NOUN* (plural **burglaries**)
A burglary is what happens when a burglar steals things from a building.
• *There had been a lot of **burglaries**.*

burial ground *NOUN* (plural **burial grounds**)
a place where the bodies of dead people are put in the ground

burp *VERB* burps, burping, burped
To burp is to make a noise by letting air from your tummy out of your mouth.

bush *NOUN* (plural **bushes**)
❶ a bush is like a small tree, with lots of branches
❷ The bush is wild land in Africa or Australia.

bush fire *NOUN* (plural **bush fires**)
A bush fire is a big fire in wild land called the **bush**.
• *The children were watching a film about **bush fires** in Australia.*

bush tucker *NOUN*
Bush tucker is food that you can find in the **bush** in Australia. It includes some kinds of insects and plants.
Insects are good bush tucker.—LEVEL 6, GRUB UP!

butler *NOUN* (plural **butlers**)
In a big house with servants, the butler is the man in charge of other servants.

a
Bb
c
d
e
f
g
h
i
j
k
l
m
n
o
p
q
r
s
t
u
v
w
x
y
z

13

Cc

call-out NOUN (plural call-outs)
A call-out is when people are told they have to go and rescue or help someone.

camcorder NOUN (plural camcorders)
A camcorder is a camera for making videos.
• Dad took the **camcorder** to sports day and made a video.

cannon NOUN (plural cannons)
A cannon is a very big gun on wheels.

canopy NOUN (plural canopies)
A canopy is a covering that hangs over something. For example, it can hang over a throne, or outside a shop, to provide shade.

capsule NOUN (plural capsules)
a container
• Mum wrote the date on the **capsule**.

captain NOUN (plural captains)
The captain of a ship or aircraft is the person in charge.

carrier pigeon NOUN (plural carrier pigeons)
a bird that takes a note or letter to someone

cart NOUN (plural carts)
a wooden vehicle
A horse and cart came along.—LEVEL 9, DUTCH ADVENTURE

cartwheel NOUN (plural cartwheels)
❶ If you do a cartwheel, you flip yourself over sideways, putting your hands on the ground.
❷ a wheel on a cart
One of the cartwheels got stuck in the tracks.—LEVEL 6, THE STEAM TRAIN

carve VERB carves, carving, carved
To carve wood or stone is to make something out of it by cutting it.

carving NOUN (plural carvings)
A carving is an object that has been made by being carved.
Anneena looked at the carving.—LEVEL 8, EGYPTIAN ADVENTURE

cascade *NOUN (plural* cascades)

A cascade of something is a large amount that suddenly drops down.

Suddenly a cascade of snow fell on Chip's head.—LEVEL 7, SURVIVAL IN THE ARCTIC

cascade *VERB* cascades, cascading, cascaded

If something cascades down, a large amount suddenly drops down.

A gush of water cascaded down.—LEVEL 9, SCULPTURES FOR THE EMPEROR

cellar *NOUN (plural* cellars)

A cellar is a room under a house.

charger *NOUN (plural* chargers)

A charger for a phone, console or computer is the thing you plug into it to put power into the battery.

• *Chip wanted to borrow Biff's* **charger** *for his game.*

chariot *NOUN (plural* chariots)

A chariot was a cart with two wheels that was pulled by horses.

• *Biff pretended to be a* **chariot** *driver in a race.*

cheese *NOUN (plural* cheeses)

a whole round piece of cheese, in its rind

Dad bought four cheeses.—LEVEL 9, DUTCH ADVENTURE

➤ **Say cheese!**
Smile for the photograph!

cheesed off *ADJECTIVE*

If someone is cheesed off, they are upset about something.

chest *NOUN (plural* chests)

a big strong box

It was a treasure chest and it was full of gold.—LEVEL 6, THE TREASURE CHEST

chewing gum *NOUN*

Chewing gum is a sticky substance that people chew.

chopsticks *NOUN*

A pair of chopsticks is a pair of small thin sticks that you use for eating.

chrysalis *(say* kriss-**a**-liss*) NOUN (plural* chrysalises)

A chrysalis is a caterpillar that will soon turn into a butterfly or moth. The hard cover around it is also called a *chrysalis*.

• *Soon, Kipper's caterpillar was a* **chrysalis**, *then it was a butterfly.*

clasp VERB clasps, clasping, clasped
If you clasp someone or something,
you hold them tightly.
If you clasp your hands
together, you join
your hands and hold
them together.
• *Biff clasped the jar
in her hands.*

clay NOUN
Clay is sticky mud that gets very hard
when it dries. Clay is used for making
pots and pottery.
• *The models were made of **clay**.*

clippers NOUN
a tool like scissors for cutting plants
• *Wilma cut the stems with **clippers**.*

clock tower NOUN (plural clock
towers)
a tall building, or part of a building, with a
large clock at the top
• *There was a **clock tower** in the market
square.*

cluster VERB clusters, clustering,
clustered
To cluster together is to form a group close
beside each other.
• *All the bees **cluster** together.*

cob NOUN (plural cobs)
A corn cob is the part of a maize plant that
corn grows on.

cockpit NOUN (plural cockpits)
The cockpit in an aircraft is the part where
the pilot sits.
• *The children looked in the helicopter
cockpit.*

collapse VERB collapses, collapsing,
collapsed
If something collapses, it falls down or
breaks into pieces.
• *Part of the cliff had **collapsed** because of
being hit by the waves.*

combat NOUN
Combat is a battle.

communicate VERB communicates,
communicating, communicated
When people communicate, they talk or
write to each other.
• *Queen Hilda and her brother
communicated by sending letters to each
other.*

communication NOUN
When people talk or write to each other, this
is communication.

companion NOUN (plural
companions)
Your companion is the person with you.
• *He turned to his **companion** and spoke.*

compete VERB competes,
competing, competed
To compete is to take part in a game or
competition.
• *It was Biff's turn to **compete**.*

countryside NOUN
The countryside is land that is not in a town.
- *The children were in the **countryside**.*

cove NOUN (plural coves)
A cove is a small area at the edge of the sea where the land curves inwards.
The tide was coming in again and the cove was filling with water.—LEVEL 8, POCKET MONEY

crackle VERB crackles, crackling, crackled
to make lots of short sharp sounds
There was a crackling sound and a terrible smell of old burnt socks.—LEVEL 8, SAVE FLOPPY!

crackle NOUN (plural crackles)
lots of short sharp sounds

creepy-crawly
NOUN (plural creepy-crawlies)
an insect, worm or other small creature

croak VERB croaks, croaking, croaked
In stories, frogs croak when they say something.
"I prefer bugs," croaked the frog.—LEVEL 5, THE FROG'S TALE

crossly ADVERB
in an angry or bad-tempered way
She stamped her foot crossly.—LEVEL 9, THE LITTER QUEEN

crowning NOUN
This is when a king or queen is crowned. The usual word is *coronation*.

cub NOUN (plural cubs)
A cub is a young lion, tiger, fox or bear.
- *Chip saw a lion **cub**.*

Cub Scout NOUN (also Cubs)
(plural Cub Scouts, Cubs)
a young member of the **Scout** organisation. Cub scouts do outdoor activities, learn skills and help people.

cyclist NOUN (plural cyclists)
A cyclist is a person who rides a bicycle.

Dd

dangle VERB dangles, dangling, dangled

To dangle is to swing or hang down loosely.
• *The rope was **dangling** from the helicopter.*

dearest ADJECTIVE

You use *dearest* to show that you are fond of someone.
• *The Queen started her letter with "My **dearest** brother".*

deed NOUN (plural deeds)

If you do a good deed, you do something good.
• *Kipper and Lee wanted to do a good **deed**, so they took the dogs for a walk.*

delightful ADJECTIVE

lovely; very, very nice
• *Her brother had sent her a **delightful** letter.*

demand VERB demands, demanding, demanded

to ask something sternly or rudely
"Who are you?" the man demanded.—LEVEL 7, DETECTIVE ADVENTURE

den NOUN (plural dens)

❶ a place for hiding or being alone
• *The children made a **den** with sticks and branches.*
❷ a wild animal's home

detail NOUN (plural details)

The details of something are the little things that are part of it.
The teacher helped Anneena with the details.—LEVEL 9, SCULPTURES FOR THE EMPEROR

detector NOUN (plural detectors)

A detector is a device that finds something.
• *The men had metal **detectors**.*

determined ADJECTIVE

If you are determined to do something, you have made up your mind to do it.
• *Dad was **determined** to have a go.*

digger NOUN (plural diggers)

A digger is a machine for digging.
• *The men dug a trench with the **digger**.*

din NOUN

A din is a loud noise.

BANG
BANG
CRASH
BANG
CRASH

dinghy *NOUN (say ding-ee)*
(plural dinghies*)*
A dinghy is a small boat.
Dad pulled the dinghy onto the beach.
—LEVEL 5, CRAB ISLAND

dingo *NOUN (plural* dingoes*)*
A dingo is a kind of wild dog in Australia.

disc *NOUN (also* disk*) (plural* discs, disks*)*
❶ a flat round object
A huge, disc-shaped object hovered in the sky.—LEVEL 9, FIREBALL IN THE SKY
❷ a flat round piece of plastic for storing information
• *Chip's film was on the **disc**.*

disposal *NOUN*
getting rid of something
• *The men from the **disposal** unit came.*

dock *NOUN (plural* docks*)*
A dock is a place where ships stop to be loaded or unloaded, or repaired.
• *The ship was in the **dock**.*

doggy *NOUN (plural* doggies*)*
Doggy is a child's word for a dog.
• *Floppy was a soggy **doggy**.*

doorbell *NOUN (plural* doorbells*)*
a bell outside a house, for visitors to ring
Just then the doorbell rang.—LEVEL 8, THE SECRET POP STAR

dragonfly *NOUN*
(plural dragonflies*)*
an insect with a long brightly coloured body

duchess *NOUN (plural* duchesses*)*
a woman with a title (like *duke* for a man), from a family with a lot of money and power
The maid was standing next to the Duchess.—LEVEL 7, DETECTIVE ADVENTURE

duck *VERB* ducks, ducking, ducked
❶ to bend down quickly so that something will not hit you
The plane took off. The men ducked as it flew over them.—LEVEL 9, THE BLUE EYE
❷ to bend or crouch down so that you will not be seen
The children ducked down as these ogres stomped past.—LEVEL 8, THE OGRE'S DINNER

duck *NOUN (plural* ducks*)*
A duck is a bird that lives near water and swims on the water.

duckling *NOUN*
(plural ducklings*)*
A duckling is a young duck.

dumpling *NOUN (plural* dumplings*)*
a kind of food, made with a kind of pastry. Some dumplings have a filling, and some are cooked in liquid.
• *Lin said they have **dumplings** at Chinese New Year.*

dyke *NOUN (plural* dykes*)*
A dyke is a long wall or bank of earth to hold back water and prevent flooding.

a
b
c
Dd
e
f
g
h
i
j
k
l
m
n
o
p
q
r
s
t
u
v
w
x
y
z

Ee

eager ADJECTIVE

very keen or interested, or really wanting something

eagerly ADVERB

in a way that shows you are very keen or interested, or really want something
• *Everyone looked **eagerly** at Biff, because they thought she was someone else.*

ease VERB eases, easing, eased

If you ease something somewhere, you move it there gently.
• *Anneena's dad put on his bee suit and **eased** the bees into the box.*

elderly ADJECTIVE

An elderly person is old, or is getting old.

embankment NOUN (plural embankments)

a long bank of earth beside or under a road or railway

emerge VERB emerges, emerging, emerged

to come out of a place
• *The hedgehog **emerged** from the bush.*

emperor NOUN (plural emperors)

An emperor is the ruler of a country or of an *empire* (more than one country).
• *The children met the Roman **Emperor**.*

entertainer NOUN (plural entertainers)

Entertainers have the job of entertaining people.

excavate VERB excavates, excavating, excavated

to dig, or to uncover something by digging
• *The mammoth's bones were **excavated**.*

excavation NOUN (plural excavations)

the work of digging things out, or the place where this work happens

exhausted ADJECTIVE
very, very tired
- Dad was **exhausted** after using his exercise bike.

experiment NOUN (plural experiments)
If you do an experiment, you do something in order to see what happens.
- His father needed the string for an **experiment**.

expert NOUN (plural experts)
Experts are people who know a lot about something, or who can do something very well.
- A team of **experts** looked at the bone.

explorer NOUN (plural explorers)
An explorer is someone who goes to a place far away to find out more about it.

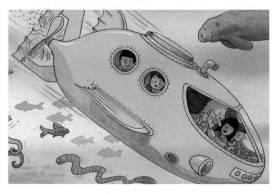

face NOUN (plural faces)
1. the front part of your head
2. a steep side of a cliff or mountain
- The children came to a steep rock **face**.

➤ **pull** or **make a face**
If you pull or make a face, you change the expression on your face. This can be to make others laugh, or to show how you are feeling.

face VERB faces, facing, faced
When you face someone or something, you look towards them.
- The man turned to **face** the crowd.

faint ADJECTIVE fainter, faintest
1. A faint sound is not very loud.
Biff heard a faint noise.—LEVEL 9, WAKE UP!
2. A faint colour, mark or light is not very bright or clear.
- Lee saw a **faint** glow.

faintly ADVERB
not very brightly or clearly
- The magic key began to glow **faintly**.

a
b
c
d
Ee
Ff
g
h
i
j
k
l
m
n
o
p
q
r
s
t
u
v
w
x
y
z

falcon NOUN (plural falcons)

A falcon is a kind of bird. Falcons are *birds of prey*. They have hooked beaks and sharp claws.
- *The **falcon** landed on the shed roof.*

fan NOUN (plural fans)

❶ a machine that moves air about
- *The **fan** made the cloth move.*

❷ something that you hold in your hand and wave in front of you to cool your face

❸ someone who likes a famous person or a sports team

fearless ADJECTIVE

A fearless person is not afraid.
- *The guards were strong and **fearless**.*

figure NOUN (plural figures)

A figure is a person, or a model of a person.
- *Anneena's clay **figure** looked like Biff.*

finger snapper

NOUN (plural finger snappers)
a piece of paper folded into four parts, used in games. You put a finger or thumb into each part and move the parts around. It is often called a *fortune teller*.

fireball NOUN (plural fireballs)

a ball of flames or fire
- *The **fireball** landed on the farm.*

first-aid kit NOUN (plural first-aid kits)

a box or bag with things like bandages and plasters in it, so you can help if someone is hurt

fir tree NOUN (plural fir trees)

Fir trees are a kind of evergreen tree.

flea NOUN (plural fleas)

A flea is a small jumping insect that sucks blood.
- *Mum didn't know how Floppy got **fleas**.*

flier NOUN (plural fliers)

A kite flier is a person flying a kite.

flop VERB flops, flopping, flopped

To flop is to fall or move in a way that looks out of control.
A strange little creature flopped out on to the ground.—LEVEL 9, FIREBALL IN THE SKY

foggy ADJECTIVE foggier, foggiest

If it is foggy, low cloud makes it hard to see.

fragile (say fraj-ile) ADJECTIVE

Something that is fragile will break easily if you drop it.

frisbee NOUN *(plural frisbees) (trademark)*
a plastic disc which you skim through the air as an outdoor game
They all went outside and played with the frisbee.—LEVEL 7, THE JIGSAW PUZZLE

frogman NOUN *(plural frogmen)*
A frogman is an underwater swimmer with a special suit, a mask, flippers and a tank of air.

front desk NOUN *(plural front desks)*
In a hotel, this is the reception, where you go when you arrive or if you need help.

frying pan
NOUN *(plural frying pans)*
a shallow pan for frying things

funny bone NOUN *(plural funny bones)*
a bone in your elbow

fun run NOUN *(plural fun runs)*
a race that you do for fun. Often, people do fun runs to raise money to help other people.

furious ADJECTIVE
very angry
The King was furious.—LEVEL 5, THE FROG'S TALE

furiously ADVERB
very angrily
"How dare he call me silly!" the Queen shouted furiously.—LEVEL 8, THE URGENT MESSAGE

fuse NOUN *(plural fuses)*
a safety device that stops electricity flowing

game pad NOUN *(plural game pads)*
a device for controlling a video game
• *Biff's **game pad** needed to be charged.*

gasp VERB gasps, gasping, gasped
❶ to breathe in suddenly when you are shocked or out of breath
Everyone gasped. The classroom was upside down.—LEVEL 5, A NEW CLASSROOM
❷ to say something while gasping
At that moment, the photographer ran up. "Have you seen a camera?" she gasped.

gasp NOUN *(plural gasps)*
A gasp is a sudden intake of breath.
• *There was a loud **gasp** from everyone as the donkeys pushed past.*

gatekeeper NOUN *(plural gatekeepers)*
the person who lets people into a place if they are allowed in

genius NOUN *(plural geniuses)*
A genius is a very, very clever person.
• *The boys liked Nadim's idea — they told him he was a **genius**.*

a
b
c
d
e
Ff
Gg
h
i
j
k
l
m
n
o
p
q
r
s
t
u
v
w
x
y
z

gesture (say jess-cher) VERB gestures, gesturing, gestured

To gesture is to make a movement which shows what you are thinking or feeling.
• *Biff asked how things had changed. The other girl **gestured** to the new hotel.*

get VERB gets, getting, got

❶ to become
• *"Don't **get** wet," said Mrs May.*
❷ To get someone angry is to make them angry.
❸ to arrive or go somewhere
"We must get home," said Mum.—LEVEL 2, A DEN IN THE WOOD
❹ to catch someone
• *The dinosaur didn't **get** Biff.*
❺ to understand something
"I don't get it," said Biff.—LEVEL 5, A MONSTER MISTAKE
❻ If you get someone to do something, you ask them or tell them to do it.
Chip got Dad to put his feet up.—LEVEL 2, GOT A JOB?

giant ADJECTIVE

huge
The children made a giant snowman.
—LEVEL 3, THE SNOWMAN

gingerbread man NOUN (plural gingerbread men)

A gingerbread man is a ginger biscuit in the shape of a person.

girder NOUN (plural girders)

A girder is a metal beam supporting part of a building or a bridge.

glow VERB glows, glowing, glowed

If something glows, it shines with a soft light.
• *The children went on an adventure each time the magic key **glowed**.*

glumly ADVERB

sadly or miserably
Alf looked glumly at the children. "What now?" he said.—LEVEL 9, WAKE UP!

gnome (say nohm) NOUN (plural gnomes)

In stories, gnomes are small creatures like fairies. They often live underground.

The gnome knew a secret way to get into the castle.—LEVEL 9, THE QUEST

goblet NOUN (plural goblets)

A goblet is a drinking glass with a long stem and a base.

● *Mum and Dad won a prize. It was a **goblet** made out of glass.*

go-kart NOUN (plural go-karts)

A go-kart is a kind of small car that people use for racing.

Gran took the children to a go-kart track.
—LEVEL 3, GRAN AND THE GO-KARTS

gong NOUN (plural gongs)

a flat round metal thing that makes a sound if you hit it. Gongs are used in music, and to show that something will happen.

goodness EXCLAMATION

This word is used showing surprise or another strong feeling.

"My goodness!" she said. "I don't believe it! Biff is wearing a dress!"—LEVEL 8, WHAT WAS IT LIKE?

"Goodness!" said the man. "Thank you so much."—LEVEL 9, WHAT A JOURNEY!

gorge NOUN (plural gorges)

A gorge is a narrow valley with steep sides.

● *The **gorge** was narrower now and the river was flowing faster.*

gotcha EXCLAMATION

I have got you; used when you have tricked or caught someone

● *Kevin said, **"Gotcha!"** when the trick sweets made Chip's and Biff's mouths go blue.*

greenhouse NOUN (plural greenhouses)

a glass building used for growing plants

grub NOUN (plural grubs)

Grubs are larvae, which are very small creatures that will become insects.

● *The badger was digging for worms and **grubs**.*

gruff ADJECTIVE gruffer, gruffest

A gruff voice does not sound soft or friendly.

● *The children could hear **gruff** voices.*

a
b
c
d
e
f
Gg
h
i
j
k
l
m
n
o
p
q
r
s
t
u
v
w
x
y
z

A B C D E F **Gg** **Hh** I J K L M N O P Q R S T U V W X Y Z

grunt VERB grunts, grunting, grunted
❶ to make a snorting sound like a pig
The crowd of monsters began to growl and grunt crossly.—LEVEL 8, AT THE MONSTER GAMES
❷ to say something in a low voice that is not soft or clear. Sometimes people grunt when they are putting a lot of effort into moving something.

guard NOUN (plural guards)
someone who protects a place or person, or stops a person from escaping
• *When the children reached the castle, they spoke to the **guard**.*

gull NOUN (plural gulls)
a **seagull** (a kind of sea bird)
• *The **gulls** took all the picnic food.*

gully NOUN (plural gullies)
A gully is a narrow channel that carries water.
• *Water gushed down the **gully**.*

gum NOUN (plural gums)
Gum is a sticky substance that people chew.
• *Wilf gave some **gum** to Chip.*

gurgling NOUN
Gurgling is a bubbling sound.
The only noise was the gurgling of the whale's tummy.—LEVEL 7, A TALL TALE

gutter NOUN (plural gutters)
In a bowling alley, the gutters are the grooves on either side of a lane. If a ball is not thrown straight, it will go into the gutter.

haggis NOUN (plural haggises)
Haggis is a kind of food from Scotland. It is made from inner parts of sheep, oats and spices.

hail NOUN
Hail is frozen drops of rain.

hammer NOUN (plural hammers)
a heavy metal ball with a handle, used in a sports event. The winner is the person who throws it furthest.

hand NOUN (plural hands)
➤ **put your hands together**
a way of asking the audience to clap
➤ **to hand**
near you, so you can use it easily
• *The frying pan was the first thing **to hand**.*

hand VERB hand, handing, handed
❶ to give someone something that you are holding
The gnome handed Wilma a mirror.—LEVEL 9, THE QUEST
❷ to deliver a person to someone who will look after them
• *The driver wanted to **hand** the children to the sheriff.*

handstand

NOUN (plural handstands)
If you do a handstand,
you balance on your
hands with your
feet in the air.
• *Chip did a cartwheel
and a handstand.*

hang **VERB** hangs, hanging, hung

❶ to be fixed or supported at the top, but
not at the bottom
• *The pole had ribbons hanging down from
the top.*
❷ to float in the air
• *Streaks of green light hung in the sky.*

➤ **hang on**
❶ to hold on to something tightly
• *Chip told Biff to hang on to the rock.*
❷ Wait; this can show that you have just
realised something or that you do not like
something.
*"Hang on," Biff gasped. "It's only six
o'clock."*—LEVEL 9, WAKE UP!

harpsichord (say harp-**sik-ord**) **NOUN**
(plural harpsichords)
an old-fashioned musical instrument like
a piano

hatch **NOUN** (plural hatches)
an opening in a wall, floor or ceiling

head **NOUN** (plural heads)

➤ **scratch your head**
to think hard about something that is
surprising or difficult to understand
• *The goblins scratched their heads. They
didn't know what to do.*

➤ **shake your head**
People shake their heads meaning "no". It
can be because they do not like something,
or it can be because they do not believe
something or do not agree with something.
*The girl shook her head. "No chance," she
said.*—LEVEL 9, TURTLE BEACH

➤ **with your head in your hands**
looking tired or upset, with your arms bent
and your hands holding your head
Percy sat with his head in his hands.—LEVEL 9,
A KNIGHT IN TOWN

head **VERB** heads, heading, headed
to go towards a person or place
• *The children headed to the train station.*

helplessly **ADVERB**
without being able to do anything
• *Everybody looked helplessly at the animal.
Nobody knew what to do.*

herb **NOUN** (plural herbs)
Herbs are plants used in foods, perfumes
and medicines. Most herbs have a strong
taste or smell.
• *The boys brought herbs to make the room
smell sweet.*

herd **NOUN** (plural herds)
A herd of animals is a group of them.

hey presto EXCLAMATION
You can say "Hey presto!" when you have just done a magic trick.

hiccup NOUN (plural hiccups)
If you have hiccups, you make short gulping sounds that you cannot control.
- *Kipper got rid of his hiccups.*

hide and seek NOUN
a game in which one person looks for the others, who are hiding

Highland Games NOUN
an outdoor event where you can see traditional Scottish activities including playing the **bagpipes**

highway NOUN (plural highways)
A highway is a main road.

holly blue NOUN
(plural holly blues)
A holly blue is a kind of butterfly with blue wings.

honey ant NOUN (plural honey ants)
Honey ants are ants whose bodies swell up with *honeydew*, a sweet food for other ants.

hoover VERB hoovers, hoovering, hoovered
To hoover a carpet is to clean it with a vacuum cleaner.

hop VERB hops, hopped, hopping
When an animal hops somewhere, it jumps there. If you hop, you jump on one leg.
- *The frog hopped off the ledge.*
➤ **hop in**
to quickly get into a car
➤ **hop on**
to quickly get on to a bus or bike

hopper NOUN (plural hoppers)
a big round ball with handles. You sit on it and bounce around.

hopscotch NOUN
a game in which you hop into squares drawn on the ground

horseshoe NOUN (plural horseshoes)
a curved metal shape that is nailed to a horse's hoof

hose NOUN (also hose-pipe) (plural hoses, hose-pipes)
a long tube of rubber or plastic that carries water from a tap
- *Mum sprayed Floppy with the hose.*

hot chocolate *NOUN (plural* hot chocolates*)*
a hot drink made with cocoa and sugar, and water or milk

housekeeper *NOUN (plural* housekeepers*)*
a person in charge of running a house. Some housekeepers are in charge of other workers.

howl *VERB* howls, howling, howled
❶ to make a long loud sound, like an animal in pain or a strong wind blowing
• *The wind was* **howling** *through the trees.*
❷ to weep loudly
• *The little boy was* **howling**. *"I'm lost,"*
he said.

huddle *VERB* huddles, huddling, huddled
If people huddle together, they get very close to each other. This can be to keep warm or to keep out of the rain.
• *The children* **huddled** *together to hear Grandpa's story.*

hump *NOUN (plural* humps*)*
A hump is a mound or round bump. Camels have humps on their backs.

ice cream van *NOUN (plural* ice cream vans*)*
A van from which you can buy ice creams.

impatiently *ADVERB*
in a way that shows you do not like waiting for something
• *Chip waited* **impatiently** *to find out what was in the metal box.*

incubator *NOUN (plural* incubators*)*
a device in which eggs are kept before the chicks hatch

inspect *VERB* inspects, inspecting, inspected

to look very carefully at something
• *The children **inspected** the ancient coins.*

inspector *NOUN* (plural **inspectors**)
a police officer who is quite important

internet café *NOUN* (plural **internet cafés**)
a café with computers for people to go online

invade *VERB* invades, invading, invaded
If people or other creatures invade a place, a lot of them enter it at the same time.
• *Kipper liked to play games about aliens **invading** Earth.*

investigate *VERB* investigates, investigating, investigated
to try to find out about something

involve *VERB* involves, involving, involved
To be involved in something is to be part of it.
• *Their next adventure **involved** a jigsaw puzzle and a frisbee.*

it *NOUN*
the person who has to find the others in the game of **hide and seek**

itching powder *NOUN*
a substance that hurts your skin and makes you want to scratch yourself

jeep *NOUN (plural* jeeps) (*trademark*)
a strong car that can go over rough ground
Suddenly a jeep drove up.—LEVEL 5, SAFARI ADVENTURE

jellyfish *NOUN (plural* jellyfish)
A jellyfish is a sea animal with a soft clear body. Some types of jellyfish can sting you.
Biff looked at a jellyfish but she didn't swim too close.—LEVEL 6, TREASURE CHEST

jig *NOUN (plural* jigs)
A jig is a lively jumping dance.

job *NOUN*
➤ **a job**
a lot of work
"What a job!" said Dad.—LEVEL 4, THE NEW HOUSE
➤ **a good job**
a good thing
• *It was **a good job** Nadim knew about computers.*

joey *NOUN (plural* joeys)
A joey is a baby animal that can be carried in its mother's pouch. Kangaroos and koalas have joeys.

judo *NOUN*
Judo is a sport in which two people try to overcome each other by using special ways of holding or throwing each other.
• *Biff and Chip were in a **judo** club.*

juggle *VERB* juggles, juggling, juggled
If you juggle, you keep throwing balls or other objects into the air and catching them again quickly.

juggler *NOUN*
(*plural* jugglers)
an entertainer who juggles
The juggler kept dropping the balls.—LEVEL 9, THE FINEST IN THE LAND

jumpy *ADJECTIVE* jumpier, jumpiest
Someone who is jumpy seems nervous, as if they expect something bad to happen at any moment.

junk *NOUN*
old things that nobody wants

a
b
c
d
e
f
g
h
i
Jj
k
l
m
n
o
p
q
r
s
t
u
v
w
x
y
z

Kk

Ll

keeper NOUN (plural **keepers**)
someone who looks after something. For example, a shop keeper looks after a shop.

kestrel NOUN (plural **kestrels**)
A kestrel is a bird. It is a kind of **falcon**. Kestrels are *birds of prey*. They have hooked beaks and sharp claws.

key NOUN (plural **keys**)
① Usually, a key is just a metal thing that opens or closes a lock. The *magic key* opens and closes adventures instead of locks.
The key took Chip to a wood.—LEVEL 9, THE TRAVELLING PLAYERS
② The keys on a piano or similar musical instrument are the parts that you press to make it work.
• *Mozart told Nadim to hit the **keys** harder than usual.*

kiln NOUN (plural **kilns**)
A kiln is a very, very hot oven for making pots or other clay objects go hard.

kilt NOUN (plural **kilts**)
A kilt is a kind of pleated skirt. It is part of traditional Scottish dress.

laboratory NOUN (plural **laboratories**)
a place where scientific work is done

lash VERB lashes, lashing, lashed
① If the rain is lashing down, it is raining very hard.
• *The rain **lashed** against the windows.*
② If you lash things together with rope, you tie them together very tightly.

leak VERB leaks, leaking, leaked
If something is leaking, it has a hole or crack that it should not have, and liquid can get through.
The water butt was leaking.—LEVEL 4, EVERYONE GOT WET

leak NOUN (plural **leaks**)
A leak is a hole or crack that should not be there, where liquid can get through.
• *Mum found a **leak** in the hosepipe.*

Lego NOUN (trademark)
Lego is a toy. It is little plastic blocks or other shapes that you join together to make models.
Floppy pushed the Lego over.—LEVEL 2, WHAT A BAD DOG!

lifelike ADJECTIVE
If something is lifelike, it looks just like a real person or thing.
• *Biff thought the models were very **lifelike**.*

life-size ADJECTIVE
the same size as a real person or thing
The soldiers were life-size models.—LEVEL 9, SCULPTURES FOR THE EMPEROR

lining NOUN *(plural linings)*
a layer on the inside of something
• *There was a hole in the **lining** of his jacket.*

lodge NOUN *(plural lodges)*
a small house in a holiday park

longship NOUN *(plural longships)*
a long narrow ship, with oars and a sail, used by the Vikings

look-alike NOUN *(plural look-alikes)*
A look-alike is someone who looks very like another person.
• *It was hard to know which was Biff and which was the **look-alike**.*

loot NOUN
Loot is things that have been stolen.
Perhaps robbers hid their loot underground!—LEVEL 7, THE TIME CAPSULE

lurch VERB lurches, lurching, lurched
to lean suddenly to one side
• *The wagon **lurched** sideways, dropping objects all over the road.*

macaroni cheese NOUN
macaroni (a kind of pasta) with cheese sauce

magic NOUN
In stories, magic makes impossible things happen.
• *The **magic** often took the children back in time.*

magic ADJECTIVE
❶ Something that is magic makes impossible things happen.
• *The **magic** key glowed again.*
❷ Magic tricks are clever tricks that seem to be impossible.
• *The lady liked doing **magic** tricks.*

magnifying glass NOUN *(plural magnifying glasses)*
an object that you look through when you want something very small to look bigger
Lee looked at one of the coins through a magnifying glass.—LEVEL 8, A LUCKY FIND

magpie *NOUN (plural* magpies*)*
A magpie is a noisy black and white bird.

maker *NOUN (plural* makers*)*
a person who makes something
The rainbow makers had to work fast.—
LEVEL 8, THE RAINBOW MACHINE

mammoth *NOUN (plural* mammoths*)*
a kind of elephant that lived long, long
ago. Mammoths had hairy skin and
curved tusks.

mammoth *ADJECTIVE*
huge
• *Dad had to make a **mammoth** decision.*

manager *NOUN (plural* managers*)*
A manager is in charge of deciding what
other people should do.
• *The hotel **manager** came to help.*
• *The pop star met his **manager**.*

mangle *NOUN (plural* mangles*)*
a device that gets rid of water from wet
cloth. Rolling parts squeeze the water out
when you turn the handle.

marble *NOUN (plural* marbles*)*
Marbles are small coloured glass balls that
you can play games with.

market square *NOUN (plural* market
squares*)*
A market square is an open space in a town,
where a market is held.

mayor *NOUN (plural* mayors*)*
A town's mayor is the leader of its council.

maypole *NOUN (plural* maypoles*)*
a tall pole with ribbons hanging from the top.
People hold the ribbons and dance round
the pole in May, making patterns with the
ribbons.

medal *NOUN (plural* medals*)*
a thing that you wear on a ribbon round
your neck or pinned to your clothes. It can
be a prize or a reward for doing something
good.
The prince gave the children a medal.
—LEVEL 6, THE SHINY KEY

medieval *ADJECTIVE (say med-ee-**ee**-val)*
to do with the Middle Ages, a time that was long, long ago
• *The children put on a **medieval** play.*

messenger *NOUN (plural messengers)*
someone who brings a message
• *The king sent his **messenger** with a letter.*

microlight *NOUN (plural microlights)*
A microlight is a very small aircraft with room for one or two people inside.
• *The **microlight** was flying lower now.*

mind *NOUN (plural minds)*
Your mind is the part of you that thinks, feels and remembers.

mind *VERB*
used for telling someone to be careful of something
"Mind you don't fall," said Biff.—LEVEL 9, STORM CASTLE
"Mind the thorns," he called.—LEVEL 5, SLEEPING BEAUTY

➤ **never mind**
used for telling someone not to worry
The children were upset. "Never mind," said Mrs May. "It was only made of paper."
—LEVEL 4, THE DRAGON DANCE

minibeast *NOUN (plural minibeasts)*
Minibeasts are very small creatures such as insects or spiders.

misunderstanding *NOUN (plural misunderstandings)*
If there is a misunderstanding, someone gets a wrong idea or impression.

moose *NOUN (plural moose)*
a big animal with antlers that lives in North America

mosaic *NOUN (say mo-**zay**-ik) (plural mosaics)*
A mosaic is a picture or design made from small coloured pieces of stone or glass.

motto *NOUN (plural mottoes)*
a short saying that tells you how to behave
• *Chip's **motto** was "Be prepared … for anything!"*

mower *NOUN (plural mowers)*
A mower is a machine for cutting grass.
A man came to cut the grass. He cut it with a mower.—LEVEL 7, THE LOST KEY

musician *NOUN (plural musicians)*
a person who makes music, by singing, playing or writing it

a
b
c
d
e
f
g
h
i
j
k
l
Mm
n
o
p
q
r
s
t
u
v
w
x
y
z

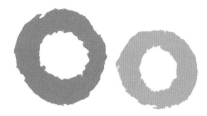

nettle NOUN (plural nettles)
A nettle, or a stinging nettle, is a plant with leaves that can hurt you.

nightmarish ADJECTIVE
very unpleasant, as if you are having a bad dream (a *nightmare*)

nightshirt NOUN (plural nightshirts)
a long shirt for wearing in bed
• *The man was wearing a **nightshirt**.*

night-vision binoculars NOUN
an object that you look through with both eyes, to see things that are far away in the dark

nugget NOUN (plural nuggets)
A nugget of gold is a rough lump of it that is found in the ground or in a river.

old-fashioned ADJECTIVE
Something that is old-fashioned is not modern.

olive NOUN (plural olives)
Olives are small bitter fruits from an *olive tree*.

orchid NOUN (say ork-**id**) (plural orchids)
Orchids are a kind of plant. Many orchids have petals that are not all the same shape.

organ NOUN (plural organs)
a musical instrument like a piano with large air pipes

otter NOUN (plural otters)
an animal with webbed feet and thick fur. Otters are good swimmers.
The otter dived into the sea and swam towards the rocks.—LEVEL 9, GREEN ISLAND

Pp

Pa NOUN
Dad

paraglider NOUN (plural paragliders)
a thing like a parachute used for gliding around in the air, or the person using it

peckish ADJECTIVE
If you are peckish, you are a bit hungry.

pedalo NOUN (plural pedaloes, pedalos)
a small boat with pedals

pharaoh (say fair-roh) NOUN
(plural pharaohs)
A pharaoh was a ruler in ancient Egypt.

photocopier NOUN (plural photocopiers)
A photocopier is a machine that prints copies of documents.

photograph album NOUN
(plural photograph albums)
a book that you put photographs into

pick-your-own NOUN
a place where you pick fruit and then pay for it
Mum took everyone to the pick-your-own.
—LEVEL 3, STRAWBERRY JAM

piper NOUN
(plural pipers)
A piper is a musician who plays a pipe or the bagpipes.

plaster NOUN
a soft mixture that goes hard when it dries, or the powder it is made from

play NOUN (plural plays)
A play is a story which people act so that other people can watch.
• *The children were taking part in a play.*

player NOUN
(plural players)
❶ a person who plays a game or sport
❷ an actor
At the end, the players give a bow.—LEVEL 9, THE TRAVELLING PLAYERS

pocket watch NOUN (plural pocket watches)
an old-fashioned watch on a chain, kept in a person's pocket

pong NOUN (plural pongs)
A pong is an unpleasant smell.

a
b
c
d
e
f
g
h
i
j
k
l
m
n
o
Pp
q
r
s
t
u
v
w
x
y
z

pop-up ADJECTIVE
Pop-up cards or books have pieces of card or paper that stand up when you open the card or book.

posh ADJECTIVE posher, poshest
very smart or elegant
• *Mum was wearing a **posh** dress.*

possibly ADVERB
➤ **cannot possibly**
If you cannot possibly do something, you definitely cannot do it.
I can't possibly send such a rude note!
—LEVEL 8, THE URGENT MESSAGE

postcard NOUN (plural postcards)
a card that you send without an envelope. People send picture postcards home from their holidays.

pottery NOUN
cups, plates and other things made of clay. The activity of making them is also called pottery.
• *Anneena went to a **pottery** class.*

prehistoric ADJECTIVE
from a very, very, very long time ago
• *The family saw a **prehistoric** animal.*

procession NOUN (plural processions)
A procession is a line of people or vehicles all moving along slowly.
• *Biff watched the **procession** as it moved along.*

project NOUN (plural projects)
A project is a piece of work.
Biff and Chip were doing a project on the Romans.—LEVEL 7, ROMAN ADVENTURE

prompt VERB prompts, prompting, prompted
In a show, if you prompt someone, you remind them what to say.
• *Chip's job was to **prompt** the others if they forgot their words.*

prompter NOUN (plural prompters)
In a show, the prompter reminds other people what to say.

propeller NOUN (plural propellers)
A propeller is a set of blades that spin round to make something move.
The propeller began to turn.—LEVEL 9, THE FLYING MACHINE

pulley NOUN (plural pulleys)
a wheel with a groove round it, used with a rope or chain to move something heavy
It was hard pulling the people across on the pulley.—LEVEL 6, SHIP IN TROUBLE

pumpkin NOUN (plural pumpkins)
A pumpkin is a very large round orange vegetable.

pup NOUN (plural pups)
a young seal or other animal

quest NOUN (plural quests)
If you go on a quest, you go to find something or do something.
• Kipper was on a **quest** to pop the balloons in the game.

quill NOUN (plural quills)
a pen made from a bird's feather
• The Queen told the servant with the **quill** what to write.

quite ADVERB
❶ a bit, or more than a bit, but not very
• At first Floppy did **quite** well, but then he got bored.
❷ completely; 100 per cent
• Anneena said her snake was **quite** harmless.

raid NOUN (plural raids)
a sudden attack

raid VERB raids, raiding, raided
to suddenly attack a place
They raided our crops again last night.
—LEVEL 8, THE BEEHIVE FENCE

raider NOUN (plural raiders)
Raiders are people who suddenly attack a place.

railroad NOUN (plural railroads)
a railway
• Wilma and Biff waited at the **railroad** station.

ramp NOUN (plural ramps)
A ramp is a man-made slope that you go up or down.

ranger NOUN (plural rangers)
someone who looks after a park or forest
• The **rangers** arrived in their jeep.

raven NOUN (plural ravens)

A raven is a large black bird. Ravens are a kind of crow.

rear-view mirror NOUN (plural rear-view mirrors)

the driver's mirror inside the windscreen of a car

recharge VERB recharges, recharging, recharged

to put more electrical power into a battery

reel NOUN (plural reels)

A reel of tape is a long piece of tape that is wound round a circular object.

reins NOUN

Reins are the thin straps that a rider uses to control a horse, by pulling on its mouth. *The driver pulled the reins.*—LEVEL 6, ON THE STAGE

reporter NOUN (plural reporters)

a person whose job is to find out the news and then talk about it on film, or write about it
• *Lee and Kipper were on TV talking to a reporter!*

richly ADVERB

in a rich or luxurious way
• *The Emperor's chariot was richly decorated.*

rink NOUN (plural rinks)

a place where you can go skating
• *Dad took Wilf to the ice rink.*

riverbank NOUN (plural riverbanks)

The riverbank is the ground near the edge of a river.

robe NOUN (plural robes)

A robe is a long loose piece of clothing.
• *The Mayor was wearing a robe.*

rock pool NOUN (plural rock pools)

a pool of sea water among rocks at the beach
• *Biff found a crab in one of the rock pools.*

rooster NOUN (plural roosters)

A rooster is a cockerel (a male chicken).

rotten ADJECTIVE

❶ Rotten food is smelly and bad to eat. *There was a terrible smell like rotten eggs.*—LEVEL 8, THE EVIL GENIE

❷ A rotten person or thing is bad or nasty.

rough *(say ruff)* **ADJECTIVE** rougher, roughest

Something that is rough is not smooth.

The plane bounced on the rough ground.
—LEVEL 9, RESCUE!

royal ADJECTIVE
to do with a king
or queen

rubbing NOUN *(plural rubbings)*
a copy of a pattern on the surface of something. You make it by placing paper over the surface and moving a crayon over the paper.

rubble NOUN
Rubble is broken bits of brick or stone.

rug NOUN *(plural rugs)*
❶ a small carpet that is not fixed to the floor
❷ a covering for the ground, so you can sit down outside or put your food down
Mum and Dad put the rug down and got the picnic out.—LEVEL 5, MUM TO THE RESCUE
❸ a thick blanket
*Chip got Dad to put his feet up. He got him a **rug**.*—LEVEL 2, GOT A JOB?

rumble NOUN *(plural rumbles)*
a long deep sound
They could hear the rumble of thunder.
—LEVEL 7, THE LIGHTNING KEY

rumble VERB rumbles, rumbling, rumbled
to make a long deep sound
There was a rumbling noise all around.
—LEVEL 7, A TALL TALE

run VERB runs, running, ran, run
❶ When you run, you use your legs to move quickly.
❷ To run somewhere is to travel or go there.
Floppy saw the pram running down the hill.
—LEVEL 9, SUPERDOG
❸ To run a person somewhere is to take them there in a car or other vehicle.
• *Mrs May said she would **run** Dad home on her scooter.*

➤ **run out**
❶ If you run out of something, you stop having enough of it.
Chip had run out of paper.—LEVEL 6, MIRROR ISLAND
❷ If a battery runs out, it stops having power.
The keyboard went dead. The battery had run out.—LEVEL 8, MEETING MOZART

➤ **run over**
If something gets run over, it gets knocked or squashed by a car or other vehicle.
• *The postman ran over mum's hat.*

rut NOUN *(plural ruts)*
a deep groove in the ground
The wagon lurched into a rut.—LEVEL 9, THE TRAVELLING PLAYERS

a b c d e f g h i j k l m n o p q **Rr** s t u v w x y z

saddle NOUN (plural saddles)
A horse's saddle is what the rider sits on. Some saddles carry luggage.

safari park NOUN (plural safari parks)
a park that people drive around to see wild animals such as lions

salamander NOUN (plural salamanders)
A salamander is an animal like a lizard.

sandbag NOUN (plural sandbags)
Sandbags are bags of sand. People put them against doors to help keep flood water out of buildings.

sandcastle NOUN (plural sandcastles)
a model of a castle built out of wet sand on a beach
- *Biff made a **sandcastle**.*

sandy ADJECTIVE sandier, sandiest
A sandy beach has sand, not just lots of little stones, on it.

sash NOUN (plural sashes)
a strip of cloth that a person wears round their waist or over one shoulder
Kim had a long sash round her waist.—
LEVEL 7, THE WILLOW PATTERN PLOT

scarecrow NOUN (plural scarecrows)
A scarecrow is something that looks like a person and is put in a field to frighten away birds.
- *Biff and Chip made the **scarecrow**'s body out of old clothes.*

scatter VERB scatters, scattering, scattered
If you scatter things, you throw them all around you.
- *The bits of paper were **scattered** on the floor.*

42

scientist NOUN *(plural scientists)*
A scientist is someone who studies science or who knows a lot about science.
• *Dad told the children about a famous scientist.*

scooter NOUN *(plural scooters)*
❶ a kind of motorcycle with small wheels
• *Mrs May arrived on her scooter.*
❷ a small electric vehicle for people who cannot walk well
A man went past on a scooter.—LEVEL 3, ROAD BURNER
❸ a toy for riding on while standing. You stand on a long flat part and move forward by pushing one foot against the ground.

Scout NOUN *(plural Scouts)*
Scouts belong to an organisation in which young people do outdoor activities, learn skills and help people.

Scout camp NOUN *(plural Scout camps)*
a trip away with the Scouts, with activities such as cooking outside and sleeping in tents

scramble VERB scrambles, scrambling, scrambled
to rush to do something, in a clumsy way

scrambled eggs NOUN
eggs that have been mixed together and cooked, forming soft lumps

scrapbook NOUN *(plural scrapbooks)*
a book with blank pages that you can fill with pictures and bits of writing
I am going to cut this page out and put it in my scrapbook.—LEVEL 7, A MAMMOTH TASK

scruffy ADJECTIVE scruffier, scruffiest
untidy

scrunched-up ADJECTIVE
A scrunched-up piece of paper has been crumpled into a ball.

sculpture NOUN *(plural sculptures)*
A sculpture is something carved or shaped out of a hard material such as stone, clay or metal.

seafood NOUN
Seafood is fish or shellfish from the sea, eaten as food.

seagull NOUN *(plural seagulls)*
Seagulls are big noisy birds that you see at the seaside.

a
b
c
d
e
f
g
h
i
j
k
l
m
n
o
p
q
r
Ss
t
u
v
w
x
y
z

seal *NOUN (plural seals)*
a blob of wax that keeps a letter or package closed. The wax has a pattern in it, showing who sent it.

seaweed *NOUN*
Seaweed is plants that grow in the sea.

see-saw *NOUN (plural see-saws)*
a long flat thing that children play on. It is balanced in the middle. A person sits at each end, making it go up and down.

set *VERB sets, setting, set*
❶ to put something somewhere
The girl set down her basket.—LEVEL 8, THE BEEHIVE FENCE
❷ to make something ready to work
Chip set his watch to the right time.—LEVEL 9, WAKE UP!
❸ to give someone a task
• *The boys had been set a problem.*
❹ to make something happen
*A man was stuck in a net. "Set me free,"
he said.*—LEVEL 4, THE MOSAIC TRAIL

➤ **set off**
to begin a journey
• *Dad set off on a bicycle to catch the thief.*

➤ **set up**
to get something ready to use
When everything was set up, Biff and Anneena went indoors.—LEVEL 8, THE BEEHIVE FENCE

sett *NOUN (plural setts)*
A badger's sett is its underground home.

settle *VERB settles, settling, settled*
to get into a comfortable position
They setttled down for the night.—LEVEL 7, SURVIVAL IN THE ARCTIC

shame *NOUN*
People use this word when they, or other people, are disappointed or upset.
Mum was disappointed. "What a shame!" said Dad.—LEVEL 4, POOR OLD MUM!

shear *VERB shears, shearing, sheared, shorn*
to cut the wool off a sheep

shelter *NOUN (plural shelters)*
a place that protects people from bad weather or from danger
Biff and Amy put up the plastic sheet to make a shelter.—LEVEL 9, SURVIVAL ADVENTURE

shelter *VERB shelters, sheltering, sheltered*
to stay in a place that is safe from bad weather or danger
• *The children sheltered from the rain.*

shepherd *NOUN (plural shepherds)*
A shepherd is a person who looks after sheep.

shepherd's pie *NOUN (plural shepherd's pies)*
Shepherd's pie is cooked minced meat with mashed potato on top.

sheriff *NOUN (plural sheriffs)*
a man in charge of an area, who made sure people kept the law

shooting star *NOUN (plural* shooting stars*)*

Shooting stars are *meteors*, bits of burning rock from space that look like streaks of light in the sky.

shower *NOUN (plural* showers*)*

a lot of small things that suddenly move or fall through the air

He threw a log on to the fire. A shower of sparks flew up.—LEVEL 7, SURVIVAL IN THE ARCTIC

shower *VERB* showers, showering, showered

❶ If a lot of small things shower you, they suddenly fall on you.

❷ to wash under a spray of water

shrub *NOUN (plural* shrubs*)*

a bush or small tree

• *The girls found a toad under a **shrub**.*

signal *NOUN (plural* signals*)*

❶ Railway signals tell train drivers to stop or go. Modern signals look like traffic lights, but older signals have parts which change position.

The train driver saw the signal and stopped.
—LEVEL 6, THE STEAM TRAIN

❷ radio waves that let a phone or TV work

signal box *NOUN (plural* signal boxes*)*

a building from which railway signals are controlled

silk *NOUN*

Silk is a kind of smooth cloth. It is made from thread that is made by caterpillars called *silkworms*.

sill *NOUN (plural* sills*)*

a shelf or flat surface at the bottom of a window

• *Chip put the pot on the window **sill**.*

sketch *NOUN (plural* sketches*)*

A sketch is a drawing that you do quickly.

• *Chip did a **sketch** of Mrs May.*

sketch *VERB* sketches, sketching, sketched

If you sketch something, you make a quick drawing of it.

skip *VERB* skips, skipping, skipped

to go quickly to another part of something

Skip to the part where I become king!
—LEVEL 9, PRINCES IN THE TOWER

slay *VERB* slays, slaying, slew, slain

In stories, to slay a dragon was to kill it.

sled *NOUN (plural* sleds*)*

a kind of sledge used for travelling over snow and ice

sleepover NOUN (plural **sleepovers**)
a night that you spend at a friend's house
Anneena had come for a sleepover with Biff.
—LEVEL 8, THE BEEHIVE FENCE

slow-worm NOUN (plural **slow-worms**)
A slow-worm looks like a small snake. It is a kind of lizard without legs.

smirk NOUN (plural **smirks**)
a smile that is not very nice. A smirk can show that you are pleased with yourself.

snap VERB **snaps, snapping, snapped**
❶ to break suddenly, with a sharp noise
Kim heard the sound of a twig snapping.
—LEVEL 7, THE WILLOW PATTERN PLOT
❷ to break something suddenly
The wind snapped off the mast.—LEVEL 8, THE EVIL GENIE
❸ to say something quickly, in a rude or angry way
"Horrid? Horrid?" snapped the Litter Queen.
—LEVEL 9, THE LITTER QUEEN
❹ If an animal snaps at something, it suddenly bites it, or tries to bite it.
The wolf snapped at Hong. It sank its teeth into his bag.—LEVEL 7, THE RIDDLE STONE PART 2
❺ To snap your fingers is to make a clicking sound using the finger and thumb of one hand. This can be to get someone's attention, in a rude way.

snap NOUN (plural **snaps**)
A snap is a snapping sound or action.

sneer VERB **sneers, sneering, sneered**
If someone sneers, they speak in a nasty mocking way, or they have a look on their face that is mocking and nasty.

sniff VERB **sniffs, sniffing, sniffed**
❶ to breathe in loudly through your nose. This can be to smell something, to stop your nose dripping, or to show that you dislike something.
• *The bear **sniffed** the air.*
❷ to say something while sniffing. This can be because you are upset.
"I don't want to go away," sniffed the boy.
—LEVEL 8, WHAT WAS IT LIKE?

snort VERB **snorts, snorting, snorted**
If an animal snorts, it makes a loud sound by forcing air out through its nose.
Biff heard something snorting outside the shelter.—LEVEL 7, SURVIVAL IN THE ARCTIC

snowmobile NOUN (plural **snowmobiles**)
A snowmobile is a kind of sledge with a motor, used for travelling over snow and ice.

soggy ADJECTIVE **soggier, soggiest**
very wet

spacesuit NOUN (plural **spacesuits**)
the outfit worn by an astronaut in space

spark NOUN (plural **sparks**)
Sparks are tiny, very hot bits that a fire sends out.
He threw a log on to the fire. A shower of sparks flew up.—LEVEL 7, SURVIVAL IN THE ARCTIC

sparkle *VERB* sparkles, sparkling, sparkled

to shine with a lot of tiny flashes of bright light
- *The golden tree and palace **sparkled** by the river.*

sparkler *NOUN* (plural sparklers)
A sparkler is a small firework that someone holds in their hand. Sparks shoot out from it.

sphinx *NOUN* (plural sphinxes)
A sphinx is a stone statue with a body like a lion's body and a head like a person's head.

splutter *VERB* splutters, spluttering, spluttered

to make spitting or choking sounds
- *The engine **spluttered** and the bus stopped.*

spring-clean *VERB* spring-cleans, spring-cleaning, spring-cleaned
to clean a house completely in spring

squint *VERB* squints, squinting, squinted

to look at something with your eyes nearly shut, trying to see
Chip squinted. "What is it?" he asked.
—LEVEL 8, AT THE MONSTER GAMES

stagecoach *NOUN* (plural stagecoaches)
a long-distance coach pulled by horses. The stagecoach took passengers and mail.

stage fright *NOUN*
If you get stage fright, you feel afraid before you perform or while you are on stage.

stately home *NOUN* (plural stately homes)
A stately home is a very big and grand house that belongs or belonged to a family with a lot of money and power.

stationmaster *NOUN* (plural stationmasters)
a person in charge of a railway station

steam train *NOUN* (plural steam trains)
an old-fashioned train with a steam engine. The steam is made by heating water with a coal fire.

stilts NOUN

a pair of poles on which you can walk high above the ground

The girl on stilts held on to the tree.—LEVEL 9, THE FINEST IN THE LAND

stomp VERB stomps, stomping, stomped

to put your feet down hard as you walk, making a lot of noise

• *The ogre **stomped** back into the cave.*

streak NOUN (plural streaks)

a long thin line or mark

• *The sky had **streaks** of green light in it.*

streak VERB streaks, streaking, streaked

To streak somewhere is to move there very quickly.

stretch limo NOUN (plural stretch limos)

a very long car that is used for taking a group of people to an event

stride VERB strides, striding, strode, stridden

to walk somewhere with firm long steps, looking determined

Then a man strode in. "Why have you stopped playing, Wolfgang?" he demanded.
—LEVEL 8, MEETING MOZART

strike VERB strikes, striking, struck

To strike something is to hit it.

• *The boy fell into the water when the boat **struck** a rock.*

sunbed NOUN (plural sunbeds)

a chair that you can lie down on outdoors

• *Biff and Chip sat in Gran's **sunbeds** to look at the stars.*

superb ADJECTIVE

excellent

He was pleased with the superb workmanship.—LEVEL 9, SCULPTURES FOR THE EMPEROR

swarm NOUN (plural swarms)

A swarm of insects is a lot of them together.

swordfish NOUN (plural swordfish)

a large sea fish. The top part of its jaw is like a pointed sword.

Tt

take *VERB* takes, taking, took, taken
❶ to bring or lead someone somewhere
The magic took the children into a new adventure.—LEVEL 6, THE SHINY KEY
❷ to need an amount of time, people or things
It took quite a long time to get to the top.
—LEVEL 9, THE LITTER QUEEN
❸ to do, make or have something. For example, you can take a test, take a photograph, or take a rest.
➤ **take off**
❶ Aircraft take off when they leave the ground.
❷ If you take off your hat or coat, or another piece of clothing, you remove it from your body.
He took his cap off.—LEVEL 8, VICTORAN ADVENTURE
➤ **take over**
to start controlling something
Don't let him take over the controls just yet.
—LEVEL 9, THE FLYING MACHINE
➤ **take part**
to do something with other people
The children were excited. They were going to take part in a play.—LEVEL 8, WHAT WAS IT LIKE?
➤ **take place**
to happen
No one has left the room since the theft took place.—LEVEL 7, DETECTIVE ADVENTURE

takeaway *NOUN* (plural takeaways)
A takeaway is a meal that you buy at a restaurant or shop and eat somewhere else.
• *Mum went to get a takeaway.*

tall story *NOUN* (plural tall stories)
something that is hard to believe

talon *NOUN* (plural talons)
Talons are strong claws on some kinds of birds.

tape measure *NOUN* (plural tape measures)
a long strip marked with numbers and lines, used for measuring

teem *VERB* teems, teeming, teemed
If it is teeming with rain, it is raining very hard.

terracotta *NOUN*
Terracotta is reddish-brown clay, used to make pots and sculptures.
• *Biff brought a soldier made of terracotta back from her adventure.*

theft *NOUN* (plural thefts)
Theft is stealing.
• *The theft took place while everyone was chatting.*

thoughtful ADJECTIVE
If you look thoughtful, you look as if you are thinking.

thoughtfully ADVERB
in a way that shows you are thinking

throne NOUN (plural thrones)
A throne is a chair for a king or queen, or for another important person.
• *The emperor sat upon his **throne**.*

thrust VERB thrusts, thrusting, thrust
to push something somewhere with a lot of force

timber yard NOUN (plural timber yards)
a place that sells wood for making things

time capsule NOUN (plural time capsules)
a container with things inside that show what life is like. Time capsules are left for people to find at a later time.

timer NOUN (plural timers)
a device for timing things
• *Percy heard the oven **timer** peeping.*

toboggan NOUN (plural toboggans)
A toboggan is a sledge for sliding downhill on snow.

tonne NOUN (plural tonnes)
1000 kilograms

tooth fairy NOUN
Some children leave teeth that have fallen out under their pillows. They believe that the tooth fairy will take the tooth and leave them some money.

topple VERB topples, toppling, toppled
to fall over
• *The tower **toppled** over before the last block went on it.*

torrent NOUN (plural torrents)
A torrent of rain is very heavy rain.

toss VERB tosses, tossing, tossed
❶ To toss a coin is to throw it in the air and see which side it lands on, as a way of deciding something.
Mr Johnson tossed a coin. "Heads or tails?" he said. —LEVEL 9, GREEN ISLAND
❷ to move about, or make something move about
Big waves tossed the boat up and down.
—LEVEL 8, THE EVIL GENIE
❸ to throw something

tourist NOUN (plural tourists)
Tourists are people visiting a place on holiday.

toxic waste NOUN
harmful leftover substances
• *Nasty people had dumped **toxic waste**.*

track NOUN (plural tracks)
❶ a road with a rough surface of mud and stones
• *The lorry went down the **track**.*
❷ rails for trains to run on
They are even laying railway track across the desert.—LEVEL 6, ON THE STAGE
❸ a road or area for racing
• *Anneena raced around the **track** in the new go-kart.*
❹ Animal tracks are paw prints or other marks left by an animal.

track VERB tracks, tracking, tracked
to follow someone
Chip and Wilf were tracking Dad.—LEVEL 5, SAFARI ADVENTURE

traffic jam NOUN (plural traffic jams)
a line of traffic, not moving

trail NOUN (plural trails)
❶ a rough road, path or track
❷ the marks or smell left behind by an animal

trailer NOUN (plural trailers)
A trailer is a container or flat surface on wheels, pulled behind a car or truck.

trample VERB tramples, trampling, trampled
to crush something with your feet
• *The elephants **trampled** the crops.*

trampoline NOUN (plural trampolines)
A trampoline is a large piece of stretchy material in a frame. You can bounce up and down on it.

trek NOUN (plural treks)
a long walk or journey

trek VERB treks, trekking, trekked
to walk a long way
"We don't want to trek down," said Dad. "It's much too far."—LEVEL 4, TOP OF THE MOUNTAIN

trench NOUN (plural trenches)
A trench is a long narrow ditch dug in the ground.

trolley NOUN (plural trolleys)
a basket on wheels, used in supermarkets
• *Kipper got the trolley.*

tube NOUN
the London underground train system

tuck *VERB* tucks, tucking, tucked

➤ **tuck in**

to start eating, with enjoyment
They all began to tuck in.—LEVEL 8, THE OGRE'S DINNER

➤ **tuck up**

If someone tucks you up, they make you feel cosy in bed by making sure the bedclothes are firmly in place.

tucker *NOUN*

an informal Australian word for food

tuneful *ADJECTIVE*

with a nice tune or sound

tunic *NOUN (plural tunics)*
a loose piece of clothing with no sleeves

turret *NOUN (plural turrets)*
Turrets are small towers on a castle or other building.

turtle *NOUN (plural turtles)*
a sea animal like a tortoise

twiddly *ADJECTIVE*
Twiddly bits in music go quickly up and down.
• *Mozart said he would add some **twiddly** bits to the tune.*

uncertainly *ADVERB*
in a way that shows you do not feel confident
"OK," said Biff, uncertainly.—LEVEL 8, AT THE MONSTER GAMES

unload *VERB* unloads, unloading, unloaded
to take things out of a car, truck, bus, plane or ship

used to *VERB*
❶ If you used to do something, you did it in the past.
• *They **used to** be friends.*
❷ If you get used to doing something, it becomes something you do without thinking
• *Chip got **used to** the bike and soon he could ride it.*

vanish *VERB* vanishes, vanishing, vanished
To vanish is to disappear.
• *The childreren **vanished** from the room.*

vegetarian *NOUN (plural vegetarians)*
A vegetarian is someone who does not eat meat.
• *The ogres were strict **vegetarians**.*

vixen *NOUN (plural vixens)*
A vixen is a female fox.

wagon *NOUN (plural wagons)*
Wagons are carts with four wheels, pulled by horses or other animals.
The wagon lurched into a rut.—LEVEL 9, THE TRAVELLING PLAYERS

wagon train *NOUN (plural wagon trains)*
a group of wagons travelling together

warrior *NOUN (plural warriors)*
a soldier

water-hole *NOUN (plural water-holes)*
In hot countries, a water-hole is a pool of water where animals go to drink.

wearily *ADVERB*
in a way that shows you are tired, or would like something to stop
• *"They often argue," he said **wearily**.*

a
b
c
d
e
f
g
h
i
j
k
l
m
n
o
p
q
r
s
t
u
Vv
Ww
x
y
z

53

weather forecast NOUN (plural weather forecasts)

information about the weather that is likely to occur
• *The boys were watching the weather forecast on TV.*

weather vane NOUN (plural weather vanes)

a decorated metal pointer that turns in the wind to show which way the wind is blowing
• *The weather vane was lifted up and put on the roof.*

weave VERB weaves, weaving, wove, woven

to make cloth or a pattern by crossing threads or strips over and under each other
• *The children learned how to weave a pattern with the ribbons.*

weaver NOUN (plural weavers)

a person who makes cloth by crossing threads under and over each other

weir NOUN (rhymes with cheer) (plural weirs)

a barrier across a river or canal to control the flow of water

whatsit NOUN (plural whatsits)

a word used when you do not know what something is called

whisk VERB whisks, whisking, whisked

to take someone somewhere very quickly
The magic whisked Chip through the door of the little house.—LEVEL 9, THE LITTER QUEEN

whizz VERB whizzes, whizzing, whizzed

❶ to send something or move somewhere very quickly
❷ to make a sound while rushing through the air

wig NOUN (plural wigs)

A wig is a head covering made of hair. The hair can be real or fake.

wildlife NOUN

wild animals

winch NOUN (plural winches)

A winch is used for lifting or pulling heavy or large things. It has a rope or cable that goes round a wheel or drum.

windmill NOUN (plural windmills)
a building or structure with large parts that turn in the wind. In the past, windmills used wind power to grind corn. Modern windmills use wind power to produce electricity.

wiper NOUN (plural wipers)
Windscreen wipers are the narrow parts that move across a car windscreen to clean it.

wishing well NOUN (plural wishing wells)
a deep hole from which people got water. People throw in coins and wish for something good to happen.

witchetty grub NOUN (plural witchetty grubs)
a kind of caterpillar

wobble VERB wobbles, wobbling, wobbled
to move unsteadily from side to side or from front to back

wobbly ADJECTIVE
If something is wobbly, it moves from side to side or from front to back.
Kipper had a wobbly tooth.—LEVEL 2, THE WOBBLY TOOTH

workmanship NOUN
Workmanship is skill in making something.
He was pleased with the superb workmanship.—LEVEL 9, SCULPTURES FOR THE EMPEROR

workmate NOUN (plural workmates)
Your workmates are the people you work with.
• *Dad and his **workmates** had done a great job.*

worksheet NOUN (plural worksheets)
a sheet of paper with a set of questions about a subject for students

workshop NOUN (plural workshops)
a place where things are made or mended
• *Dad went to the **workshop** and got them to make the model.*

worth ADJECTIVE
❶ If something is worth an amount of money, you can sell it for that amount of money.
It looks quite old, so maybe it's worth a lot of money.—LEVEL 8, THE FLYING CARPET
❷ If something is worth doing, it is good to do it, even if there is a bad side.
"It was worth a sore toe," said Gran.—LEVEL 6, TWO LEFT FEET

wriggly ADJECTIVE
A wriggly creature twists and turns its body a lot.
• *Biff didn't want to eat a **wriggly** grub.*

a
b
c
d
e
f
g
h
i
j
k
l
m
n
o
p
q
r
s
t
u
v
Ww
x
y
z

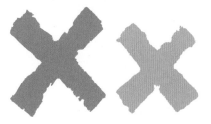

X-ray NOUN (plural X-rays)
An X-ray shows the inside of your body.

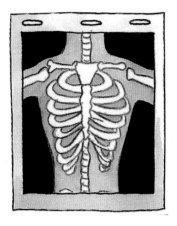

Only a few words start with *x*.

Lots of words start with ex-, for instance *exit, exercise* and *explain*. You can find more words starting with ex- on pages 20 and 21.

yap VERB yaps, yapping, yapped
to bark in a noisy shrill way

yap EXCLAMATION
Yap shows that a dog is barking in a noisy shrill way.

yucky ADJECTIVE yuckier, yuckiest
disgusting
"Hey, no yucky frogs in here!" shouted the cook.—LEVEL 5, THE FROG'S TALE

yuk EXCLAMATION (also yuck)
This word shows that you feel disgusted.
"Have some bug pie," said a troll. "Yuk!" said Kipper.—LEVEL 5, KIPPER AND THE TROLLS

Zz

zap *VERB* zaps, zapping, zapped
to attack or destroy something
• *In her computer game, Biff **zapped** giants.*

zebra crossing *NOUN* (plural zebra crossings)
a place to cross the road, with white stripes on the road surface

zip wire *NOUN* (plural zip wires)
a cable between a high place and a lower place. People sit or hang below it, clipped on, and slide down for fun.
• *Dad flew down the hillside on the **zip wire**.*

zookeeper *NOUN* (plural zookeepers)
A zookeeper is someone whose job is looking after animals in a zoo.

a
b
c
d
e
f
g
h
i
j
k
l
m
n
o
p
q
r
s
t
u
v
w
x
y
Zz

57

Phrases

Sometimes, when we use words together their meaning changes. Here are some examples of phrases with a different meaning from what you might expect.

come on
❶ Let's go! Keep going! Hurry up!
➤ *"**Come on**," said Wilf.*
❷ to start, or start working
➤ *Suddenly the lights **came on**.*

come round
to come to your house to see you
➤ *Wilma **came round** to play.*

put out
To put out a fire is to stop it burning.

fall out
If people fall out with each other, they argue or stop being friends.

put on
❶ to start wearing clothes
➤ *Chip **put on** his boots.*
❷ to perform a show for others to see
➤ *The children often **put on** plays.*
❸ to start a machine
➤ *Chip **put** the TV **on**.*

pick someone up
to fetch someone from somewhere
➤ *Mum came to **pick** the children **up**.*

about to
If something is about to happen, it is going to happen very soon.
➤ *A new adventure was **about to** start!*

do something up
❶ to repair or redecorate something
➤ *Dad said they would **do** the cot **up**.*
❷ to fasten something
➤ *Kipper **did up** his coat.*

I'm afraid

unfortunately

➤ *"**I'm afraid** we can't do that," the man told Wilf.*

all along

from the start

➤ *The children knew the answer **all along**.*

hit and miss

If something is hit and miss, it is good sometimes and not very good at other times.

I bet

I'm sure.

➤ *"**I bet** I can go faster!" said Anneena.*

in a bit

in a little while; soon

➤ *Mum said she would get dinner **in a bit**.*

Wait and see! or You'll see!

You will understand soon.

➤ *The children asked Mrs May, but she just said, "**Wait and see!**"*

It's had it!

If something has had it, it is broken and useless.

➤ *The bunk beds have **had it**.*

That's funny!

Sometimes, we use words in an unusual way, to make a joke.
Here are some examples from the *Oxford Reading Tree* stories.

Wizard Blot often made mistakes.
➤ A blot is a mark, or another thing that spoils the look of something.

In *Kid Rocket*, there is a bad person called **Doctor Rotten**.

Lord Plum had the same name as a piece of fruit!
➤ A plum is a juicy fruit with a stone. Plums can be yellow, red or purple.

Pram dipping is looking for interesting things in the water in an old pram.
➤ The usual thing is *pond dipping*. You use a net to find interesting plants and creatures in a pond.

A **frogman** is a diver but Dad joked about being a frogman when he had a frog on his head.

Fang, **Hook** and **Snap** were nasty dogs.
➤ A fang is a sharp tooth. A hook can be sharp. If a dog snaps at you, it bites you, or tries to bite you.

Professor Tangle often got in a muddle.
➤ If things are in a tangle, they are in a mess or a muddle.

A **funny bone** is a bone in your elbow but Dad joked about a funny bone when Floppy did something funny with a bone.

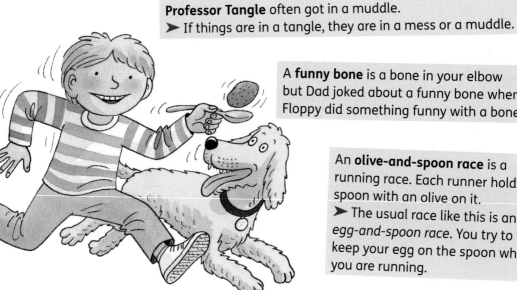

An **olive-and-spoon race** is a running race. Each runner holds a spoon with an olive on it.
➤ The usual race like this is an *egg-and-spoon race*. You try to keep your egg on the spoon while you are running.

People and Places

Here are some famous people and places mentioned in the *Oxford Reading Tree* stories.

Bach was a famous composer.

Robert Baden-Powell was the man who started the Scouts.

Buckingham Palace is where the British king or queen lives when he or she is in London.

The **Eiffel Tower** is a tall metal tower in Paris (the capital of France). Lots of tourists visit it.

Essex is an area in the south of England.

In stories, **King Arthur** was a king long, long ago. He and his knights sat at a round table so that no one was at the top (the important end).

Latin is the language that was spoken by the ancient Romans.

Loch Ness is a lake in Scotland. Some people say they have seen a monster in the lake. The monster is called the Loch Ness monster.

In a story in the Bible and in the Koran, a man called **Noah** made a ship (called the **Ark**) to save people and animals from a big flood.

Queen Victoria ruled Britain and Northern Ireland for most of the 19th century.

In stories, **Robin Hood** was a thief but he was a good man. He stole things from rich people and gave them to poor people.

The **Romans** came from ancient Rome, a city that is now in Italy. The Ancient Romans ruled many countries.

Sherlock Holmes is a detective in stories written by Arthur Conan Doyle.

In stories, **Saint George** killed a fierce **dragon**.

The **Saxons** were people who came to England from Europe in the 5th and 6th centuries.

In stories, **Sinbad** was a sailor.

In stories, **Sleeping Beauty** stayed asleep for many, many years, until a prince kissed her. She was in a castle with thorns all around it.

Tower Bridge is a famous bridge in London. It has a tower each side and can be raised to let big ships pass.

Trafalgar Square is an open space in London. It has a very tall structure called Nelson's column. The statue on top is of Lord Nelson.

The **Vikings** were people who came from Scandinavia to other parts of Europe from the 8th to the 11th century.

Wolfgang Amadeus Mozart was a famous composer.

Onomatopoeic words

Some words sound like the thing that they describe. Try saying these aloud to see what they mean.

aaah aahh ... tishoo CLUMP

CLANK BOO

clang eek HISS FIzz

glub WHOOSH WoW

shoo HIC

phew Mmm THUD bah

ZOOM

DING

shh Hooray

PUFF

Common and tricky words

I

no
so
go
oh no!

people
Mr
Mrs
Miss

could
should
would

was
because

to
do
into

her
here
were

are
our

father
mother
brother
sister

of
off

to
too

goes
does
shoes

said
again

you
your
out
about

the
they
their
there

me
we
he
she
be

when
who
where
why
what
which

above
come
love
some

Days and months

Monday
Tuesday
Wednesday
Thursday

Friday
Saturday
Sunday

January
February
March
April
May
June

July
August
September
October
November
December

Collins

CAMBRIDGE IGCSE® CO-ORDINATED SCIENCES CHEMISTRY

Sam Goodman and Chris Sunley

William Collins' dream of knowledge for all began with the publication of his first book in 1819.

A self-educated mill worker, he not only enriched millions of lives, but also founded a flourishing publishing house. Today, staying true to this spirit, Collins books are packed with inspiration, innovation and practical expertise. They place you at the centre of a world of possibility and give you exactly what you need to explore it.

Collins. Freedom to teach.

An imprint of HarperCollins*Publishers*
The News Building
1 London Bridge Street
London
SE1 9GF

Browse the complete Collins catalogue at
www.collins.co.uk

© HarperCollins*Publishers* Limited 2017

10 9 8 7 6 5 4 3 2 1

ISBN 978-0-00-821021-2

Sam Goodman and Chris Sunley assert their moral right to be identified as the authors of this work.

British Library Cataloguing in Publication Data
A catalogue record for this publication is available from the British Library.

Commissioned by **Joanna Ramsay**
Project editor **Rebecca Evans**
Project managed by **Catharine Tucker**
Developed by **Amanda Harman**
Proofread by **Karen Falla**
Cover design by **Angela English**
Cover artwork by **sbayram/iStock**
Internal design by **Jouve India Private Limited**
Typesetting by **QBS Media Services Private Limited**
Illustrations by **Jouve India Private Limited** and **QBS Media Services Private Limited**
Production by **Lauren Crisp**
Printed and bound by **Grafica Veneta S. P. A.**

All exam-style questions and sample answers have been written by the authors. In examinations marks may be given differently.

® IGCSE is the registered trademark of Cambridge International Examinations.

Acknowledgements

The publishers wish to thank the following for permission to reproduce photographs. Every effort has been made to trace copyright holders and to obtain their permission for the use of copyright materials. The publishers will gladly receive any information enabling them to rectify any error or omission at the first opportunity.

(t = top, c = centre, b = bottom, r = right, l = left)

Cover & p1 sbayram/iStock, pp 10–11 Denis Vrublevski/Shutterstock, p 12a jele/Shutterstock, p 12b Achim Baque/Shutterstock , p 16 cobalt88/Shutterstock, p 17 Lightspring/Shutterstock, p 18a Andrew Lambert Photography/Science Photo Library, p 18b Andrew Lambert Photography/Science Photo Library, p 18c Andrew Lambert Photography/Science Photo Library, p 23 Charles D. Winters/Science Photo Library, p 24 haveseen/Shutterstock, p 25 Andrew Lambert Photography/Science Photo Library, p 27 Martyn F. Chillmaid/Science Photo Library, p 28 eldar nurkovic/Shutterstock, p 32 FikMik/Shutterstock, p 34 Andrew Lambert Photography/Science Photo Library, p 35 Martyn F. Chillmaid/Science Photo Library, p 37 MrJafari/Shutterstock, p 39 David Parker & Julian Baum/Science Photo Library, p 42 Ho Philip/Shutterstock, p 43 Smit/Shutterstock, p 46 Blaz Kure/Shutterstock, p 47a jordache/Shutterstock, p 47b travis manley/Shutterstock, p 47 c Marc Dietrich/Shutterstock, p 48 Voronin76/Shutterstock, p 54a broukoid/Shutterstock, p 54b Tyler Boyes/Shutterstock, p 55a Dmitry Kalinovsky/Shutterstock, p 55b Tatiana Grozetskaya/Shutterstock, p 62 Martyn F. Chillmaid/Science Photo Library, p 68 ggw/Shutterstock, p 69 Andrew Lambert Photography/Science Photo Library, p 72 PHOTOTAKE Inc./Alamy, p 76 Andrew Lambert Photography/Science Photo Library, p 80 ARENA Creative/Shutterstock, p 87 Science Photo Library, pp 92–93 Galyna Andrushko/Shutterstock, p 94 Maximilian Stock Ltd/Science Photo Library, p 97 Charles D. Winters/Science Photo Library, p 108 EdBockStock/Shutterstock, p 114 badahos/Shutterstock, p 120a Iakov Kalinin/Shutterstock, p 120b john t. fowler/Alamy, p 123 Anna Baburkina/Shutterstock, p 132 Martyn F. Chillmaid/Science Photo Library, p 133a dgmata/Shutterstock, p 133b Ken Brown/iStockphoto, p 134 Charles D. Winters/Science Photo Library, p 136 Cyril Hou/Shutterstock, p 138 Andrew Lambert Photography/Science Photo Library, p 139 Phil Degginger/Alamy, p 145 Martyn F. Chillmaid/Science Photo Library, p 150a Andrew Lambert Photography/Science Photo Library, p 150b Andrew Lambert Photography/Science Photo Library, p 152a Blaz Kure/Shutterstock, p 152b Andrew Lambert Photography/Science Photo Library, p 155 Charles D. Winters/Science Photo Library, p 158 jcwait/Shutterstock, p 160a Johann Helgason/Shutterstock, p 160b Andrew Lambert Photography/Science Photo Library, p 161 Andrew Lambert Photography/Science Photo Library, p 164 Andrew Lambert Photography/Science Photo Library, pp 172–173 Piotr Zajc/Shutterstock, p 174 Shebeko/Shutterstock, p 179 Andrew Lambert Photography/Science Photo Library, p 180 Charles D. Winters/Science Photo Library, p 182 Andrew Lambert Photography/Science Photo Library, p 183 design56/Shutterstock, p 184 Andrew Lambert Photography/Science Photo Library, p 190 Slaven/Shutterstock, p 198 Centrill Media/Shutterstock, p 200 Ehrman Photographic/Shutterstock, p 203a Lawrence Migdale/Science Photo Library, p 203b Richard treptow/Science Photo Library, p 203c Julia Reschke/Shutterstock, p 207a kilukilu/Shutterstock, p 207b Fokin Oleg/Shutterstock, p 207c Parnumas Na Phatthalung/Shutterstock, p 207d Holly Kuchera/Shutterstock, p 207e Danicek/Shutterstock, p 212 David_Monniaux/Wikimedia Commons, p 213 Joe Gough/Shutterstock, p 217 Romas_Photo/Shutterstock, p 218 Martyn F. Chillmaid/Science Photo Library, p 219 Jackiso/Shutterstock, p 221 Meryll/Shutterstock, p 222a Ratikova/Shutterstock, p 222b sciencephotos/Alamy, p 224 Nando Machado/Shutterstock, p 227 muzsy/Shutterstock, p 229 Prixel Creative/Shutterstock, p 236 beboy/Shutterstock, p 240 niepo/Shutterstock, p 242 Francois Etienne du Plessis/Shutterstock, p 244–245 Photobank gallery/Shutterstock, p 246 juliasv/Shutterstock, p 247 Paul Rapson/Science Photo Library, p 268 BESTWEB/Shutterstock, p 253a Dawid Zagorski/Shutterstock, p 253b Yvan/Shutterstock, p 253c speedpix/Alamy, p 255 ggw/Shutterstock, p 256 Joe Gough/Shutterstock, p 257 Gwoeii/Shutterstock, p 260 JoLin/Shutterstock, p 261 Tonis Valing/Shutterstock, p 262 David R. Frazier Photolibrary, Inc./Alamy, p 266 Jim Parkin/Alamy, p 269 kaband/Shutterstock, p 270 EpicStockMedia/Shutterstock, p 370 Ed Phillips/Shutterstock,

Contents

Getting the best from the book

Welcome to Collins *Cambridge IGCSE Co-ordinated Sciences Chemistry*.

This textbook has been designed to help you understand all of the requirements of the Chemistry section of the Cambridge IGCSE Co-ordinated Sciences course.

SAFETY IN THE SCIENCE LESSON

This book is a textbook, not a laboratory or practical manual. As such, you should not interpret any information in this book that relates to practical work as including comprehensive safety instructions. Your teachers will provide full guidance for practical work and cover rules that are specific to your school.

A brief introduction to the section to give context to the science covered in the section.

Starting points will help you to revise previous learning and see what you already know about the ideas to be covered in the section.

The section contents shows the separate topics to be studied matching the syllabus order.

Modern physical chemistry originated in the 19th century. It is not as clearly defined a category as organic chemistry, but it is still a useful description of this branch of science. Physical chemistry focuses on chemical processes at the 'macro level' (where properties can be observed) more than at the 'micro level' (too small to see) of individual atoms, molecules and ions. However, observed physical properties can still be explained in terms of what the atoms, molecules or ions are doing.

In this section you will explore the chemical reactions that can be caused by using electricity, a process known as electrolysis. You will then investigate some chemical reactions that produce significant amounts of heat energy, as well as some strange ones that seem to absorb energy and make everything cooler. The speed or rate of chemical reactions will also be explored, together with chemists' strategies to try to control them. You will learn about redox reactions, which are reactions involving reduction and oxidation, as well as about acids, bases and salts. Finally, you will look at some of the simple analytical techniques that can be used to identify ions and gases.

2 Physical chemistry

STARTING POINTS

1. How many non-renewable fuels can you name? What products do they form when they burn?

2. Give an example of a very rapid, almost instantaneous, chemical reaction. Now give an example of a very slow one.

3. Explain how you can easily distinguish between an acid and an alkali.

4. What is a catalyst? Name two examples where catalysts are used in everyday life.

5. Acids react with alkalis in neutralisation reactions. What is meant by neutralisation?

SECTION CONTENTS

a) Electricity and chemistry

b) Energy changes in chemical reactions

c) Chemical reactions

d) Acids, bases and salts

Knowledge check shows the ideas you should have already encountered in previous work before starting the topic.

Learning objectives cover what you need to learn in this topic.

Examples of investigations are included with questions matched to the investigative skills you will need to learn.

△ Fig. 3.54 The chalk cliffs of southern England are composed largely of calcium carbonate.

Carbonates

INTRODUCTION

Carbonates are salts of **carbonic acid**, a weak acid that is made when carbon dioxide dissolves in water. They react with dilute hydrochloric acid and dilute sulfuric acid forming carbon dioxide. Many metals exist in nature as metal carbonates – the most important of these is calcium carbonate or limestone. Limestone is used for building but it has other important uses as well.

KNOWLEDGE CHECK
✓ Know that dilute acids react with carbonates to form salts, carbon dioxide and water.
✓ Know how to detect the presence of carbon dioxide.

LEARNING OBJECTIVES
✓ Be able to describe the manufacture of lime (calcium oxide) from calcium carbonate (limestone) in terms of the chemical reactions involved.
✓ Know that lime is used in treating acidic soil and neutralising acidic industrial waste products.
✓ Be able to describe the thermal decomposition of calcium carbonate (limestone).

HOW IS LIMESTONE USED?

For centuries limestone has been heated in lime kilns to make 'quicklime' (lime) or calcium oxide, CaO:

$$CaCO_3(s) \xrightarrow{1200\ ^\circ C} CaO(s) + CO_2(g)$$

limestone → quicklime

This is an example of **thermal decomposition**, the use of heat ('thermal') to break up a substance.

A modern rotary kiln is shown in Fig. 3.55.

△ Fig. 3.55 A modern rotary kiln.

When water is added to calcium oxide (quicklime), a vigorous exothermic (heat-producing) reaction takes place, and slaked lime – calcium hydroxide, Ca(OH)₂ – is formed:

$$CaO(s) + H_2O(l) \rightarrow Ca(OH)_2(s)$$

quicklime → slaked lime

Slaked lime is an alkali, which is the basis of many of its uses.
The major uses of limestone, quicklime and slaked lime are listed below.

Limestone ($CaCO_3$):
• crushed and used as aggregate for road building
• added as a powder to lakes to **neutralise** acidity
• mixed and heated with clay to make cement
• used to extract iron in the blast furnace.

Quicklime (CaO):
• added to soil to neutralise acidity
• used as a drying agent in industry
• used to neutralise acid gases, such as sulfur dioxide, SO_2, produced by power stations (flue-gas desulfurisation).

INORGANIC CHEMISTRY

240

CARBONATES

241

Dissolving crystals in water

Fig. 1.10 shows purple crystals of potassium manganate(VII) dissolving in water.

△ Fig. 1.10 Crystals of potassium manganate(VII) dissolving in water. The picture on the left shows the water immediately after the crystal was added; the picture on the right shows the water 1 hour later.

There are no water currents, so only particle theory can explain this. The particles of the crystal gradually move into the water and mix with the water particles.

Mixing gases

These photos show a jar of air and a jar of bromine gas. Bromine gas is red-brown and heavier than air. The jar of air has been placed on top of the jar of bromine and the lids removed so the gases can mix (left-hand part of Fig. 1.11).

After about 24 hours the bromine gas and the air have spread throughout both jars. Particle theory says that the particles of bromine gas can move around randomly so that they can fill both gas jars. This also occurs with hydrogen and air (Fig. 1.12).

△ Fig. 1.11 Diffusion of bromine.

△ Fig. 1.12 Demonstration of diffusion with a jar of oxygen and a jar of hydrogen.

PRINCIPLES OF CHEMISTRY

18

EXTENDED

Developing investigative skills

Two students set up the experiment shown in Fig. 1.13. They carefully clamped the long glass tube horizontally. At the same time, they inserted the cotton wool plugs soaked in the two solutions at each end of the tube and replaced the rubber bungs.

△ Fig. 1.13 Results of experiment.

After about 15 minutes a white ring was seen in the tube.

Note: The white ring was formed where the ammonia gas from the concentrated ammonia solution met the hydrogen chloride gas from the concentrated hydrochloric acid. Together they formed a white substance called ammonium chloride.

Using and organising techniques, apparatus and materials

The concentrated ammonia solution is corrosive – it burns and is dangerous to the eyes. Concentrated hydrochloric acid is corrosive – it burns and its vapour irritates the lungs.

❶ How should the cotton wool plugs have been handled when putting them into the tube?
❷ What other safety precaution(s) should the two students have used?

Observing, measuring and recording

❸ Which gas moved furthest in the 15 minutes before the ring formed?
❹ Approximately how much further did this gas travel compared to the other gas?

Handling experimental observations and data

❺ The rate of diffusion of a gas depends on the mass of its particles. What conclusion can you draw about the relative masses of the two gases in this experiment?

END OF EXTENDED

THE PARTICULATE NATURE OF MATTER

19

Getting the best from the book *continued*

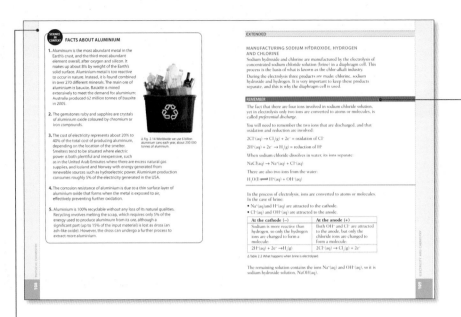

Remember boxes provide tips and guidance to help you during your course and to prepare for examination.

Science in context boxes put the ideas you are learning into real-life context. It is not necessary for you to learn the content of these boxes as they do not form part of the syllabus. However, they do provide interesting examples of scientific application that are designed to enhance your understanding.

Science Link boxes help you to deepen your understanding of the connections between the different sciences. It is not necessary for you to learn the content of these boxes as they do not form part of the syllabus.

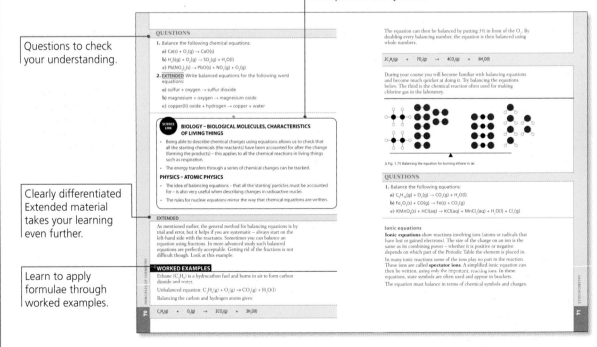

Questions to check your understanding.

Clearly differentiated Extended material takes your learning even further.

Learn to apply formulae through worked examples.

A full checklist of all the information you need to cover the complete syllabus requirements for each topic.

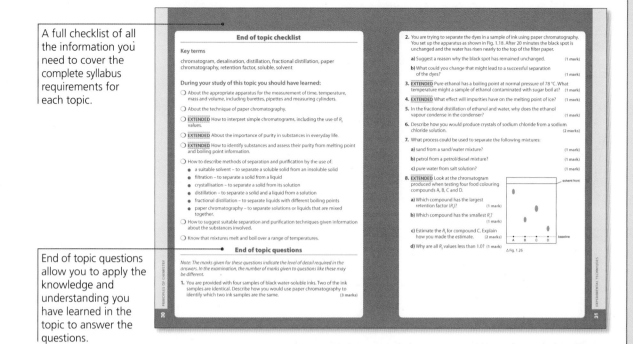

End of topic questions allow you to apply the knowledge and understanding you have learned in the topic to answer the questions.

Each section includes exam-style questions to help you prepare for your exam in a focused way.

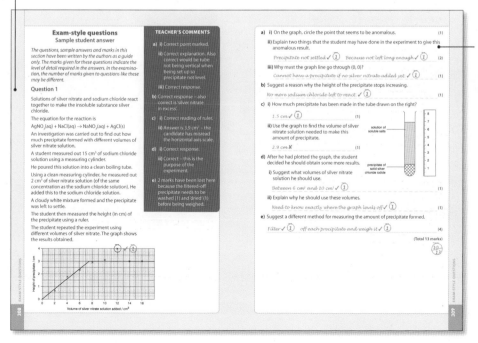

The first question has a sample answer with teacher's comments to show best practice.

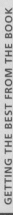

This section provides the basic ideas that the rest of your course is built on. You may have covered some aspects in your previous work, but it is important to understand the key principles thoroughly before seeing how these can be applied across all the other sections. The section covers some of the experimental techniques you will meet in your course.

First you will look at the existing evidence for the particulate nature of matter. Next, you will consider the structure of an atom and why the atoms of different elements have different properties. You will look at the different ways in which atoms of elements join together when they form compounds, and how the method of combination will determine the properties of the compound formed. You will develop your skills in writing word and symbol equations; and, as well as being able to use an equation to work out the products of a reaction, you will be able to calculate how much of the product can be made in the reaction. These quantitative aspects of chemistry are crucially important in the chemical industry.

STARTING POINTS

1. What is an atom?

2. Name some of the particles that are found in an atom.

3. What name is given to a particle formed when two atoms combine together?

4. You will be learning about the states of matter. Do you know what these states are?

5. One type of chemical bonding you will study is called ionic bonding. Find out what an ion is.

6. Diamond and graphite are both covalent substances. They contain the same atoms but have very different structures and properties. What do you know about what diamond and graphite are used for?

SECTION CONTENTS

a) The particulate nature of matter

b) Experimental techniques

c) Atoms, elements and compounds

d) Stoichiometry

1
Principles of chemistry

△ Diamond and graphite are both forms of carbon but have quite different properties.

△ Fig. 1.1 Water in all its states of matter.

The particulate nature of matter

INTRODUCTION

Nearly all substances may be classified as solid, liquid or gas – the states of matter. In science these states are often shown in shorthand as (s), (l) and (g) after the formula or symbol (these are called **state symbols**). Particle theory is based on the idea that all substances are made up of extremely tiny particles. The particles in these three states are arranged differently and have different types of movement and different energies. In many cases, matter changes into different states quite easily. The names of many of these processes are in everyday use, such as melting and condensing. Using simple models of the particles in solids, liquids and gases can help to explain what happens when a substance changes state.

KNOWLEDGE CHECK

✓ Be able to classify substances as solid, liquid or gas.
✓ Be familiar with some of the simple properties of solids, liquids and gases.
✓ Know that all substances are made up of particles.

LEARNING OBJECTIVES

✓ Be able to state the distinguishing properties of solids, liquids and gases.
✓ Be able to describe the structure of solids, liquids and gases in terms of particle separation, arrangement and types of motion.
✓ Be able to describe the changes of state in terms of melting, boiling, evaporation, freezing and condensation.
✓ Be able to demonstrate understanding of the terms atom, molecule and ion.
✓ Be able to describe and explain diffusion.
✓ **EXTENDED** Be able to explain changes of state in terms of particle theory.
✓ **EXTENDED** Be able to describe the dependence of rate of diffusion on molecular mass.

△ Fig. 1.2 Water covers nearly four-fifths of the Earth's surface. In this photo you can see that all three states of matter can exist together: solid water (the ice) is floating in liquid water (the ocean), and the surrounding air contains water vapour (clouds).

HOW DO SOLIDS, LIQUIDS AND GASES DIFFER?

The three states of matter each have different properties, depending on how strongly the particles are held together.

- **Solids** have a fixed volume and shape.
- **Liquids** have a fixed volume but no definite shape. They take up the shape of the container in which they are held.
- **Gases** have no fixed volume or shape. They spread out to fill whatever container or space they are in.

Substances don't always exist in the same state; depending on the physical conditions, they change from one state to another (interconvert).

Some substances can exist in all three states in the natural world. A good example of this is water.

QUESTIONS

1. What is the state symbol for a liquid?

2. Which is the only state of matter that has a fixed shape?

3. In what ways does fine sand behave like a liquid?

Why do solids, liquids and gases behave differently?

The behaviour of solids, liquids and gases can be explained if we think of all matter as being made up of very small particles that are in constant motion. This idea has been summarised in the **particle theory** of matter.

In solids, the particles are held tightly together in a fixed position, so solids have a definite shape. However, the particles are vibrating about their fixed positions because they have energy.

In liquids, the particles are held tightly together but have enough energy to move around. Liquids have no definite shape and will take on the shape of the container they are in.

In gases, the particles are further apart with enough energy to move apart from each other and are constantly moving. Gas particles can spread apart to fill the container they are in.

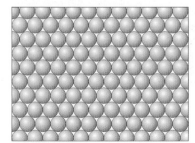

△ Fig. 1.3 Particles in a solid.

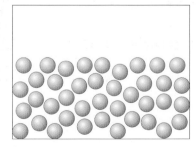

△ Fig. 1.4 Particles in a liquid.

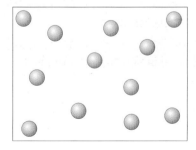

△ Fig. 1.5 Particles in a gas.

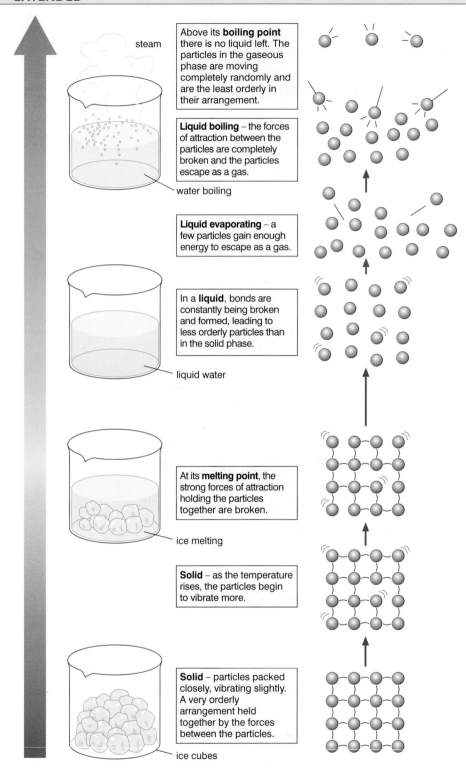

steam

Above its **boiling point** there is no liquid left. The particles in the gaseous phase are moving completely randomly and are the least orderly in their arrangement.

Liquid boiling – the forces of attraction between the particles are completely broken and the particles escape as a gas.

water boiling

Liquid evaporating – a few particles gain enough energy to escape as a gas.

In a **liquid**, bonds are constantly being broken and formed, leading to less orderly particles than in the solid phase.

liquid water

At its **melting point**, the strong forces of attraction holding the particles together are broken.

ice melting

Solid – as the temperature rises, the particles begin to vibrate more.

Solid – particles packed closely, vibrating slightly. A very orderly arrangement held together by the forces between the particles.

ice cubes

Δ Fig. 1.6 Particles in the different states of matter.

END OF EXTENDED

HOW DO SUBSTANCES CHANGE FROM ONE STATE TO ANOTHER?

To change solids into liquids and then into gases, heat energy must be put in. The heat provides the particles with enough energy to overcome the forces holding them together.

To change gases into liquids and then into solids involves cooling, so removing heat energy. This makes the particles come closer together as the substance changes from gas to liquid and the particles bond together as the liquid becomes a solid.

The temperatures at which one state changes to another have specific names:

Name of temperature	Change of state
Melting point	Solid to liquid
Boiling point	Liquid to gas
Freezing point	Liquid to solid
Condensation point	Gas to liquid

Δ Table 1.1 Changes of state.

The particles in a liquid can move around. They have different energies, so some are moving faster than others. The faster particles have enough energy to escape from the surface of the liquid and it changes into the gas state (also called **vapour** particles). This process is **evaporation**. The rate of evaporation increases with increasing temperature because heat gives more particles the energy to be able to escape from the surface.

Fig. 1.7 summarises the changes in states of matter. Note that melting and freezing happen at the same temperature – as do boiling and condensing.

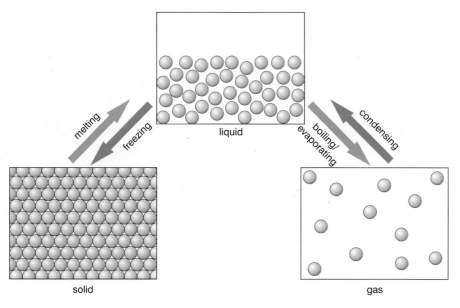

Δ Fig. 1.7 Changes of state. Note that melting and freezing happen at the same temperature – as do boiling and condensing.

THE STATES OF MATTER

There are three states of matter – or are there? To complicate this simple idea, some substances show the properties of two different states of matter. Some examples are given below.

Liquid crystals

Liquid crystals are commonly used in displays in computers and televisions. Within particular temperature ranges the particles of the liquid crystal can flow like a liquid, but remain arranged in a pattern in which the particles cannot rotate.

△ Fig. 1.8 An LCD (liquid crystal display) television.

Superfluids

When some liquids are cooled to very low temperatures they form a second liquid state, described as a *superfluid* state. Liquid helium at just above absolute zero has infinite fluidity and will 'climb out' of its container when left undisturbed – at this temperature the liquid has zero viscosity. (You may like to look up 'fluidity' and 'viscosity'.)

Plasma

Plasmas, or ionised gases, can exist at temperatures of several thousand degrees Celsius. An example of a plasma is the charged air produced by lightning. Stars like our sun also produce plasma. Like a gas, a plasma does not have a definite shape or volume but the strong forces between its particles give it unusual properties, such as conducting electricity. Because of this combination of properties, plasma is sometimes called the fourth state of matter.

QUESTIONS

1. What type of movement do the particles in a solid have?

2. In which state are the particles held together more strongly: in solid water, liquid water or water vapour?

3. What is the name of the process that occurs when the faster-moving particles in a liquid escape from its surface?

4. What name is given to the temperature at which a solid changes into a liquid?

SCIENCE LINK

PARTICLES

- Particles make up the structure of all living things in Biology and everything in the Universe that we study in Physics.

- Biological processes in cells happen through the movement of particles.

- Larger-scale processes such as digestion, respiration and photosynthesis are driven by the interactions of particles.

- In Physics, ideas about particles help explain the structure of buildings, how heat energy is transferred, how electrical circuits work, what happens to cause the weather...the list goes on.

- Particle ideas – the different sizes, how particles join together, how particles are arranged and how they move – are ideas that return again and again.

ELEMENTS, ATOMS AND MOLECULES

All matter is made from **elements**. Elements are substances that cannot be broken down into anything simpler, because they are made up of only one kind of the same small particle. These small particles are called **atoms**.

Almost always, the atoms in an element combine with other atoms to form **molecules**. For example, the particles in water are molecules containing two hydrogen atoms joined up with one oxygen atom. The formula is therefore H_2O. There are also particles called **ions** (see page 43).

△ Fig. 1.9 Model of a water molecule.

DIFFUSION EXPERIMENTS

Scientists have confidence in particle theory because of the evidence from simple experiments.

The random mixing and moving of particles in liquids and gases is known as **diffusion**. The examples given below show the effects of diffusion.

THE PARTICULATE NATURE OF MATTER

17

Dissolving crystals in water

Fig. 1.10 shows purple crystals of potassium manganate(VII) dissolving in water.

△ Fig. 1.10 Crystals of potassium manganate(VII) dissolving in water. The picture on the left shows the water immediately after the crystal was added; the picture on the right shows the water 1 hour later.

There are no water currents, so only particle theory can explain this. The particles of the crystal gradually move into the water and mix with the water particles.

Mixing gases

These photos show a jar of air and a jar of bromine gas. Bromine gas is red-brown and heavier than air. The jar of air has been placed on top of the jar of bromine and the lids removed so the gases can mix (left-hand part of Fig. 1.11).

After about 24 hours the bromine gas and the air have spread throughout both jars. Particle theory says that the particles of bromine gas can move around randomly so that they can fill both gas jars. This also occurs with hydrogen and air (Fig. 1.12).

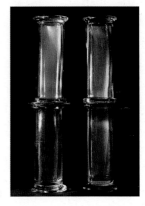

△ Fig. 1.11 Diffusion of bromine.

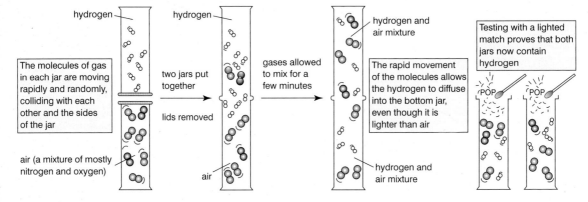

△ Fig. 1.12 Demonstration of diffusion with a jar of oxygen and a jar of hydrogen.

Developing investigative skills

Two students set up the experiment shown in Fig. 1.13. They carefully clamped the long glass tube horizontally. At the same time, they inserted the cotton wool plugs soaked in the two solutions at each end of the tube and replaced the rubber bungs.

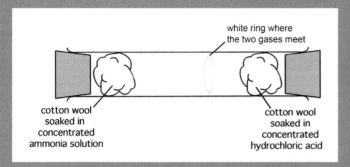

△ Fig. 1.13 Results of experiment.

After about 15 minutes a white ring was seen in the tube.

Note: The white ring was formed where the ammonia gas from the concentrated ammonia solution met the hydrogen chloride gas from the concentrated hydrochloric acid. Together they formed a white substance called ammonium chloride.

Using and organising techniques, apparatus and materials

The concentrated ammonia solution is corrosive – it burns and is dangerous to the eyes. Concentrated hydrochloric acid is corrosive – it burns and its vapour irritates the lungs.

❶ How should the cotton wool plugs have been handled when putting them into the tube?

❷ What other safety precaution(s) should the two students have used?

Observing, measuring and recording

❸ Which gas moved furthest in the 15 minutes before the ring formed?

❹ Approximately how much further did this gas travel compared to the other gas?

Handling experimental observations and data

❺ The rate of diffusion of a gas depends on the mass of its particles. What conclusion can you draw about the relative masses of the two gases in this experiment?

END OF EXTENDED

QUESTIONS

1. What is *diffusion*?

2. Explain how the purple colour of the potassium manganate(VII) shown in Fig. 1.10 spreads through the water.

3. A bottle of perfume is broken at one end of a room. Explain why the perfume can soon be smelled all over the room.

4. What is the name of the particle that is found in all elements?

End of topic checklist

Key terms

atom, boiling, condensation, diffusion, element, evaporation, freezing, gas, liquid, melting, particle theory, solid, state symbols, vapour

During your study of this topic you should have learned:

○ About the different properties of solids, liquids and gases.

○ How to describe the structure of solids, liquids and gases in terms of particle separation, arrangement and types of motion.

○ How to describe changes of state in terms of melting, boiling, evaporation, freezing and condensation.

○ About the terms atom, molecule and ion.

○ How to describe and explain diffusion.

○ **EXTENDED** How to explain changes of state in terms of particle theory.

○ **EXTENDED** How to describe and explain how the rate of diffusion depends on molecular mass.

End of topic questions

Note: The marks given for these questions indicate the level of detail required in the answers. In the examination, the number of marks given to questions like these may be different.

1. In which of the three states of matter are the particles moving fastest? **(1 mark)**

2. Describe the arrangement and movement of the particles in a liquid. **(2 marks)**

3. In which state of matter do the particles just vibrate about a fixed point? **(1 mark)**

4. Sodium (melting point 98 °C) and aluminium (melting point 660 °C) are both solids at room temperature. From their melting points, what can you conclude about the forces of attraction between the particles in the two metals? **(1 mark)**

5. What is the name of the process involved in each of the following changes of state:

   a) $Fe(s) \rightarrow Fe(l)$? **(1 mark)**

   b) $H_2O(l) \rightarrow H_2O(g)$? **(1 mark)**

   c) $H_2O(g) \rightarrow H_2O(l)$? **(1 mark)**

   d) $H_2O(l) \rightarrow H_2O(s)$? **(1 mark)**

6. Ethanol liquid turns into ethanol vapour at 78 °C. What is the name of this temperature? **(1 mark)**

7. Explain how water in the Earth's polar regions can produce water vapour even when the temperature is very low. **(2 marks)**

8. A student wrote in her exercise book, 'The particle arrangement in a liquid is more like the arrangement in a solid than in a gas'. Do you agree with this statement? Explain your reasoning. **(2 marks)**

9. What word is used to describe the rapid mixing and moving of particles in gases? **(1 mark)**

10. Look at Fig. 1.11 showing gas jars of air and bromine. Explain why bromine gas fills the top gas jar even though it is denser than air. **(2 marks)**

11. **EXTENDED** The molecular masses of some gases are shown in the table.

Which gas would diffuse at the greatest rate? Explain your answer. **(2 marks)**

Gas	Molecular mass
Oxygen	32
Nitrogen	28
Chlorine	71

Experimental techniques

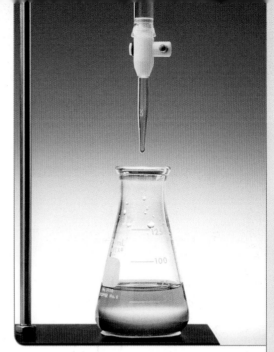

INTRODUCTION

Practical work is a very important part of studying chemistry. In your practical work you will need to develop your skills so that you can safely, correctly and methodically use and organise techniques, apparatus and materials. This involves being able to use appropriate apparatus for measurement to give readings to the required degree of accuracy. It is important to be able to use techniques that will determine the purity of a substance and, if necessary, techniques that can be used to purify mixtures of substances.

△ Fig. 1.14 Using the neutralisation method for a titration.

KNOWLEDGE CHECK

✓ Be familiar with some simple equipment for measuring time, temperature, mass and volume.
✓ Know that some substances are mixtures of a number of different components.

LEARNING OBJECTIVES

✓ Be able to name appropriate apparatus for accurate measurement of time, temperature, mass and volume including burettes, pipettes and measuring cylinders.
✓ Be able to describe paper chromatography.
✓ Be able to interpret simple chromatograms.
✓ Recognise that mixtures melt and boil over a range of temperatures.
✓ **EXTENDED** Be able to identify substances and assess their purity from the melting point and boiling point information.
✓ Understand the importance of purity in substances in everyday life.
✓ **EXTENDED** Be able to use R_f values in interpreting simple chromatograms.
✓ Be able to describe methods of separation and purification by the use of a suitable solvent, filtration, crystallisation, distillation, fractional distillation and paper chromatography.
✓ Be able to suggest suitable separation and purification techniques, given information about the substances involved.

MEASUREMENT

In your study of chemistry you will carry out practical work. It is essential to use the right apparatus for the task.

Time is measured with clocks, such as a wall clock. The clock should be accurate to about 1 second. You may be able to use your own wristwatch or a stopclock.

Temperature is measured using a thermometer. The range of the thermometer is commonly −10 °C to +110 °C with intervals of 1 °C.

Mass is measured with a balance or scales.

Volume of liquids can be measured with burettes, pipettes and measuring cylinders.

△ Fig. 1.15 Measuring equipment.

CRITERIA OF PURITY

Paper chromatography

Paper **chromatography** is a way of separating solutions or liquids that are mixed together.

Black ink is a mixture of different coloured inks. The diagrams in Fig. 1.16 show how paper chromatography is used to find the colours that make up a black ink.

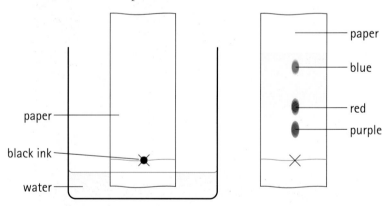

paper

blue

red

purple

paper

black ink

water

△ Fig. 1.16 Paper chromatography separates a solution to find the colours in black ink. The left part of the diagram shows the paper before the inks have been separated, and the right part shows the paper after the inks have been separated.

A spot of ink is placed on the × mark and the paper is suspended in water. As the water rises up the paper, the different dyes travel different distances and so are separated on the **chromatogram**.

Paper chromatography can be used to identify what an unknown liquid is made of. This is called interpreting a chromatogram.

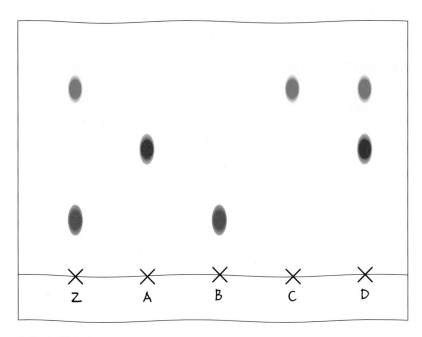

△ Fig. 1.17 A chromatogram.

The unknown liquid Z is compared with known liquids – in this case A to D.

Z must be made of B and C because the pattern of their dots matches the pattern shown by Z.

△ Fig. 1.18 A piece of filter paper is marked with black ink and dipped into water in a beaker.

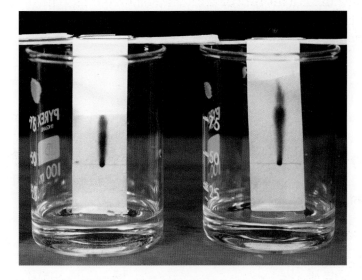

△ Fig. 1.19 After a few minutes the chromatogram has been created by the action of the water on the ink.

Retention factors

Substances can also be identified using chromatography by measuring their **retention factor** on the filter paper. The retention factor (R_f) for a particular substance compares the distance the substance has travelled up the filter paper with the distance travelled by the **solvent**. The retention factor can be calculated using the following formula:

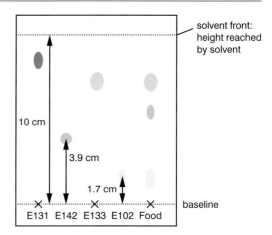

$$R_f = \frac{\text{Distance moved by a substance from the baseline}}{\text{Distance moved by the solvent from the baseline}}$$

△ Fig. 1.20 The R_f value for the food additive E102 is 0.17.

As the solvent will always travel further than the substance, R_f values will always be less than 1.

The purity of solids and liquids

It is very important that manufactured foods and drugs contain only the substances the manufacturers want in them – that is, they must not contain any contaminants.

The simplest way of checking the purity of solids and liquids is using heat to find the temperature at which they melt or boil.

An impure solid will have a lower melting point than the pure solid.

A liquid containing a dissolved solid (solute) will have a higher boiling point than the pure solvent.

The best examples to use to remember these facts are water and ice:

• Pure water boils at 100 °C – salted water for cooking vegetables boils at about 102 °C.
• Pure ice melts at 0 °C – ice with salt added to it melts at about −4 °C.

QUESTIONS

1. The start line, or baseline, in chromatography should be drawn in pencil. Explain why.

2. In a chromatography experiment, why must the solvent level in the beaker be below the baseline?

3. In a chromatography experiment to compare the dyes in two different inks, one of the inks does not move at all from the baseline. Suggest a reason for this.

4. A sample of water contains some dissolved impurities. What would you expect the boiling point of the sample to be?

5. EXTENDED Look at the diagram in Fig. 1.20. Explain why the retention factor for the food additive E102 is 0.17.

METHODS OF PURIFICATION

Techniques for purifying solids and liquids rely on finding different properties of the substances that make up the impure mixture.

Purifying impure solids

The method is:

1. Add a solvent that the required solid is **soluble** in, and dissolve it.

2. Filter the mixture to remove the insoluble impurity.

3. Heat the solution to remove some solvent and leave it to crystallise.

4. Filter off the crystals, wash with a small amount of cold solvent and dry them – this is the pure solid.

Δ Fig. 1.21 Filtration of copper(II) hydroxide.

An example of using this technique would be separating salt from 'rock salt' (the impure form of sodium chloride). Water is added to dissolve the salt but leave the other solids undissolved. Filter off the insoluble impurities, warm the salt solution and leave it to crystallise to form salt crystals.

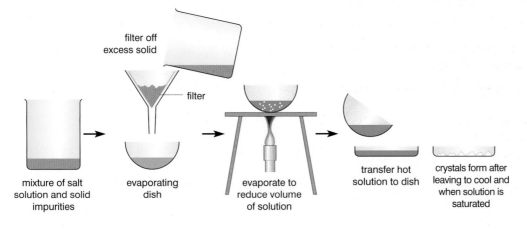

filter off excess solid

filter

mixture of salt solution and solid impurities

evaporating dish

evaporate to reduce volume of solution

transfer hot solution to dish

crystals form after leaving to cool and when solution is saturated

Δ Fig. 1.22 Separating impurities in rock salt.

Purifying impure liquids

There are two methods:

1. Liquids contaminated with soluble solids dissolved in them.

The method is **distillation**.

The solution is heated, the solvent boils and turns into a vapour. It is condensed back to the pure liquid and collected.

This is the technique used in **desalination** plants, which produce pure drinking water from sea water. The solids are left behind after boiling off the water.

△ Fig.1.23 Distillation apparatus.

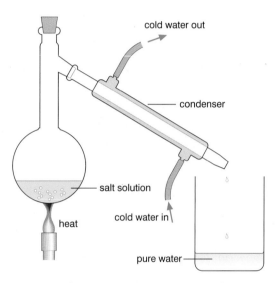

△ Fig. 1.24 Distillation of salt water.

2. Liquids contaminated with other liquids.

In this case the technique is **fractional distillation**, which uses the difference in boiling points of the different liquids mixed together.

The mixture is boiled, and the liquid with the lowest boiling point turns to a vapour first, rises up the fractionating column and is condensed back to liquid in the condenser. The next lowest boiling point liquid comes off, and so on until all the liquids have been separated. You can identify the fraction you want to collect by the temperature reading on the thermometer. The fractionating column increases the purity of the distilled product by reducing the amount of other substances in the vapour when it condenses.

Fractional distillation is the method used in the separation of crude oil and collecting ethanol from the fermentation mixture.

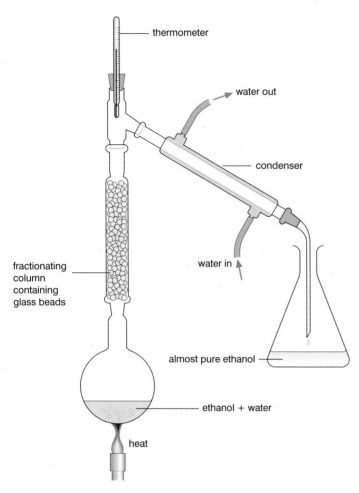

thermometer

water out

condenser

fractionating
column
containing
glass beads

water in

almost pure ethanol

ethanol + water

heat

△ Fig. 1.25 Apparatus for fractional distillation of an alcohol/water mixture.

QUESTIONS

1. What is a *solvent*?

2. What does the term *soluble* mean?

3. What method would you use to separate a pure liquid from a solution of a solid and the liquid?

4. To separate two liquids by fractional distillation they must have different:

   a) melting points

   b) boiling points

   c) colours

   d) viscosities.

End of topic checklist

Key terms

chromatogram, desalination, distillation, fractional distillation, paper chromatography, retention factor, soluble, solvent

During your study of this topic you should have learned:

○ About the appropriate apparatus for the measurement of time, temperature, mass and volume, including burettes, pipettes and measuring cylinders.

○ About the technique of paper chromatography.

○ **EXTENDED** How to interpret simple chromatograms, including the use of R_f values.

○ **EXTENDED** About the importance of purity in substances in everyday life.

○ **EXTENDED** How to identify substances and assess their purity from melting point and boiling point information.

○ How to describe methods of separation and purification by the use of:

● a suitable solvent – to separate a soluble solid from an insoluble solid

● filtration – to separate a solid from a liquid

● crystallisation – to separate a solid from its solution

● distillation – to separate a solid and a liquid from a solution

● fractional distillation – to separate liquids with different boiling points

● paper chromatography – to separate solutions or liquids that are mixed together.

○ How to suggest suitable separation and purification techniques given information about the substances involved.

○ Know that mixtures melt and boil over a range of temperatures.

End of topic questions

Note: The marks given for these questions indicate the level of detail required in the answers. In the examination, the number of marks given to questions like these may be different.

1. You are provided with four samples of black water-soluble inks. Two of the ink samples are identical. Describe how you would use paper chromatography to identify which two ink samples are the same. **(3 marks)**

2. You are trying to separate the dyes in a sample of ink using paper chromatography. You set up the apparatus as shown in Fig. 1.18. After 20 minutes the black spot is unchanged and the water has risen nearly to the top of the filter paper.

    a) Suggest a reason why the black spot has remained unchanged.   **(1 mark)**

    b) What could you change that might lead to a successful separation of the dyes?   **(1 mark)**

3. **EXTENDED** Pure ethanol has a boiling point at normal pressure of 78 °C. What temperature might a sample of ethanol contaminated with sugar boil at?   **(1 mark)**

4. **EXTENDED** What effect will impurities have on the melting point of ice?   **(1 mark)**

5. In the fractional distillation of ethanol and water, why does the ethanol vapour condense in the condenser?   **(1 mark)**

6. Describe how you would produce crystals of sodium chloride from a sodium chloride solution.   **(2 marks)**

7. What process could be used to separate the following mixtures:

    a) sand from a sand/water mixture?   **(1 mark)**

    b) petrol from a petrol/diesel mixture?   **(1 mark)**

    c) pure water from salt solution?   **(1 mark)**

8. **EXTENDED** Look at the chromatogram produced when testing four food colouring compounds A, B, C and D.

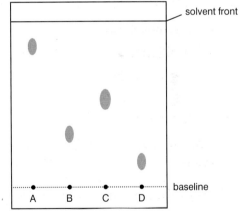

    a) Which compound has the largest retention factor (R_f)?   **(1 mark)**

    b) Which compound has the smallest R_f?   **(1 mark)**

    c) Estimate the R_f for compound C. Explain how you made the estimate.   **(2 marks)**

    d) Why are all R_f values less than 1.0? **(1 mark)**

△ Fig. 1.26

Atoms, elements and compounds

△ Fig. 1.27 A model showing molecular structure.

INTRODUCTION

This topic is about the structure, or the makeup, of all substances. Some substances exist in nature as elements, others as compounds that are formed when elements combine chemically. The topic starts by considering the structure of the atoms that make up elements. It shows how the arrangement of elements in the Periodic Table is determined by the structure of their atoms. The properties of metals and non-metals are explained and an introduction to the combination of atoms forming compounds is provided. The following topics look in more detail at how atoms combine together to form ions and molecules, and the structure of metals.

KNOWLEDGE CHECK

✓ Know the three states of matter and how to use particle theory to explain the conversion of one state into another.
✓ Understand how diffusion experiments provide evidence for the existence of particles.
✓ Know that compounds are formed when elements combine together chemically.
✓ Understand that compounds are formed when the atoms of two or more elements combine together.

LEARNING OBJECTIVES

✓ Be able to identify physical and chemical changes, and understand the differences between them.
✓ **EXTENDED** Understand that some chemical reactions can be reversed by changing the reaction conditions.
✓ Be able to describe the differences between elements, mixtures and compounds, and between metals and non-metals.
✓ Be able to describe the structure of an atom in terms of a central nucleus containing protons and neutrons, and 'shells' of electrons.
✓ Be able to describe the build-up of electrons in 'shells' and understand the significance of the noble gas electronic structures and of outer electrons.
✓ Be able to state the relative charges and approximate relative masses of protons, neutrons and electrons.
✓ Be able to define *proton number* (atomic number) as the number of protons in the nucleus of an atom and *nucleon number* (mass number) as the total number of protons and neutrons in the nucleus of an atom.
✓ Be able to use proton number and the simple structure of atoms to explain the basis of the Periodic Table, with special reference to the elements with proton numbers 1 to 20.
✓ Be able to define *isotopes* as atoms of the same element that have the same proton number but different nucleon number.

✓ **EXTENDED** Understand that isotopes have the same chemical properties because they have the same number of electrons in their outer shells.

✓ Be able to describe the formation of ions by electron loss or gain.

✓ Be able to describe the formation of ionic bonds between elements from Groups I and VII.

✓ **EXTENDED** Be able to describe the formation of ionic bonds more generally as being between metallic and non-metallic elements.

✓ **EXTENDED** Be able to describe the lattice structure of ionic compounds as a regular arrangement of alternating positive and negative ions.

✓ Be able to state that non-metallic elements form simple molecules with covalent bonds between atoms.

✓ Be able to describe the formation of single covalent bonds in H_2, Cl_2, H_2O, CH_4, NH_3 and HCl as the sharing of pairs of electrons leading to the noble gas configuration.

✓ Be able to describe the differences in volatility, solubility and electrical conductivity between ionic and covalent compounds.

✓ **EXTENDED** Be able to represent the bonding in more complex covalent molecules such as N_2, C_2H_4, CH_3OH and CO_2.

✓ **EXTENDED** Be able to explain the differences in melting point and boiling point of ionic and covalent compounds in terms of attractive forces.

✓ Be able to describe the giant covalent structures of graphite and diamond as different forms of carbon.

✓ **EXTENDED** Be able to relate the structures of diamond and graphite to their uses, for example graphite as a lubricant and a conductor and diamond in cutting tools.

✓ **EXTENDED** Be able to describe the macromolecular structure of silicon(IV) oxide (silicon dioxide).

PHYSICAL AND CHEMICAL CHANGES

A chemical change, or chemical reaction, is quite different from physical changes that occur, for example, when sugar dissolves in water.

In a chemical change, one or more new substances are produced. In many cases an observable change is apparent, for example, the colour changes or a gas is produced.

An apparent change in mass can occur. This change is often quite small and difficult to detect unless accurate balances are used. Mass is conserved in *all* chemical reactions – the apparent change in mass usually occurs because one of the reactants or products is a gas (whose mass may not have been measured).

An energy change is almost always involved. In most cases energy is released and the surroundings become warmer. In some cases energy is absorbed from the surroundings, and so the surroundings become colder. Note: Some physical changes, such as evaporation, also have energy changes.

ELEMENTS, COMPOUNDS AND MIXTURES

All matter can be classified into the three categories of elements, compounds and mixtures.

A **mixture** contains more than one substance (elements or compounds). In a mixture, the individual substances can be separated by simple means. This is because the substances in a mixture have not combined chemically.

Most elements can be classified as either **metals** or **non-metals**. In the Periodic Table, the metals are arranged on the left and in the middle, and the non-metals are on the right.

Metals and non-metals have quite different physical and chemical properties.

Δ Fig. 1.28 Non-metals: from left: silicon, chlorine, sulfur.

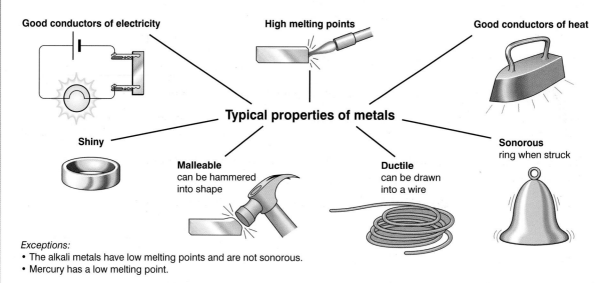

Good conductors of electricity

High melting points

Good conductors of heat

Typical properties of metals

Shiny

Malleable can be hammered into shape

Ductile can be drawn into a wire

Sonorous ring when struck

Exceptions:
• The alkali metals have low melting points and are not sonorous.
• Mercury has a low melting point.

Δ Fig. 1.29 Typical properties of metals.

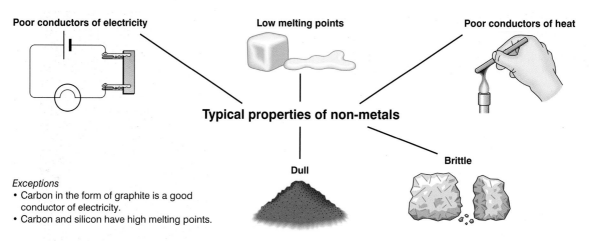

Poor conductors of electricity

Low melting points

Poor conductors of heat

Typical properties of non-metals

Dull

Brittle

Exceptions
• Carbon in the form of graphite is a good conductor of electricity.
• Carbon and silicon have high melting points.

Δ Fig.1.30 Typical properties of non-metals.

An **alloy** is formed when a metal is mixed with other elements.

QUESTIONS

1. What is the main difference between a physical change and a chemical change?

2. What is the difference between a *mixture* and a *compound*?

3. Metals are often *malleable*. What does this mean?

4. a) What is an *alloy*?

   b) What elements are contained in the alloy brass?

EXTENDED

Some chemical reactions can be reversed by changing the reaction conditions.

When **hydrated** blue copper(II) sulfate crystals are heated, a white powder is formed (anhydrous copper(II) sulfate) and water is lost as steam. If water is added to this white powder, hydrated blue copper(II) sulfate is formed again. The reaction is **reversible**:

hydrated copper(II) sulfate crystals	$\rightleftharpoons$	anhydrous copper(II) sulfate	+	water
$CuSO_4.5H_2O(s)$	$\rightleftharpoons$	$CuSO_4(s)$	+	$5H_2O(l)$

A reversible reaction can go from left to right or from right to left – notice the double-headed $\rightleftharpoons$ arrow used when writing these equations.

A similar reaction occurs when hydrated cobalt(II) chloride crystals are heated.

hydrated cobalt(II) chloride	$\rightleftharpoons$	anhydrous cobalt(II) chloride	+	water
$CoCl_2.6H_2O(s)$	$\rightleftharpoons$	$CoCl_2(s)$	+	$6H_2O(l)$

The pink hydrated cobalt(II) chloride crystals turn to blue anhydrous cobalt(II) chloride on strong heating. If water is added to the blue anhydrous cobalt(II) chloride, the pink hydrated cobalt(II) chloride is reformed.

END OF EXTENDED

△ Fig. 1.31 When hydrated copper(II) sulfate crystals are heated they turn from blue to white. The reaction can then be reversed by adding water.

BIOLOGY – BIOLOGICAL MOLECULES

- The behaviour of the different types of particles – atoms, molecules and ions – is important in describing how the different life processes happen.

- The combination of atoms of different elements into molecules leads to the chemicals required for life to exist.

- Although some of the molecules required for life processes are very complicated, they arise through the same rules of combination that apply to the simplest compounds.

- Particular elements must be present for living things to survive correctly – for example, plants need particular 'nutrients', a number of which are simply chemical elements.

PHYSICS – ATOMIC PHYSICS

- Knowing how the atom itself has an internal structure is critical to the development of ideas that can explain why radioactivity happens.

ATOMIC STRUCTURE

In 1808 the British chemist John Dalton published a book outlining his theory of atoms. These were the main points of his theory:

- All matter is made of small, indivisible spheres called atoms.
- All the atoms of a given element are identical and have the same mass.
- The atoms of different elements have different masses.
- Chemical compounds are formed when different atoms join together.

All the molecules of a chemical **compound** have the same type and number of atoms.

An element is the smallest part of a substance that can exist on its own. When two or more elements combine together a compound is formed.

Since 1808, atomic theory has developed considerably and yet many of Dalton's ideas are still correct. Modern theory is built on an understanding of the particles that make up atoms – the so-called sub-atomic particles.

Sub-atomic particles

The smallest amount of an element that still behaves like that element is an atom. Each element has its own unique type of atom. Atoms are made up of smaller, sub-atomic particles. The three main sub-atomic particles are **protons**, **neutrons** and **electrons**.

These particles are very small and have very little mass. However, it is possible to compare their masses using a relative scale. Their charges may also be compared in a similar way. The proton and neutron have the same mass, and the proton and electron have equal but opposite charges.

Sub-atomic particle	Relative mass	Relative charge
Proton	1	+1
Neutron	1	0
Electron	about $\frac{1}{2000}$	−1

△ Table 1.2 Relative masses and charges of sub-atomic particles.

Protons and neutrons are found in the centre of the atom in a cluster called the **nucleus**. The electrons form a series of 'shells' around the nucleus.

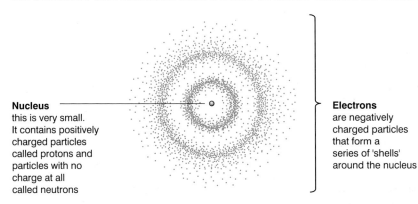

Nucleus
this is very small.
It contains positively
charged particles
called protons and
particles with no
charge at all
called neutrons

Electrons
are negatively
charged particles
that form a
series of 'shells'
around the nucleus

△ Fig. 1.32 Structure of an atom.

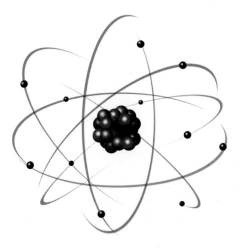

△ Fig. 1.33 Diagrams are another way of representing the structure of an atom.

Proton number and nucleon number

In order to describe the numbers of protons, neutrons and electrons in an atom, scientists use two numbers. These are called the **proton number** (or **atomic number**) and the **nucleon number** (or **mass number**). The proton number, as you might expect, describes the number of protons in the atom. The nucleon number describes the number of particles in the nucleus of the atom – that is, the total number of protons and neutrons.

Proton numbers are used to arrange the elements in the Periodic Table. The atomic structures of the first ten elements in the Periodic Table are shown in Table 1.3.

Hydrogen is the only atom that has no neutrons.

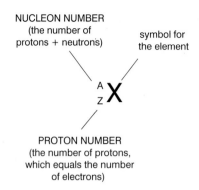

NUCLEON NUMBER
(the number of
protons + neutrons)

symbol for
the element

$^{A}_{Z}X$

PROTON NUMBER
(the number of protons,
which equals the number
of electrons)

△ Fig. 1.34 Chemical symbol showing nucleon number and proton number.

Element	Proton number	Nucleon number	Number of protons	Number of neutrons	Number of electrons
Hydrogen	1	1	1	0	1
Helium	2	4	2	2	2
Lithium	3	7	3	4	3
Beryllium	4	9	4	5	4
Boron	5	11	5	6	5
Carbon	6	12	6	6	6
Nitrogen	7	14	7	7	7
Oxygen	8	16	8	8	8
Fluorine	9	19	9	10	9
Neon	10	20	10	10	10

△ Table 1.3 Atomic structures of the first ten elements.

QUESTIONS

1. Which sub-atomic particle has the smallest relative mass?

2. Why do atoms have the same number of protons as electrons?

3. An aluminium atom can be represented as $^{27}_{13}$Al.

    a) What is aluminium's nucleon number?

    b) How many neutrons does this atom of aluminium have?

Isotopes

Atoms of the same element with the same number of protons and electrons but different numbers of neutrons are called **isotopes**. For example, there are two isotopes of chlorine:

Symbol	Number of protons	Number of neutrons
$^{35}_{17}$Cl	17	18
$^{37}_{17}$Cl	17	20

△ Table 1.4 Isotopes of chlorine.

The chemical properties of an element depend on the number of electrons in the outer electron shell. As isotopes of the same element have the same number of electrons they have the same chemical properties.

SCIENCE IN CONTEXT

SUB-ATOMIC PARTICLES

△ Fig. 1.35 The Large Hadron Collider at CERN in Switzerland.

Protons, neutrons and electrons are the particles from which atoms are made. However, in the past 20 years or so scientists have discovered a number of other sub-atomic particles: quarks, leptons, muons, neutrinos, bosons and gluons. The properties of some of these particles have become well known, but there is still much to learn about the others. Finding out about these, and possibly other sub-atomic particles, is one of the challenges of the 21st century.

To study the smallest known particles, a particle accelerator has been built underground at CERN near Geneva, Switzerland. This giant instrument, called the Large Hadron Collider (LHC), has a circumference of 27 km. It attempts to recreate the conditions that existed just after the 'Big Bang' by colliding beams of particles at very high speed – only about 5 m/s slower than the speed of light. It promises to revolutionise scientific understanding of the nature of atoms. Who knows – school science in 10 or 20 years' time may be very different from your lessons today!

QUESTIONS

1. What are *isotopes*?

Arrangements of electrons in the atom

An atom's electrons are arranged in **shells** around the nucleus. These do not all contain the same number of electrons – the shell nearest to the nucleus can take only two electrons, whereas the next one out from the nucleus can take eight.

Electron shell	Maximum number of electrons
1	2
2	8
3	8 (initially, with up to 18 after element 20)

△ Table 1.5 Maximum number of electrons in a shell.

Oxygen has a proton number of 8, so it has 8 electrons. Of these, two are in the first shell and six are in the second shell. This arrangement is written 2,6. A phosphorus atom with a proton number of 15 has 15 electrons, arranged 2,8,5. The electrons in the outer electron shell that are involved in chemical bonding are known as the **valency electrons**.

Atom diagrams

The atomic structure of an atom can be shown simply in a diagram.

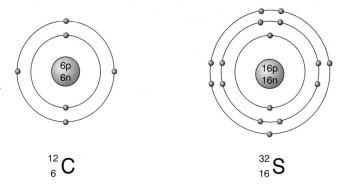

$$^{12}_{6}\text{C}$$

$$^{32}_{16}\text{S}$$

△ Fig. 1.36 Atom diagrams for carbon and sulfur showing the numbers of protons and neutrons and the electron arrangements.

The arrangement of electrons in an atom is called its **electronic configuration**.

Electronic configuration: The first 20 elements of the Periodic Table

There are over 100 different elements. They are arranged in the Periodic Table according to their chemical and physical properties.

The chemical properties of elements depend on the arrangement of electrons in their atoms. The electronic structure of the first 20 elements is shown in Table 1.6.

Element	Symbol	Proton number	Electron number	Electronic configuration
Hydrogen	H	1	1	1
Helium	He	2	2	2
Lithium	Li	3	3	2,1
Beryllium	Be	4	4	2,2
Boron	B	5	5	2,3
Carbon	C	6	6	2,4
Nitrogen	N	7	7	2,5
Oxygen	O	8	8	2,6
Fluorine	F	9	9	2,7
Neon	Ne	10	10	2,8
Sodium	Na	11	11	2,8,1
Magnesium	Mg	12	12	2,8,2
Aluminium	Al	13	13	2,8,3
Silicon	Si	14	14	2,8,4
Phosphorus	P	15	15	2,8,5
Sulfur	S	16	16	2,8,6
Chlorine	Cl	17	17	2,8,7
Argon	Ar	18	18	2,8,8
Potassium	K	19	19	2,8,8,1
Calcium	Ca	20	20	2,8,8,2

△ Table 1.6 Electronic structure of the first 20 elements.

Periodicity and electronic configuration

In the Periodic Table lithium, sodium and potassium are placed on the left, and neon and argon are placed on the right. The proton number increases from lithium to neon, moving through a section, or **period**, of the Periodic Table. The number of electrons in the outer shell increases. This is called **periodicity**.

Electronic configuration and chemical properties

Elements that have similar electronic configurations have similar chemical properties.

Lithium (2,1), sodium (2,8,1) and potassium (2,8,8,1) all have one electron in their outer shell. These are all highly reactive metals. They are called Group I elements.

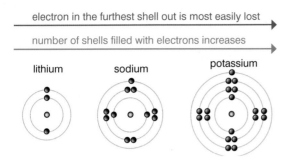

electron in the furthest shell out is most easily lost →

number of shells filled with electrons increases →

lithium   sodium   potassium

△ Fig. 1.37 Electronic configurations of lithium, sodium and potassium.

Fluorine (2,7), chlorine (2,8,7), bromine (2,8,18,7) and iodine (2,8,18,18,7) all have seven electrons in their outer shell. These elements are all highly reactive non-metals. They are called Group VII elements, or halogens.

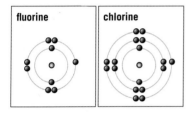

fluorine   chlorine

△ Fig. 1.38 Electronic configuration of fluorine and chlorine.

Similarly, all the elements in Group III of the Periodic Table have three electrons in their outer electron shell.

The elements helium (2), neon (2,8), argon (2,8,8), krypton (2,8,18,8) and xenon (2,8,18,18,8) either have a full outer shell or have eight electrons in their outer shell and therefore the atoms do not lose or gain electrons easily. This means that these gases are unreactive. They are called **noble gases**.

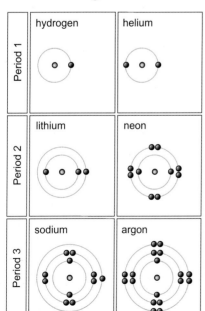

Period 1 | hydrogen | helium
Period 2 | lithium | neon
Period 3 | sodium | argon

△ Fig. 1.39 Electronic configurations of helium, neon and argon.

△ Fig. 1.40 Neon lighting in Hong Kong.

1. **a)** How many electrons does magnesium have in its outer electron shell?

   b) In which group of the Periodic Table is magnesium?

2. Draw atom diagrams for:

   a) aluminium

   b) calcium.

3. Why are noble gases unreactive?

IONS AND IONIC BONDS

When the atoms of elements react and join together, they form compounds. When one of the reacting atoms is a metal, the compound formed is called an ionic compound. They do not contain molecules; instead they are made of particles called ions. Ionic compounds have similar physical properties, many of which are quite different from the properties of substances made up of atoms or molecules.

△ Fig. 1.41 Sodium chloride is an example of an ionic compound.

THE FORMATION OF IONS

Atoms bond with other atoms in a **chemical reaction** to make a compound. For example, sodium reacts with chlorine to make sodium chloride. **Ionic compounds** contain a metal combined with one or more non-metals. They are not made up of molecules – they are made up of **ions**.

Ions are formed from atoms by the gain or loss of electrons. Both metals and non-metals try to achieve complete (filled) outer electron shells or the electron configuration of the nearest noble gas.

Metals lose electrons from their outer shells and form positive ions. Non-metals gain electrons in their outer shells and form negative ions.

The bonding process can be represented in dot and cross diagrams. Look at the reaction between sodium and chlorine as an example.

Sodium is a metal. It has a proton number of 11 and so has 11 electrons, arranged 2,8,1. Its atom diagram looks like this:	Chlorine is a non-metal. It has a proton number of 17 and so has 17 electrons, arranged 2,8,7. Its atom diagram looks like this:

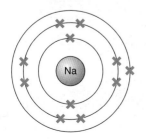

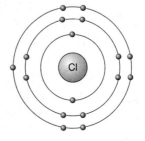

△ Fig. 1.42 Dot and cross diagrams for sodium and chlorine.

Sodium has one electron in its outer shell. It can achieve a full outer shell by losing this electron. The sodium atom transfers its outermost electron to the chlorine atom.	Chlorine has seven electrons in its outer shell. It can achieve a full outer shell by gaining an extra electron. The chlorine atom accepts an electron from the sodium.

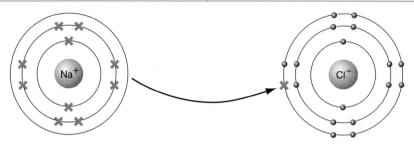

△ Fig. 1.43 Dot and cross diagram for sodium chloride, NaCl.

The sodium is no longer an atom; it is now an ion. It does not have equal numbers of protons and electrons, so it is no longer neutral. It has one more proton than it has electrons, so it is a positive ion with a charge of 1+. The ion is written as Na⁺.	The chlorine is no longer an atom; it is now an ion. It does not have equal numbers of protons and electrons, so it is no longer neutral. It has one more electron than it has protons, so it is a negative ion with a charge of 1−. The ion is written as Cl⁻.

EXTENDED

METALS CAN TRANSFER MORE THAN ONE ELECTRON TO A NON-METAL

Magnesium combines with oxygen to form magnesium oxide. The magnesium (electron arrangement 2,8,2) transfers two electrons to the oxygen (electron arrangement 2,6). Magnesium therefore forms an Mg^{2+} ion and oxygen forms an O^{2-} ion.

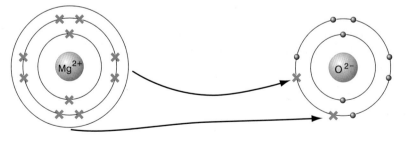

△ Fig. 1.44 Dot and cross diagram for magnesium oxide, MgO.

Aluminium has an electron arrangement 2,8,3. When it combines with fluorine with an electron arrangement 2,7, three fluorine atoms are needed for each aluminium atom. The formula of aluminium fluoride is therefore AlF_3.

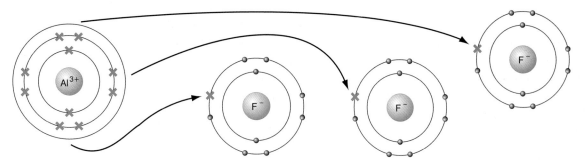

△ Fig. 1.45 Dot and cross diagram for aluminium fluoride, AlF_3.

REMEMBER

Many students find it difficult to remember the difference between oxidation and reduction. In ionic bonding the atom that loses electrons is said to be *oxidised*. The atom that gains the electrons is said to be *reduced*. So, aluminium is oxidised and fluorine is reduced when aluminium fluoride is made.

END OF EXTENDED

QUESTIONS

1. Draw a dot and cross diagram to show how lithium and fluorine atoms combine to form lithium fluoride. You must show the starting atoms and the finishing ions. (Proton numbers: Li 3; F 9)

2. **EXTENDED** Draw a dot and cross diagram to show how calcium and sulfur atoms combine to form calcium sulfide. You must show the starting atoms and finishing ions. (Proton numbers: Ca 20; S 16)

3. **EXTENDED** How do you know that phosphorus oxide is not an ionic compound?

Electronic configuration and ionic charge

When atoms form ions, they are trying to achieve the electronic configuration of their nearest noble gas. Some common ions and their electronic configurations are shown in Table 1.7.

Ion	Electronic configuration
Li^+	2
Na^+	2,8
Mg^{2+}	2,8
F^-	2,8
Cl^-	2,8,8
O^{2-}	2,8

△ Table 1.7 Electronic configurations of some ions.

PROPERTIES OF IONIC COMPOUNDS

Ionic compounds have high melting points and high boiling points because of strong electrostatic forces between the ions.

The strong electrostatic attraction between oppositely charged ions is called an **ionic bond**.

Ionic compounds form giant lattice structures. For example, when sodium chloride is formed by ionic bonding, the ions do not pair up. Each sodium ion is surrounded by six chloride ions, and each chloride ion is surrounded by six sodium ions.

The electrostatic attractions between the ions are very strong. The properties of sodium chloride can be explained using this model of its structure.

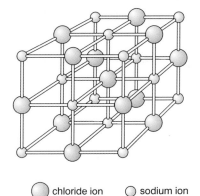

chloride ion ◯ sodium ion

△ Fig. 1.46 In solid sodium chloride, the ions are held firmly in place. All ionic compounds have giant ionic lattice structures like this.

△ Fig. 1.47 Crystals of sodium chloride.

Properties of sodium chloride	Explanation in terms of structure
Hard crystals	Strong forces of attraction between the oppositely charged ions
High melting point (801 °C)	Strong forces of attraction between the oppositely charged ions
Dissolves in water	The water is also able to form strong electrostatic attractions with the ions – the ions are 'plucked' off the lattice structure
Does not conduct electricity when solid	Strong forces between the ions prevent them from moving
Conducts electricity when molten or dissolved in water	The strong forces between the ions have been broken down and so the ions are able to move

△ Table 1.8 Properties of sodium chloride.

Magnesium oxide is another ionic compound. Its ionic formula is $Mg^{2+}O^{2-}$.

MgO has a much higher melting point and boiling point than NaCl because of the increased charges on the ions. The forces holding the ions together are stronger in MgO than in NaCl.

END OF EXTENDED

 SCIENCE IN CONTEXT

MAGNESIUM OXIDE

Magnesium oxide is a very versatile compound. It is used extensively in the construction industry, both in making cement and in making fire-proof construction materials. The fact that it has a melting point of over 2800 °C makes it ideal for this use.

▷ Fig. 1.48 The heat resistance of magnesium oxide means that it is used to line furnaces.

SCIENCE IN CONTEXT

IONIC CRYSTALS

△ Fig. 1.49 Gemstones are examples of ionic crystals.

All ionic compounds form giant structures, and all have relatively high melting and boiling points. The charges on the ions determine the strength of the electrostatic attraction between the ions, and hence the melting and boiling points of the compound compared to others.

Another factor that affects the strength of the electrostatic attraction is the relative sizes of the positive and negative ions and how well they are able to pack together. The overall arrangement of the ions is determined by attractive forces between oppositely charged ions and repulsive forces between similarly charged ions. In sodium chloride, for example, six chloride ions fit around one sodium ion without the chloride ions getting too close together and repelling one another. Similarly, six sodium ions can fit around one chloride ion. This structure is sometimes called a 6:6 lattice (see Fig. 1.46 for a diagram of this structure).

Caesium is a metal in the same group of the Periodic Table as sodium, but caesium ions are much bigger than sodium ions. In the structure of caesium chloride, eight chloride ions can fit around each caesium ion. So although sodium and caesium are in the same group, their chlorides have different structures.

Some of the most valuable gemstones are ionic compounds. Rubies and sapphires, for example, are both aluminium oxide. The different colours of the gemstones are due to traces of other metals such as iron, titanium and chromium.

QUESTIONS

1. **EXTENDED** Why does an ionic compound such as magnesium oxide not conduct electricity when it is solid?

2. **EXTENDED** Suggest a reason why magnesium oxide has a higher melting point than sodium chloride.

MOLECULES AND COVALENT BONDS

Unlike ionic compounds, covalent substances are formed when atoms of non-metals combine. Although covalent substances all contain the same type of bond, their properties can be quite different – some are gases, others are very hard solids with high melting points. Plastics are a common type of covalent substance. Because chemists now understand how the molecules form and link together, they can produce plastics with almost the perfect properties for a particular use, from soft and flexible (as in contact lenses) to hard and rigid (as in electrical sockets).

△ Fig. 1.50 All plastics are covalent substances.

How covalent bonds are formed

Covalent bonding involves electron sharing and occurs between atoms of non-metals. It results in the formation of a **molecule**.

The non-metal atoms try to achieve complete outer electron shells or the electron arrangement of the nearest noble gas by sharing electrons.

A single **covalent bond** is formed when two atoms each contribute one electron to a shared pair of electrons. For example, hydrogen gas exists as H_2 molecules. Each hydrogen atom needs to fill its electron shell. They can do this by sharing electrons.

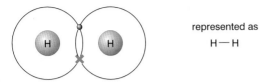

represented as

H—H

△ Fig. 1.51 The dot and cross diagram and displayed formula of H_2.

A covalent bond is the result of attraction between the bonding pair of electrons (negative charges) and the nuclei (positive charges) of the atoms involved in the bond. A single covalent bond can be represented by a single line. The formula of a hydrogen molecule can be written as a displayed formula, H—H. The hydrogen atoms and oxygen atoms in water are also held together by single covalent bonds.

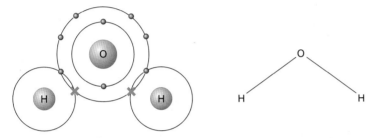

△ Fig. 1.52 Water contains single covalent bonds.

The hydrogen and carbon atoms in methane are held together by single covalent bonds.

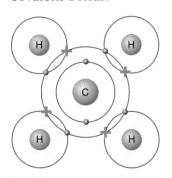

△ Fig. 1.53 Methane contains four single covalent bonds.

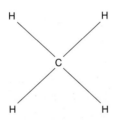

△ Fig. 1.54 The displayed formula for methane.

The hydrogen chloride molecule, HCl, is also held together by a single covalent bond.

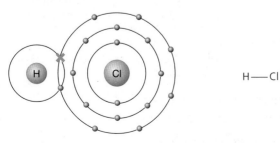

H—Cl

△ Fig. 1.55 Hydrogen chloride has a single covalent bond.

Ethane has a slightly more complex electron arrangement.

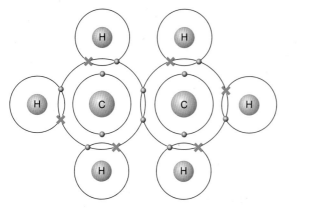

△ Fig. 1.56 Covalent bonds in ethane.

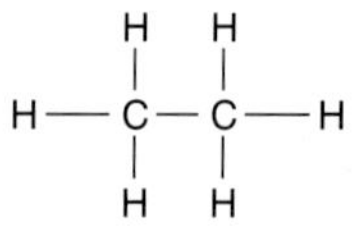

△ Fig. 1.57 Displayed formula for ethane.

The alcohol methanol is covalently bonded as shown in Fig. 1.58.

Methanol $CH_3 OH$

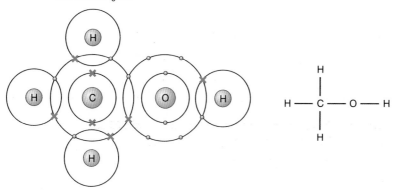

△ Fig. 1.58 Covalent bonds in methanol.

Some molecules contain double covalent bonds. In carbon dioxide, the carbon atom has an electron arrangement of 2,4 and needs an additional four electrons to complete its outer electron shell. It needs to share its four electrons with four electrons from oxygen atoms (electron arrangement 2,6). So two oxygen atoms are needed, each sharing two electrons with the carbon atom.

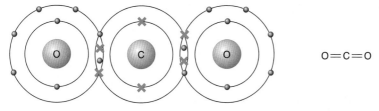

△ Fig. 1.59 Carbon dioxide contains double bonds.

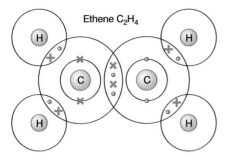

Ethene C₂H₄

H H
| |
C═C
| |
H H

△ Fig. 1.60 Ethene contains a double bond.

Some molecules contain triple covalent bonds. In the nitrogen molecule, each nitrogen atom has an electron arrangement of 2,5 and needs an additional three electrons to complete its outer electron shell.

It needs to share three of its outer electrons with another nitrogen atom. This forms a triple bond, which is shown as N≡N.

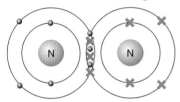

◁ Fig. 1.61 A nitrogen molecule contains a triple bond.

END OF EXTENDED

QUESTIONS

1. Draw a dot and cross diagram and displayed formula to show how the covalent bonds are formed in chlorine gas (Cl_2). The proton number of chlorine is 17.

2. Draw a dot and cross diagram and displayed formula to show how the covalent bonds are formed in the gas ammonia (NH_3). The proton number of hydrogen is 1; the proton number of nitrogen is 7.

3. **EXTENDED** Draw a dot and cross diagram and displayed formula to show the double bond in an oxygen molecule (O_2). The proton number of oxygen is 8.

4. **EXTENDED** Draw a dot and cross diagram and displayed formula to show the covalent bonds in hydrazine (N_2H_4). The proton number of hydrogen is 1; the proton number of nitrogen is 7.

How many covalent bonds can an element form?

The number of covalent bonds a non-metal atom can form is linked to its position in the Periodic Table. Metals (Groups I, II, III) do not form covalent bonds. The noble gases in Group 0, for example helium, neon and argon, are unreactive and also do not usually form covalent bonds.

Group in the Periodic Table	I	II	III	IV	V	VI	VII	VIII(0)
Covalent bonds formed	–	–	–	4	3	2	1	–

△ Table 1.9 Group number and number of covalent bonds formed.

Molecular crystals

Covalent compounds can form simple molecular crystals. Many covalent crystals exist only in the solid form at low temperatures. Some simple molecular crystals are ice, solid carbon dioxide and iodine.

EXTENDED

Properties of covalent compounds

Substances with molecular structures are usually gases, liquids or solids with low melting points and boiling points.

Covalent bonds are strong bonds. They are **intramolecular** bonds – formed *within* each molecule. Much weaker **intermolecular** forces attract the individual molecules to each other.

The properties of covalent compounds can be explained using a simple model involving these two types of bond or forces.

Properties of hydrogen	Explanation in terms of structure
Hydrogen is a gas with a very low melting point (−259 °C).	The intermolecular forces of attraction between the molecules are weak.
Hydrogen does not conduct electricity.	There are no ions or free electrons present. The covalent bond (intramolecular bond) is a strong bond and the electrons cannot be removed from it easily.

△ Table 1.10 Properties of hydrogen.

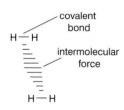

△ Fig. 1.62 Force in and between hydrogen molecules.

END OF EXTENDED

Comparing the properties of covalent and ionic compounds

Simple covalent compounds typically have very different properties from ionic compounds. A comparison can be seen in Table 1.11. The volatility of a compound is a measure of how easily it forms a vapour. Compounds with low melting and boiling points are often described as being volatile.

Property	Ionic compounds	Simple covalent compounds
Volatility	Non-volatile (high melting and boiling points)	Volatile (low melting and boiling points)
Solubility	Often soluble in water	Mostly insoluble in water
Electrical conductivity	Conduct electricity only when dissolved in water or molten (the ions separate and are free to move, carrying their electric charge)	Low electrical conductivity – are non-electrolytes (do not contain ions and so cannot carry an electrical current; however, some covalent compounds do form ions when dissolved in water)

△ Table 1.11 Comparison of simple covalent compounds with ionic compounds.

EXTENDED

Type of compound	Intermolecular force	Property
Ionic	Strong	High melting and boiling points
Simple covalent	Weak	Low melting and boiling points

END OF EXTENDED

QUESTIONS

1. **EXTENDED** Why does a covalently bonded compound such as carbon dioxide have a relatively low melting point?

2. Would you expect a covalently bonded compound such as ethanol to conduct electricity? Explain your answer.

MACROMOLECULES

Diamond and graphite

Some covalently bonded compounds do not exist as simple molecular structures in the way that hydrogen does. Diamond, for example, has a giant structure with each carbon atom covalently bonded to four others (Fig. 1.64). Another form of carbon is graphite. Graphite has a different giant structure, as seen in Fig. 1.65. Different forms of the same element, like these, are called **allotropes**. In diamond, each carbon atom forms four strong covalent bonds. In graphite, each carbon atom forms three strong covalent bonds. There are weak forces of attraction between the layers in graphite (Fig. 1.65).

△ Fig. 1.63 A cut diamond is one of the hardest substances in nature.

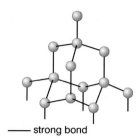

—— strong bond

△ Fig. 1.64 Structure of diamond.

△ Fig. 1.65 Graphite is made of the same atoms as diamond but with a different molecular structure.

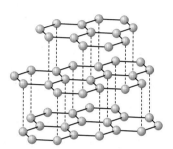

Structure of graphite.

The atoms in both diamond and graphite are held together by strong covalent bonds, which result in very high sublimation or melting points. Diamond has a melting point of about 3730 °C.

EXTENDED

In diamond, all the bonding is extremely strong, which makes diamond an extremely hard substance – one of the hardest natural substances known. This is why diamonds are used in cutting.

In graphite, carbon atoms form layers of hexagons in the plane of their strong covalent bonds. The weak forces of attraction are between the layers. Because the layers can slide over each other, graphite is flaky and can be used as a lubricant. Graphite can also conduct electricity, because the fourth unbonded electron from each carbon atom is **delocalised** and so can move along the layer.

END OF EXTENDED

SCIENCE IN CONTEXT

DIAMONDS

Diamond is the hardest naturally occurring material in the world. It is formed by high pressures and high temperatures deep underground. Volcanic eruptions often bring the diamonds closer to the surface, where they can be mined. In some cases diamonds can be mined almost on the surface of the land, whereas in other cases tunnels need to be dug deep into the ground. Diamonds are mined throughout Africa. The ore is called kimberlite, and diamonds are found in kimberlite gravels and pipe formations.

After mining, the ore is crushed, washed and screened by X-rays to find the diamonds. Finally the diamonds are sorted by hand, then washed and classified for sale. Diamond mining and recovery is a very clean operation. Processing of the ore uses no toxic chemicals and produces no chemical pollutants. However, getting the diamonds from deep in the ground can be very dangerous for the miners.

△ Fig. 1.66 This saw has diamonds on its cutting edges.

The quality of diamonds used in jewellery is judged in terms of the four Cs: carat weight, colour, clarity (how transparent the diamond is and how well it reflects light) and cut (the shape of the diamond). One carat is 0.2 g. Although the carat weight is the most important, prices can vary widely depending on the other three factors. In 2009 the largest producers were Russia and Botswana, each producing about 32 million carats of uncut diamonds. In the same year the world demand for diamonds was estimated at 39 billion dollars. Diamonds are clearly big business!

△ Fig. 1.67 An open cast diamond mine in Yakutia, Russia.

Silicon(IV) oxide

Silicon(IV) oxide (silicon dioxide, SiO_2) is another giant covalent molecule. It is the main component of sand.

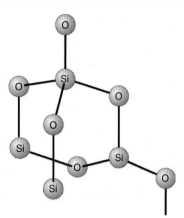

△ Fig. 1.68 The structure of silicon(IV) oxide.

You can see from its structure that every silicon atom has four covalent bonds. The structure is similar to the diamond structure in Fig. 1.64, which is why silicon(IV) oxide has a high melting point and is hard like diamond.

Structures can usually be identified as being 'giant' or 'molecular' from their melting points.

Structure	Atom	Molecule	Ion
Giant	Diamond, graphite and metals have high melting points	Sand (silicon(IV) oxide) has a high melting point	All ionic compounds such as sodium chloride have high melting points
Simple molecular	Noble gases such as helium have low melting points	Carbon dioxide, water have low melting points	None

△ Table 1.12 Giant structures have higher melting points than simple molecular structures.

QUESTIONS

1. Explain why diamond has a very high melting point.

2. How is the structure of graphite different from that of diamond?

End of topic checklist

Key terms

allotropes, chemical reaction, compound, covalent bond, delocalised electrons, electron, electronic configuration, intermolecular, intramolecular, ion, ionic bond, ionic compound, isotopes, metal, mixture, molecule, neutron, noble gases, non-metal, nucleon number (mass number), nucleus, period, periodicity, proton, proton number (atomic number), shell, volatile

During your study of this topic you should have learned:

○ About physical and chemical changes and the difference between them.

○ EXTENDED That some chemical reactions can be reversed by changing the reaction conditions.

○ About the differences between elements, mixtures and compounds, and between metals and non-metals.

○ About the structure of an atom in terms of a central nucleus containing protons and neutrons, and 'shells' of electrons.

○ About the relative charges and approximate relative masses of protons, neutrons and electrons.

○ How to define *proton number* (atomic number) and *nucleon number* (mass number).

○ How to use proton numbers and the simple structure of atoms to explain the basis of the Periodic Table, with special reference to the elements with proton numbers 1 to 20.

○ That the arrangement of electrons in an atom can be worked out from the atom's position in the Periodic Table.

○ How to describe the build-up of electrons in 'shells' and understand the significance of the noble gas electronic structures and of valency or outer electrons.

○ How to define *isotopes*.

○ EXTENDED Understand that isotopes have the same properties because they have the same number of electrons in their outer shell.

○ How to describe the formation of ions by electron loss or gain.

○ How to describe the formation of ionic bonds between elements from Groups I and VII.

End of topic checklist continued

○ **EXTENDED** How to describe the formation of ionic bonds between metallic and non-metallic elements.

○ **EXTENDED** How to describe the lattice structure of ionic compounds as a regular arrangement of alternating positive and negative ions.

○ That non-metallic elements form simple molecules with covalent bonds between atoms.

○ How to describe the formation of single covalent bonds in H_2, Cl_2, H_2O, CH_4, NH_3 and HCl as the sharing of pairs of electrons leading to the noble gas configuration.

○ How to describe the differences in volatility, solubility and electrical conductivity between ionic and covalent compounds.

○ **EXTENDED** How to represent the bonding in more complex covalent molecules such as N_2, C_2H_4, CH_3OH and CO_2.

○ **EXTENDED** How to explain the differences in melting point and boiling point of ionic and covalent compounds in terms of forces.

○ How to describe the giant covalent structures of graphite and diamond as different forms of carbon.

○ **EXTENDED** How to relate the structures of diamond and graphite to their uses, for example graphite as a lubricant and a conductor and diamond in cutting tools.

○ **EXTENDED** How to describe the macromolecular structure of silicon(IV) oxide (silicon dioxide).

End of topic questions

Note: The marks given for these questions indicate the level of detail required in the answers. In the examination, the number of marks given to questions like these may be different.

1. What is the relative mass of a proton? (1 mark)

2. Explain the meaning of:

   a) *proton number* (atomic number) (1 mark)

   b) *nucleon number* (mass number). (1 mark)

3. Chlorine has two common isotopes, chlorine-35 and chlorine-37.

   a) What is an *isotope*? (1 mark)

   b) What are the numbers of protons, neutrons and electrons in each isotope? (2 marks)

4. Copy and complete the table. (4 marks)

Atom	Number of protons	Number of neutrons	Number of electrons	Electron arrangement
$^{28}_{14}Si$				
$^{24}_{12}Mg$				
$^{32}_{16}S$				
$^{40}_{18}Ar$				

5. The table shows information about the structure of six particles (A–F).

Particle	Protons	Neutrons	Electrons
A	8	8	10
B	12	12	10
C	6	6	6
D	8	10	10
E	6	8	6
F	11	12	11

a) In each of questions i) to v), choose one of the six particles A–F. Each letter may be used once, more than once or not at all.

Choose a particle that:

i) has a nucleon number of 12 (1 mark)

ii) has the highest nucleon number (1 mark)

iii) has no overall charge (1 mark)

iv) has an overall positive charge (1 mark)

v) is the same element as particle E. (1 mark)

b) Draw an atom diagram for particle E. (2 marks)

6. Draw an atom diagram for:

a) oxygen (2 marks)

b) potassium. (2 marks)

7. For each of parts a) to d) say whether the statement is TRUE or FALSE.

There is a relationship between the group number of the first 20 elements in the Periodic Table and:

a) the number of protons in an atom of the element (1 mark)

b) the number of neutrons in an atom of the element (1 mark)

c) the number of electrons in an atom of the element (1 mark)

d) the number of electrons in the outer electron shell of the element. (1 mark)

8. EXTENDED There are two common isotopes of chlorine, chlorine-35 and chlorine-37. Explain why these different isotopes have exactly the same chemical properties. (2 marks)

9. For each of the following reactions, say whether the compound formed is ionic or not:

a) hydrogen and chlorine (1 mark)

b) carbon and hydrogen (1 mark)

c) sodium and oxygen (1 mark)

d) chlorine and oxygen (1 mark)

e) calcium and bromine. (1 mark)

10. Write down the formulae of the ions formed by the following elements:

a) potassium (1 mark)

b) aluminium (1 mark)

c) sulfur (1 mark)

d) fluorine. (1 mark)

11. The table below shows the electronic arrangement of three atoms, X, Y and Z. Copy and complete the table to show the electronic arrangements and charges of the ions these atoms will form. (3 marks)

Atom	Electronic arrangement of the atom	Electronic arrangement of the ion	Charge on the ion
X	2,6		
Y	2,8,8,2		
Z	2,1		

12. **EXTENDED** Draw dot and cross diagrams to show how the following atoms combine to form ionic compounds. (You must show the electronic arrangements of the starting atoms and the finishing ions.)

   a) potassium and oxygen (proton numbers: K 19; O 8)   **(2 marks)**

   b) magnesium and chlorine (proton numbers: Mg 12; Cl 17)   **(2 marks)**

13. **EXTENDED** Explain why an ionic substance such as potassium chloride:

   a) has a high melting point   **(2 marks)**

   b) can conduct electricity.   **(2 marks)**

14. **EXTENDED** Explain why magnesium oxide has a higher melting point and boiling point than sodium chloride.   **(2 marks)**

15. **EXTENDED** Draw dot and cross diagrams to show the bonding in the following compounds:

   a) hydrogen fluoride, HF   **(2 marks)**

   b) carbon disulfide, CS_2 **(2 marks)**

   c) ethanol, C_2H_5OH.   **(2 marks)**

16. **EXTENDED** Candle wax is a covalently bonded compound. Explain why candle wax has a relatively low melting point.   **(2 marks)**

17. Ozone (O_3) is a gas found in the Earth's atmosphere. How do you know that ozone is covalently bonded and not ionically bonded?   **(2 marks)**

18. **EXTENDED** Explain why methane (CH_4), which has strong covalent bonds between the carbon atom and the hydrogen atoms, is a gas at room temperature and pressure and has a very low melting point.   **(2 marks)**

19. **EXTENDED** Substance X has a simple molecular structure.

   a) In which state(s) of matter might you expect it to exist at room temperature and pressure? Explain your answer.   **(2 marks)**

   b) How would you expect the boiling point of X to compare with the boiling point of an ionic compound such as sodium chloride? Explain your answer.

   (2 marks)

20. **EXTENDED** Use the structure of graphite to explain:

   a) how carbon fibres can add strength to tennis rackets.   **(2 marks)**

   b) how graphite conducts electricity.   **(2 marks)**

21. **EXTENDED a)** Diamond is probably the hardest naturally occurring material in the world. Explain this by referring to the structure of diamond.   **(2 marks)**

   b) Apart from jewellery, name another use of diamond.   **(1 mark)**

Stoichiometry

INTRODUCTION

Stoichiometry is the branch of chemistry concerned with the relative quantities of reactants and products in a chemical reaction. A study of stoichiometry depends on balanced chemical equations which, in turn, depend on knowledge of the chemical symbols for the elements and the formulae of chemical compounds. This topic starts by considering how simple chemical formulae are written and then looks in detail at chemical equations. The topic then focuses on how chemical equations can be used to work out how much reactant is needed to make a certain amount of product.

△ Fig. 1.69 When this reaction is described as S(s) + O_2(g) → SO_2(g), it is understood by chemists all over the world.

KNOWLEDGE CHECK

✓ Know that elements are made up of atoms.
✓ Know that compounds are formed when atoms combine together.
✓ Know that molecules are formed in covalent bonding and that ions are formed in ionic bonding.

LEARNING OBJECTIVES

✓ Be able to use the symbols of the elements and write the formulae of simple compounds.
✓ Be able to deduce the formula of a simple compound from the relative number of atoms present.
✓ Be able to deduce the formula of a simple compound from a model or a diagrammatic representation.
✓ Be able to construct and use word equations.
✓ Be able to interpret and balance simple symbol equations.
✓ **EXTENDED** Be able to determine the formula of an ionic compound from the charges on the ions present.
✓ **EXTENDED** Be able to construct symbol equations with state symbols, including ionic equations.
✓ **EXTENDED** Be able to deduce the balanced equation for a chemical reaction, given relevant information.
✓ **EXTENDED** Be able to define relative atomic mass (A_r) as the average mass of naturally occurring atoms of an element on a scale where the ^{12}C atom has a mass of exactly 12 units.
✓ **EXTENDED** Be able to define relative molecular mass (M_r) as the sum of the relative atomic masses.

✓ **EXTENDED** Know that relative formula mass (M_r) is used for ionic compounds.

✓ **EXTENDED** Know that the mole is a specific number of particles called the Avogadro constant.

✓ **EXTENDED** Be able to use the molar gas volume (24 dm³ at room temperature and pressure).

✓ **EXTENDED** Be able to calculate stoichiometric reacting masses, volumes of gases and solutions and concentrations of solutions expressed in g/dm³ and mol/dm³.

HOW ARE CHEMICAL FORMULAE WRITTEN?

When elements chemically combine, they form compounds. A compound can be represented by a **chemical formula**.

All substances are made up from simple building blocks called elements. Each element has a unique **chemical symbol**, containing one or two letters. Elements discovered a long time ago often have symbols that don't seem to match their name. For example, silver has the chemical symbol Ag. This is derived from *argentum*, the Latin name for silver.

'COMBINING POWERS' OF ELEMENTS

There are a number of ways of working out chemical formulae. In this topic you will start with the idea of a 'combining power' for each element and then look at how the charges on ions can be used for ionic compounds. Later in the course you will be introduced to oxidation states and how these can be used to work out chemical formulae.

There is a simple relationship between an element's *group number* in the Periodic Table and its combining power. Groups are the vertical columns in the Periodic Table. The combining power is linked to the *number of electrons* in the outer shell of atoms of the element.

Group number	I	II	III	IV	V	VI	VII	0
Combining power	1	2	3	4	3	2	1	0

△ Table 1.13 Combining powers of elements.

Groups I–IV: combining power = group number

Groups V–VII: combining power = 8 − (group number)

If an element is not in one of the main groups, its combining power is included in the name of the compound containing it. For example, copper is a transition metal and is in the middle block of the Periodic Table. In copper(II) oxide, copper has a combining power of 2.

Sometimes an element does not have the combining power you would predict from its position in the Periodic Table. The combining power of these elements is also included in the name of the compound containing it. For example, phosphorus is in Group V, so you would expect it to have a combining power of 3, but in phosphorus(V) oxide its combining power is 5.

The only exception is hydrogen. Hydrogen is not included in a group, nor is its combining power given in the name of compounds containing hydrogen. It has a combining power of 1.

SIMPLE COMPOUNDS

Many compounds contain just two elements. For example, when magnesium burns in oxygen, a white ash of magnesium oxide is formed. To work out the chemical formula of magnesium oxide:

1. Write down the name of the compound.

2. Write down the chemical symbols for the elements in the compound.

3. Use the Periodic Table to find the 'combining power' of each element. Write the combining power of each element under its symbol.

4. If the numbers can be cancelled down, do so.

5. Swap the combining powers. Write them after the symbol, slightly below the line (as a 'subscript').

6. If any of the numbers are 1, you do not need to write them.

Magnesium oxide has the chemical formula you would have probably guessed: MgO.

The chemical formula of a compound is not always immediately obvious, but if you follow these rules you will have no problems.

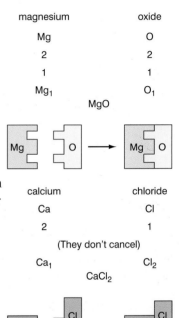

△ Fig. 1.70 Working out the chemical formulae for magnesium oxide and calcium chloride.

Compounds containing more than two elements

Some elements exist bonded together in what is called a **radical**. For example, in copper(II) sulfate, the sulfate part of the compound is a radical.

There are a number of common radicals, each having its own combining power. You cannot work out these combining powers easily from the Periodic Table – you have to learn them. Notice that all the radicals exist as ions.

Combining power = 1	Combining power = 2	Combining power = 3
Hydroxide OH^-	Carbonate CO_3^{2-}	Phosphate PO_4^{3-}
Hydrogencarbonate HCO_3^-	Sulfate SO_4^{2-}	
Nitrate NO_3^-		
Ammonium NH_4^+		

△ Table 1.14 Combining compounds for common radicals.

The same rules for working out formulae apply to radicals as to elements. For example:

Copper(II) sulfate		Potassium nitrate	
Cu	SO_4	K	NO_3
2	2	1	1
$CuSO_4$		KNO_3	

△ Table 1.15 Combining elements and radicals.

If the formula contains more than one radical unit, the radical must be put in brackets. For example:

calcium hydroxide	
Ca	OH
2	1
$Ca(OH)_2$	

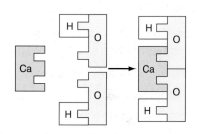

△ Fig. 1.71 Working out the chemical formula for calcium hydroxide.

The brackets are used just as they are used in mathematics: the number outside a bracket multiplies everything inside it. Be careful how you use the brackets – for example, do not be tempted to write calcium hydroxide as $CaOH_2$ rather than $Ca(OH)_2$. This is wrong.

$CaOH_2$ contains one Ca, one O, two H ✗
$Ca(OH)_2$ contains one Ca, two O, two H ✓

EXTENDED

The formula of an ionic compound can be worked out from the ions present. For example, sodium chloride is an ionic compound.

Sodium is in Group I and forms an ion with a charge of 1+, Na^+

Chlorine is in Group VII and forms an ion with a charge of 1–, Cl^-

When these ions combine, the charges must cancel each other out:

NaCl (the 1+ and 1– charges cancel)

What is the formula of lead(II) bromide, which contains Pb^{2+} and Br^- ions?

To cancel the 2+ charge, two 1– charges are needed, so the formula is $PbBr_2$.

END OF EXTENDED

QUESTIONS

1. Work out the chemical formulae of the following compounds:

   a) potassium bromide

   b) calcium oxide

   c) aluminium chloride

   d) carbon hydride (methane).

2. Work out the chemical formulae of the following compounds:

   a) copper(II) nitrate

   b) aluminium hydroxide

   c) ammonium sulfate

   d) iron(III) carbonate.

3. **EXTENDED** Work out the chemical formulae of the following compounds:

   a) a compound containing Zn^{2+} ions and Cl^- ions

   b) a compound containing Cr^{3+} ions and O^{2-} ions

   c) a compound containing Fe^{2+} and OH^- ions.

WRITING CHEMICAL EQUATIONS

In a chemical equation the starting chemicals are called the **reactants** and the finishing chemicals are called the **products**.

Follow these rules to write a chemical equation.

1. Write down the word equation.

2. Write down the symbols (for elements) and formulae (for compounds).

3. Balance the equation, to make sure there are the same number of each type of atom on each side of the equation.

4. **EXTENDED** Include the **state symbols** solid (s); liquid (l); gas (g); solution in water (aq).

State	State symbol
Solid	(s)
Liquid	(l)
Gas	(g)
Solution	(aq)

△ Table 1.16 States and their symbols.

Remember that some elements are **diatomic**. They exist as molecules containing two atoms.

Element	Formula
Hydrogen	H_2
Oxygen	O_2
Nitrogen	N_2
Chlorine	Cl_2
Bromine	Br_2
Iodine	I_2

△ Table 1.17 Some diatomic elements.

WORKED EXAMPLES

1. When a lighted splint is put into a test tube of hydrogen, the hydrogen burns with a 'pop'. In fact the hydrogen reacts with oxygen in the air (the reactants) to form water (the product). Write the chemical equation for this reaction.

Word equation: hydrogen + oxygen $\rightarrow$ water

Symbols and formulae: H_2 + O_2 $\rightarrow$ H_2O

Balance the equation: $2H_2$ + O_2 $\rightarrow$ $2H_2O$

For every two molecules of hydrogen that react, one molecule of oxygen is needed and two molecules of water are formed.

EXTENDED

Add the state symbols: $2H_2(g) + O_2(g) \rightarrow 2H_2O(l)$

END OF EXTENDED

2. What is the equation when sulfur burns in air?

Word equation: sulfur + oxygen $\rightarrow$ sulfur dioxide

Symbols and formulae: S + O_2 $\rightarrow$ SO_2

Balance the equation: S + O_2 $\rightarrow$ SO_2

EXTENDED

Add the state symbols: $S(s) + O_2(g) \rightarrow SO_2(g)$

END OF EXTENDED

△ Fig. 1.72 Methane is burning in the oxygen in the air to form carbon dioxide and water.

BALANCING EQUATIONS

Balancing equations can be quite tricky. It is essentially done by trial and error. However, the golden rule is that *balancing numbers can only be put in front of the formulae.*

For example, to balance the equation for the reaction between methane and oxygen:

	Reactants	Products
Start with the unbalanced equation	$CH_4 + O_2$	$CO_2 + H_2O$
Count the number of atoms on each side of the equation	1C ✓, 4H, 2O	1C ✓, 2H, 3O
There is a need to increase the number of H atoms on the products side of the equation. Put a '2' in front of the H_2O	$CH_4 + O_2$	$CO_2 + 2H_2O$
Count the number of atoms on each side of the equation again	1C ✓, 4H ✓, 2O	1C ✓, 4H ✓, 4O
There is a need to increase the number of O atoms on the reactant side of the equation. Put a '2' in front of the O_2	$CH_4 + 2O_2$	$CO_2 + 2H_2O$
Count the atoms on each side of the equation again	1C ✓, 4H ✓, 4O ✓	1C ✓, 4H ✓, 4O ✓

△ Table 1.18 Steps in balancing the equation for the reaction between methane and oxygen.

No atoms have been created or destroyed in the reaction. The equation is balanced.

$$CH_4(g) \quad + \quad 2O_2(g) \quad \rightarrow \quad CO_2(g) \quad + \quad 2H_2O(l)$$

△ Fig. 1.73 The number of each type of atom is the same on the left and right sides of the equation.

In balancing equations involving radicals such as sulfate, hydroxide and nitrate, you can use the same procedure. For example, when lead(II) nitrate solution is mixed with potassium iodide solution, lead(II) iodide and potassium nitrate are produced (Fig. 1.74).

1. Words:

lead(II)   +   potassium   →   lead(II)   +   potassium
nitrate   iodide   iodide   nitrate

2. Symbols:

$$Pb(NO_3)_2 \quad + \quad KI \quad \rightarrow \quad PbI_2 \quad + \quad KNO_3$$

3. Balance the nitrates:

$$Pb(NO_3)_2 \quad + \quad KI \quad \rightarrow \quad PbI_2 \quad + \quad 2KNO_3$$

4. Balance the iodides:

$$Pb(NO_3)_2(aq) \quad + \quad 2KI(aq) \quad \rightarrow PbI_2(s) \quad + \quad 2KNO_3(aq)$$

◁ Fig. 1.74 This reaction occurs simply on mixing the solutions of lead(II) nitrate and potassium iodide. Lead iodide is an insoluble yellow solid.

QUESTIONS

1. Balance the following chemical equations:

  a) $Ca(s) + O_2(g) \rightarrow CaO(s)$

  b) $H_2S(g) + O_2(g) \rightarrow SO_2(g) + H_2O(l)$

  c) $Pb(NO_3)_2(s) \rightarrow PbO(s) + NO_2(g) + O_2(g)$

2. EXTENDED Write balanced equations for the following word equations:

  a) sulfur + oxygen $\rightarrow$ sulfur dioxide

  b) magnesium + oxygen $\rightarrow$ magnesium oxide

  c) copper(II) oxide + hydrogen $\rightarrow$ copper + water

SCIENCE LINK

BIOLOGY – BIOLOGICAL MOLECULES, CHARACTERISTICS OF LIVING THINGS

- Being able to describe chemical changes using equations allows us to check that all the starting chemicals (the reactants) have been accounted for after the change (forming the products) – this applies to all the chemical reactions in living things such as respiration.

- The energy transfers through a series of chemical changes can be tracked.

PHYSICS – ATOMIC PHYSICS

- The idea of balancing equations – that all the 'starting' particles must be accounted for – is also very useful when describing changes in radioactive nuclei.

- The rules for nuclear equations mirror the way that chemical equations are written.

EXTENDED

As mentioned earlier, the general method for balancing equations is by trial and error, but it helps if you are systematic – always start on the left-hand side with the reactants. Sometimes you can balance an equation using fractions. In more advanced study such balanced equations are perfectly acceptable. Getting rid of the fractions is not difficult though. Look at this example:

WORKED EXAMPLES

Ethane (C_2H_6) is a hydrocarbon fuel and burns in air to form carbon dioxide and water.

Unbalanced equation: $C_2H_6(g) + O_2(g) \rightarrow CO_2(g) + H_2O(l)$

Balancing the carbon and hydrogen atoms gives:

$C_2H_6(g) + O_2(g) \rightarrow 2CO_2(g) + 3H_2O(l)$

The equation can then be balanced by putting 3½ in front of the O_2. By doubling every balancing number, the equation is then balanced using whole numbers.

$$2C_2H_6(g) \quad + \quad 7O_2(g) \quad \rightarrow \quad 4CO_2(g) \quad + \quad 6H_2O(l)$$

During your course you will become familiar with balancing equations and become much quicker at doing it. Try balancing the equations below. The third is the chemical reaction often used for making chlorine gas in the laboratory.

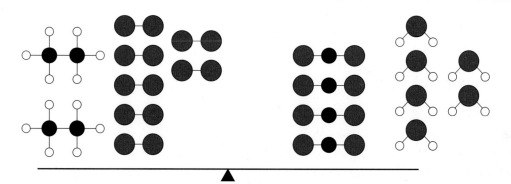

△ Fig. 1.75 Balancing the equation for burning ethane in air.

QUESTIONS

1. Balance the following equations:

a) $C_5H_{10}(g) + O_2(g) \rightarrow CO_2(g) + H_2O(l)$

b) $Fe_2O_3(s) + CO(g) \rightarrow Fe(s) + CO_2(g)$

c) $KMnO_4(s) + HCl(aq) \rightarrow KCl(aq) + MnCl_2(aq) + H_2O(l) + Cl_2(g)$

Ionic equations

Ionic equations show reactions involving ions (atoms or radicals that have lost or gained electrons). The size of the charge on an ion is the same as its combining power – whether it is positive or negative depends on which part of the Periodic Table the element is placed in.

In many ionic reactions some of the ions play no part in the reaction. These ions are called **spectator ions**. A simplified ionic equation can then be written, using only the important, reacting ions. In these equations, state symbols are often used and appear in brackets.

The equation must balance in terms of chemical symbols and charges.

1. In the reaction to produce lead(II) iodide, the potassium ions and nitrate ions are spectators – the important ions are the lead(II) ions and the iodide ions.

The simplified ionic equation is:

$Pb^{2+}(aq) + 2I^-(aq) \rightarrow PbI_2(s)$

	Reactants	Products
	$Pb^{2+}(aq) + 2I^-(aq)$	$PbI_2(s)$
Symbols	1Pb ✓, 2I ✓	1Pb ✓, 2I ✓
Charges	2+ and 2– = 0 ✓	0 ✓

The equation shows that *any* solution containing lead(II) ions will react with *any* solution containing iodide ions to form lead(II) iodide.

2. Any solution containing copper(II) ions and any solution containing hydroxide ions can be used to make copper(II) hydroxide, which appears as a solid:

$Cu^{2+}(aq) + 2OH^-(aq) \rightarrow Cu(OH)_2(s)$

	Reactants	Products
	$Cu^{2+}(aq) + 2OH^-(aq)$	$Cu(OH)_2(s)$
Symbols	1Cu ✓, 2O ✓, 2H ✓	1Cu ✓, 2O ✓, 2H ✓
Charges	2+ and 2– = 0 ✓	0 ✓

△ Fig. 1.76 Copper(II) hydroxide.

END OF EXTENDED

RELATIVE ATOMIC MASS

Atoms are far too light to be weighed. Instead, scientists have developed a **relative atomic mass** scale. The lightest atom, hydrogen, was chosen at first as the unit that all other atoms were weighed against.

On this scale, a carbon atom weighs the same as 12 hydrogen atoms, so carbon's relative atomic mass was given as 12.

Using this relative mass scale you can see, for example, that:

- 1 atom of magnesium is 24 × the mass of 1 atom of hydrogen.
- 1 atom of magnesium is 2 × the mass of 1 atom of carbon.
- 1 atom of copper is 2 × the mass of 1 atom of sulfur.

	Hydrogen	**Carbon**	**Oxygen**	**Magnesium**	**Sulfur**	**Calcium**	**Copper**
Symbol	H	C	O	Mg	S	Ca	Cu
Relative atomic mass	1	12	16	24	32	40	64
Relative size of atom							

△ Table 1.19 Relative atomic masses and sizes of atoms.

Since 1961 the reference point of the relative atomic scale has been carbon-12.

The relative atomic mass, A_r, is the average mass of naturally occurring atoms of an element on a scale where the ^{12}C atom has a mass of exactly 12 units. This takes into account the abundance of all existing isotopes of that element.

RELATIVE FORMULA MASSES, M_r

A **relative formula mass** (M_r) can be worked out from the relative atomic masses of the atoms in the formula.

The relative formula mass of a molecule (or the relative molecular mass) can be worked out by simply adding up the relative atomic masses of the atoms in the molecule. For example:

Water, H_2O (A_r: H = 1; O = 16)

The relative formula mass (M_r) = 1 + 1 + 16 = 18

Note: The subscript $_2$ only applies to the hydrogen atom.

Carbon dioxide, CO_2 (A_r: C = 12; O = 16)

M_r = 12 + 16 + 16 = 44

Note: The subscript $_2$ only applies to the oxygen atom.

A similar approach can be used for any formula, including ionic formulae.

1. Sodium chloride, NaCl (A_r: Na = 23; Cl = 35.5)
The relative formula mass (M_r) = 23 + 35.5 = 58.5

2. Potassium nitrate, KNO_3 (A_r: K = 39; N = 14; O = 16)

M_r = 39 + 14 + 16 + 16 + 16 = 101

(Note: The subscript $_3$ only applies to the oxygen atoms.)

3. Calcium hydroxide, $Ca(OH)_2$ (A_r: Ca = 40; O = 16; H = 1)

M_r = 40 + (16 + 1) 2 = 40 + 34 = 74

(Note: The subscript $_2$ applies to everything inside the bracket.)

4. Magnesium nitrate, $Mg(NO_3)_2$ (A_r: Mg = 24; N = 14; O = 16)

M_r = 24 + (14 + 16 + 16 + 16) 2 = 24 + (62)2 = 24 + 124 = 148

QUESTIONS

1. What is the formula mass of methane, CH_4? (A_r: H = 1; C = 12)

2. What is the formula mass of ethanol, C_2H_5OH? (A_r: H = 1; C = 12; O = 16)

3. What is the formula mass of ozone, O_3? (A_r: O = 16)

MOLES

A **mole** is an amount of substance. It is a very large number, approximately 6×10^{23}. This number is called the **Avogadro number** or **Avogadro constant**.

For example, you can have a mole of atoms, a mole of molecules or a mole of electrons. A mole of atoms is about 6×10^{23} atoms.

The relative atomic mass of an element tells you the mass of a mole of atoms of that element. So, for example, a mole of carbon atoms has a mass of 12 grams.

The relative formula mass (M_r) tells you the mass of a mole of that substance. For example, a mole of sodium chloride, NaCl, has a relative formula mass of 58.5, so one mole has a mass of 58.5 g.

WORKED EXAMPLE

1. How many moles of atoms are there in 72 g of magnesium?
(A_r of magnesium = 24)

Write down the formula:	$moles = \dfrac{mass}{A_r}$
Rearrange if necessary:	(None needed)
Substitute the numbers:	$moles = \dfrac{72}{24}$
Write the answer and units:	moles = 3 moles

2. What is the mass of 0.1 mole of carbon atoms? (A_r of carbon = 12)

Write down the formula:	$moles = \dfrac{mass}{A_r}$
Rearrange if necessary:	$mass = moles \times A_r$
Substitute the numbers:	$mass = 0.1 \times 12$
Write the answer and units:	mass = 1.2 g

EXPERIMENTS TO FIND THE FORMULAE OF SIMPLE COMPOUNDS

Finding the formula of magnesium oxide

Magnesium ribbon can be heated in a crucible to make a white powder called magnesium oxide. The magnesium reacts with oxygen from the air. The reaction is called oxidation because the magnesium combines with oxygen.

If you measure the masses of the magnesium used and the magnesium oxide formed in this reaction, you can use the relative atomic masses of magnesium and oxygen to work out the formula of the compound made.

Measurement	Mass in grams (g)
Mass of crucible + lid	30.00
Mass of crucible + lid + magnesium	30.24
Mass of crucible + lid + magnesium oxide	30.40
Mass of magnesium	30.24 − 30.00 = 0.24
Mass of magnesium oxide	30.40 − 30.00 = 0.40
Mass of oxygen	30.40 − 30.24 = 0.16

△ Table 1.20 Typical results when 0.24 g of magnesium is oxidised.

The result is that 0.24 g of magnesium joins with 0.16 g of oxygen.

Therefore 24 g of magnesium would join with 16 g of oxygen. The relative atomic mass of magnesium is 24 and that of oxygen is 16. So 1 magnesium atom combines with 1 oxygen atom, or 1 mole of magnesium atoms joins with 1 mole of oxygen atoms. This means that the formula of magnesium oxide is MgO.

△ Fig. 1.77 Magnesium ribbon is put in a crucible with a lid on it. The crucible is heated until the magnesium is red hot. The lid is lifted very slightly (to allow oxygen in) and put back down. This lets the magnesium burn but prevents loss of magnesium oxide.

WORKED EXAMPLES

Copper(II) oxide can be heated in hydrogen to produce copper and water. This reaction can be used to find the formula of copper(II) oxide.

In an experiment 12.8 g of copper was produced from 16.0 g of copper(II) oxide.

Relative atomic masses: H = 1, O = 16, Cu = 64

Word equation: copper(II) oxide + hydrogen → copper + water

Masses   16.0 g   12.8 g

So the mass of oxygen that was combined with the copper = 16.0 − 12.8 = 3.2 g.

Therefore 32 g of oxygen would combine with 128 g of copper.

Therefore $\frac{32}{16}$ = 2 moles of oxygen would combine with

$\frac{128}{64}$ = 2 moles of copper.

Therefore 1 mole of oxygen would combine with 1 mole of copper.

Therefore the formula for copper(II) oxide is CuO.

Developing investigative skills

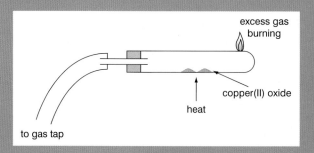

△ Fig. 1.78 Apparatus to find the chemical formula of a sample of copper(II) oxide.

Two students set out to find the chemical formula of a sample of copper(II) oxide. First they weighed an empty combustion tube, then used a spatula to put a full measure of copper(II) oxide near the centre of the tube, being careful not to spill any of the powder near the opening of the tube. They then reweighed the tube and set up the apparatus as shown in Fig. 1.78. (Note: copper(II) oxide is harmful if swallowed.)

The gas was turned on very slowly and after about 10 seconds a lighted splint was held over the jet. The gas flow was adjusted until a flame about 1 cm high was burning at the jet. The copper(II) oxide was then heated strongly in a Bunsen flame for about 15 minutes until all the copper(II) oxide had been turned into copper. At this point the tube was allowed to cool, but with the gas still flowing through the tube and being burned at the jet.

When the tube was cold, the gas was turned off and the tube and contents reweighed. The results are shown in the table:

Mass of tube + copper(II) oxide	= 24.15 g
Mass of tube + copper	= 23.92 g
Mass of tube	= 23.15 g
Mass of copper(II) oxide	=
Mass of copper	=
Mass of oxygen combined with the copper	=

Using and organising techniques, apparatus and materials

❶ Why was it important not to spill any of the copper(II) oxide near the opening of the tube?

❷ Why was the gas supply turned on very slowly?

❸ Why was the tube allowed to cool before turning the gas supply off?

Observing, measuring and recording

❹ What colour change would you expect to see as the copper(II) oxide changes into copper?

❺ Use the results to work out the masses of copper(II) oxide, copper and oxygen.

Handling experimental observations and data

❻ Use your results to calculate the number of moles of copper and the number of moles of oxygen (A_r: O = 16; Cu = 64).

❼ What is the ratio of moles of copper: moles of oxygen? (Write this as Cu:O 1:?)

Evaluating methods

❽ What do your calculations suggest is the most likely formula of copper(II) oxide?

❾ List the main sources of error in the experiment.

QUESTIONS

1. In the experiment used to find the formula of magnesium oxide:

  a) why is the lid of the crucible lifted whilst the magnesium is being heated?

  b) why is the crucible lid lifted only very slightly during the heating of the magnesium?

  c) what is the colour of magnesium oxide?

H_2O: a water molecule contains two hydrogen atoms and one oxygen atom.

Alternatively:

H_2O: 1 mole of water molecules is made from two moles of hydrogen atoms and 1 mole of oxygen atoms.

The formula of a compound can be calculated if the numbers of moles of the combining elements are known.

WORKED EXAMPLES

1. What is the simplest formula of a hydrocarbon that contains 60 g of carbon combined with 20 g of hydrogen? (A_r: H = 1; C = 12)

	C	**H**
Write down the mass of each element:	60	20
Work out the number of moles of each element:	$\dfrac{60}{12} = 5$	$\dfrac{20}{1} = 20$
Find the simplest ratio (divide by the smaller number):	$\dfrac{5}{5} = 1$	$\dfrac{20}{5} = 4$
Write the formula showing the ratio of atoms:	CH_4	

2. What is the simplest formula of calcium carbonate if it contains 40% calcium, 12% carbon and 48% oxygen? (A_r: C = 12; O = 16; Ca = 40)

	Ca	C	O
Write down the mass of each element (in 100 g of calcium carbonate):	40	12	48
Work out the number of moles of each element:	$\dfrac{40}{40} = 1$	$\dfrac{12}{12} = 1$	$\dfrac{48}{16} = 3$
Find the simplest ratio:	Already in the simplest ratio		
Write the formula showing the ratio of atoms:	$CaCO_3$		

REMEMBER

When calculating moles of elements, you must be careful to make sure you know what the question refers to. For example, you may be asked for the mass of 1 mole of nitrogen gas. N = 14, but nitrogen gas is diatomic, that is N_2, so the mass of 1 mole of N_2 = 28 g. This applies to other diatomic elements, such as Cl_2, Br_2, I_2, O_2 and H_2.

QUESTIONS

1. In an experiment, 5.6 g of iron reacts to form 8.0 g of iron oxide. What is the formula of iron oxide? (A_r: O = 16; Fe = 56)

2. 16.2 g of zinc oxide is reduced by carbon to form 13.0 g of zinc. What is the formula of zinc oxide? (A_r: O = 16; Zn = 65)

LINKING REACTANTS AND PRODUCTS

Chemical equations allow quantities of reactants and products to be linked together. They tell you how much of the products you can expect to make from a fixed amount of reactants.

In a balanced equation, the numbers in front of each symbol or formula indicate the numbers of moles represented. The numbers of moles can then be converted into masses in grams.

For example, when magnesium (A_r = 24) reacts with oxygen (A_r = 16):

Write down the balanced equation: $2Mg(s)$ + $O_2(g)$ → $2MgO(s)$

Write down the number of moles: 2 + 1 → 2

Convert moles to masses: 48 g + 32 g → 80 g

So when 48 g of magnesium reacts with 32 g of oxygen, 80 g of magnesium oxide is produced. From this you should be able to work out the mass of magnesium oxide produced from any mass of magnesium.

◁ Fig. 1.79 In an oxidation reaction, magnesium reacts with oxygen – the reaction can be used in fireworks and flares producing a brilliant white colour.

WORKED EXAMPLES

1. What mass of magnesium oxide can be made from 6 g of magnesium? (A_r: O = 16; Mg = 24)

Equation:	$2Mg(s)$	+	$O_2(g)$	$\rightarrow$	$2MgO(s)$
Moles:	2		1		2
Masses:	48 g		32 g		80 g
÷ 8	6 g				10 g

Therefore 6 g of Mg will form 10 g of MgO.

Note: In this example, there was no need to work out the mass of oxygen needed. It was assumed that there would be as much as was necessary to convert all the magnesium to magnesium oxide.

2. What mass of ammonia can be made from 56 g of nitrogen? (A_r: H = 1; N = 14)

Equation:	$N_2(g)$	+	$3H_2(g)$	$\rightarrow$	$2NH_3(g)$
Moles:	1		3		2
Masses:	28 g		6 g		34 g
× 2	56 g				68 g

Mass of ammonia = 68 g.

MOLES OF SOLUTIONS

A **solution** is made when a **solute** dissolves in a **solvent**. The **concentration** of a solution depends on how much solute is dissolved in how much solvent. Fig. 1.80 shows how to make up a solution of 1 mol/dm³ copper(II) sulfate.

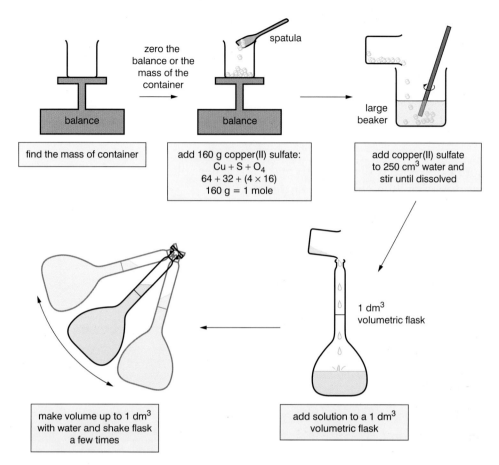

 shows the following labels:

zero the balance or the mass of the container

spatula

balance

balance

large beaker

find the mass of container

add 160 g copper(II) sulfate:
$Cu + S + O_4$
$64 + 32 + (4 \times 16)$
$160 \text{ g} = 1 \text{ mole}$

add copper(II) sulfate to 250 cm³ water and stir until dissolved

1 dm³ volumetric flask

make volume up to 1 dm³ with water and shake flask a few times

add solution to a 1 dm³ volumetric flask

Δ Fig. 1.80 Making a 1 mol/dm³ solution of copper(II) sulfate.

The concentration of a solution can be expressed in terms of g/dm³ of copper(II) sulfate.

WORKED EXAMPLE

1. A solution is made by dissolving 1 g of sodium hydroxide in distilled water to make 250 cm³ of solution. What is the concentration of the sodium hydroxide solution?

1 g in 250 cm³ is the same concentration as 4 g in 1 dm³ (remember 1 dm³ is 1000 cm³).

So, the concentration of the solution = 4 g/dm³.

The concentration of a solution can also be expressed in terms of moles per dm³ (1000 cm³), or mol/dm³. 1 mole can be written 1 M.

1 mole of solute dissolved to make 1000 cm³ of solution produces a 1 mol/dm³ solution.

2 moles dissolved to make a 1000 cm³ solution produces a 2 mol/dm³ solution.

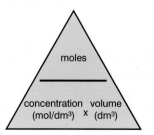

moles

concentration volume
(mol/dm³) × (dm³)

Δ Fig. 1.81 This triangle will help you to calculate concentrations of solutions.

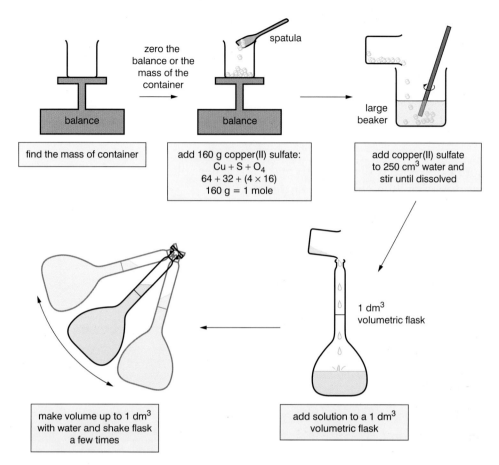

0.5 moles dissolved to make a 1000 cm³ solution produces
a 0.5 mol/dm³ solution.

1 mole dissolved to make a 500 cm³ solution produces
a 2 mol/dm³ solution.

1 mole dissolved to make a 250 cm³ solution produces
a 4 mol/dm³ solution.

If the same amount of solute is dissolved to make a smaller volume
of solution, the solution will be more concentrated.

2. How much sodium chloride can be made by reacting 100 cm³ of
1.0 mol/dm³ hydrochloric acid with excess sodium hydroxide
solution? (A_r: Na = 23; Cl = 35.5)

Equation:	$HCl(aq)$ + $NaOH(aq)$ → $NaCl(aq)$ + $H_2O(l)$			
Moles:	1	1	1	1
Masses/volumes:	1000 cm³ of 1 mol/dm³		58.5 g	
Therefore	100 cm³ of 1 mol/dm³		5.85 g	

(the quantities are scaled down by 10 times.)

EXTENDING THE MOLE CONCEPT

The mole is the amount of substance that contains 6.023×10^{23} particles. The particles can be atoms, molecules or ions.

Atoms	Elements only	all metals some non-metals noble gases	Aluminium one mole of aluminium **atoms** (mass 27.0g) Carbon one mole of carbon **atoms** (mass 12.0g) Helium airship one mole of helium **atoms** (mass 4.0g)	one mole of **atoms** contains 6.023×10^{23} atoms
Molecules	Elements or Compounds		Oxygen one mole of oxygen **molecules** (mass 32.0g) Bromine one mole of bromine **molecules** (mass 160g) Iodine one mole of iodine **molecules** (mass 254g) Ammonia one mole of ammonia **molecules** (mass 17.0g) Water one mole of water **molecules** (mass 18.0g)	one mole of **molecules** contains 6.023×10^{23} molecules
Ions	Compounds only		Sodium chloride one mole of sodium chloride 1 mole of sodium chloride contains: 6.023×10^{23} sodium **ions** and 6.023×10^{23} chloride **ions**	

Δ Fig. 1.82 Moles of atoms, molecules and ions.

Developing investigative skills

A student wanted to find the concentration of a solution of potassium hydroxide. She decided to use a titration method using a 0.10 M ('M' is short for 'moles per cubic decimetre') solution of sulfuric acid. (Note: dilute sulfuric acid may cause harm to eyes or a cut. Potassium hydroxide can be corrosive and can cause severe burns and damage to the eyes. Methyl orange indicator is toxic if swallowed.)

$$2KOH(aq) + H_2SO_4(aq) \rightarrow K_2SO_4(aq) + 2H_2O(l)$$

The method she used is described below:

❶ Wearing eye protection, she washed a pipette and a burette carefully making sure they were drained after washing.

❷ She used the pipette to transfer 25.00 cm^3 of the potassium hydroxide solution into a clean conical flask and added 3 drops of methyl orange indicator.

❸ She filled the burette with sulfuric acid solution, making sure that there were no air bubbles in the jet of the burette. Finally she took the first reading of the volume of acid in the burette.

❹ She ran the acid into the alkali in the conical flask, swirling the flask all the time. When she thought the indicator colour was close to changing, she added the acid more slowly until the colour changed. She then took the second reading on the burette.

She repeated the procedure steps 2 to 4 twice, making sure that between each titration she washed the conical flask carefully. Her results are shown in the table.

Volume of potassium hydroxide solution = 25.00 cm^3

Burette reading	1st titration	2nd titration	3rd titration
2nd reading (cm^3)	17.50	19.50	20.50
1st reading (cm^3)	0.00	2.50	3.50
Difference (cm^3)	17.50	17.00	17.00

Using and organising techniques, apparatus and materials

❺ Describe precisely how the student should have washed a) the pipette and b) the burette at the beginning of the experiment.

❻ How could the pipette be used most safely to measure out the 25.00 cm^3 of potassium hydroxide solution?

❼ How can a burette be filled most easily without spilling acid?

❽ What could the student have done to make the colour change easier to observe? What colour change was she looking for?

❾ How should she have washed out the conical flask between titrations to prevent contamination?

⑩ Why are the second and third titrations likely to be more accurate than the first?

⑪ What volume of sulfuric acid would you use in your calculation? Explain your answer.

⑫ Use the results and the balanced equation to work out the concentration of the potassium hydroxide solution. (Hint: start by writing down the number of moles of H_2SO_4 used.)

QUESTIONS

1. What mass of calcium oxide can be made from the **decomposition** of 50 g of calcium carbonate? (A_r: C = 12; O = 16; Ca = 40)

   Equation: $CaCO_3(s) \rightarrow CaO(s) + CO_2(g)$

2. How many moles of solute are there in the following solutions?

   a) 2000 cm³ of 1 M sodium chloride solution

   b) 100 cm³ of 0.1 M copper(II) sulfate solution

   c) 500 cm³ of 0.5 M sodium hydroxide solution.

MOLES OF GASES

In reactions involving gases it is often more convenient to measure the *volume* of a gas rather than its mass.

There are many gases and they are crucially important in science. In experiments or industrial processes it's often necessary to know the amount of a gas – but a gas is difficult to weigh. Molar volumes make it possible to find out the amount of a gas by using volume rather than mass.

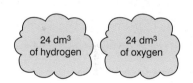

△ Fig. 1.83 Each of these contains 1 mole of molecules.

One mole of any gas occupies the same volume under the same conditions of temperature and pressure. The conditions chosen are usually room temperature (25 °C) and normal atmospheric pressure (1 atmosphere).

The volume of one mole of any gas contains the Avogadro number of molecules (particles) of that gas. This means that equal volumes of all gases at the same temperature and pressure must contain the same number of molecules. This is sometimes called **Avogadro's law**.

One mole of any gas occupies 24 000 cm³ (24 dm³) at room temperature and pressure (rtp). The following equation can be used to convert gas volumes into moles and vice versa:

$$moles = \frac{volume\ in\ cm^3}{24\ 000}$$

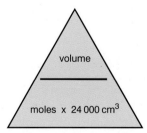

△ Fig. 1.84 The triangle can be used to decide whether to multiply or divide the quantities.

1. How many moles of molecules are there in the following:

    a) 88 g of carbon dioxide, CO_2? (A_r: C = 12; O = 16)

    b) 9 g of water, H_2O? (A_r: H = 1; O = 16)

    c) 2.8 g of ethene, C_2H_4? (A_r: H = 1; C = 12)

2. How many moles of molecules are there in the following:

    a) 12 000 cm³ of sulfur dioxide, SO_2, at room temperature and pressure?

    b) 2400 cm³ of methane, CH_4, at room temperature and pressure?

    c) 48 000 cm³ of oxygen, O_2, at room temperature and pressure?

WORKED EXAMPLES

1. What volume of hydrogen is formed at room temperature and pressure when 4 g of magnesium is added to excess dilute hydrochloric acid? (A_r: H = 1; Mg = 24; molar volume at room temperature and pressure = 24 000 cm³)

Balanced equation: $Mg(s) + 2HCl(aq) \rightarrow MgCl_2(aq) + H_2(g)$

Moles: 1   2   1   1

Masses/volumes: 24 g   24 000 cm³

Number of moles of magnesium $= \dfrac{4}{24} = 0.167$

Therefore 0.167 moles hydrogen gas will be produced.

Therefore volume of hydrogen gas $= 0.167 \times 24\,000$

$$= 4000 \text{ cm}^3$$

Note: The hydrochloric acid is in excess. This means that there is enough to react with all the magnesium.

2. What volume of carbon dioxide will be produced when 124 g of copper carbonate is broken down by heating?

(A_r: C = 12; O = 16; Cu = 64; molar volume at room temperature and pressure = 24 000 cm³)

Words: copper carbonate $\rightarrow$ copper oxide + carbon dioxide

Balanced equation: $CuCO_3(s)$ $\rightarrow$ $CuO(s)$ + $CO_2(g)$

Moles: 1   1   1

Masses/vols: 124 g   24 000 cm³

The relative formula mass of $CuCO_3$ is 64 + 12 + 16 + 16 + 16 = 124 g.

As there is exactly one mole of reactant, there must be one mole of each of the products. So, one mole of CO_2 is produced or 24 000 cm³.

END OF EXTENDED

AMEDEO AVOGADRO

Amedeo Avogadro was born in Italy in 1776. At age 20 he graduated from university with a degree in religious law. However, his real interests were science and mathematics, and this was where he started to devote his university research. At the beginning of the 19th century, scientists across the world were trying to work out the relative masses of different atoms. There was much confusion and disagreement about the existence of other particles, which we now call molecules. Against this background of confusion, in 1811 Avogadro published a research paper on 'determining the relative masses of elementary molecules'. It was in this paper that he proposed his hypothesis:

'All gases under the same conditions of temperature and pressure contain the same number of molecules.'

△ Fig. 1.85 Amedeo Avogadro.

The scientific community paid little attention to his work at the time. There were doubts about the existence of molecules and conflicting evidence coming from the research of more well-known and respected scientists. In fact, it was not until four years after his death in 1856 that his idea was accepted, following work done by a highly respected scientist called Cannizzaro. So Avogadro died without ever knowing the importance of his contribution to the development of science. It was only in 1911 that Avogadro's contribution to chemistry was formally recognised when, in honour of his work, the number of molecules in one mole of a substance was called the Avogadro number, equal to approximately 6×10^{23}.

How many other great advances or discoveries in science have not been recognised during the lifetime of the scientist concerned?

End of topic checklist

Key terms

Avogadro constant, Avogadro's law, chemical formula, chemical symbol, concentration, decomposition, diatomic, ionic equation, mole, product, radical, reactant, relative atomic mass (A_r), relative formula mass (M_r), relative molecular mass (M_r), spectator ions

During your study of this topic you should have learned:

○ How to use the symbols of the elements to write the formulae of simple compounds.

○ How to deduce the formula of a simple compound from the numbers of atoms present.

○ How to deduce the formula of a simple compound from a model or a diagrammatic representation.

○ How to construct and use word equations.

○ How to interpret and balance simple symbol equations.

○ **EXTENDED** How to determine the formula of an ionic compound from the charges on the ions present.

○ **EXTENDED** How to construct symbol equations with state symbols, including ionic equations.

○ **EXTENDED** How to deduce the balanced equation for a chemical reaction, given relevant information.

○ **EXTENDED** The definition of relative atomic mass (A_r).

○ **EXTENDED** The definition of relative molecular mass (M_r) as the sum of the relative atomic masses.

○ **EXTENDED** That relative formula mass (M_r) is used for compounds.

○ **EXTENDED** The definition of the mole and Avogadro constant.

○ **EXTENDED** How to use the molar gas volume (24 dm^3 at room temperature and pressure).

○ **EXTENDED** How to calculate stoichiometric reacting masses and volumes of gases and solutions expressed in g/dm^3 and mol/dm^3 (M).

End of topic questions

Note: The marks given for these questions indicate the level of detail required in the answers. In the examination, the number of marks given to questions like these may be different.

1. Work out the chemical formulae of the following compounds:

   a) sodium chloride   (1 mark)

   b) magnesium fluoride   (1 mark)

   c) aluminium nitride   (1 mark)

   d) lithium oxide   (1 mark)

   e) carbon(IV) oxide (carbon dioxide).   (1 mark)

2. Work out the chemical formulae of the following compounds:

   a) iron(III) oxide   (1 mark)

   b) phosphorus(V) chloride   (1 mark)

   c) chromium(III) bromide   (1 mark)

   d) sulfur(VI) oxide (sulfur trioxide)   (1 mark)

   e) sulfur(IV) oxide (sulfur dioxide).   (1 mark)

3. Work out the chemical formulae of the following compounds:

   a) potassium carbonate   (1 mark)

   b) ammonium chloride   (1 mark)

   c) sulfuric acid   (1 mark)

   d) magnesium hydroxide   (1 mark)

   e) ammonium sulfate.   (1 mark)

4. **EXTENDED** Write symbol equations from the following word equations:

   a) carbon + oxygen → carbon dioxide   (1 mark)

   b) iron + oxygen → iron(III) oxide   (1 mark)

   c) iron(III) oxide + carbon → iron + carbon dioxide (1 mark)

   d) calcium carbonate + hydrochloric acid → calcium chloride + carbon dioxide + water.   (1 mark)

5. **EXTENDED** What is the formula mass of:

   a) ethene, C_2H_4?   (1 mark)

   b) sulfur dioxide, SO_2?   (1 mark)

   c) methanol, CH_3OH?   (1 mark)

   (A_r: H = 1; C = 12; O = 16; S = 32)

6. EXTENDED Magnesium burns in oxygen to form magnesium oxide:

$2Mg(s) + O_2(g) \rightarrow 2MgO(s)$

(A_r: O = 16; Mg = 24)

Calculate:

a) the mass of magnesium required to make 8 g of magnesium oxide   **(3 marks)**

b) the mass of oxygen required to make 8 g of magnesium oxide.   **(1 mark)**

7. EXTENDED What mass of sodium hydroxide can be made by reacting 2.3 g of sodium with water?   **(3 marks)**

$2Na(s) + 2H_2O(l) \rightarrow 2NaOH(aq) + H_2(g)$

(A_r: H = 1; O = 16; Na = 23)

8. EXTENDED How many moles are in the following?

a) 64 g of S_8 **(1 mark)**

b) 9.8 g of H_2SO_4 **(1 mark)**

c) 21 g of Li.   **(1 mark)**

(A_r: S = 32; H = 1; O = 16; Li = 7)

9. EXTENDED What is the mass of the following?

a) 2.5 moles of Sr   **(1 mark)**

b) 0.25 moles of MgO   **(1 mark)**

c) 0.1 moles of C_2H_5Br.   **(1 mark)**

(A_r: Sr = 88; Mg = 24; O = 16; C = 12; H = 1; Br = 80)

10. EXTENDED How many moles are in the following?

a) 24 000 cm^3 of hydrogen gas, measured at room temperature and pressure   **(1 mark)**

b) 1200 cm^3 of nitrogen gas measured at room temperature and pressure.   **(1 mark)**

11. EXTENDED 0.64 g of copper when heated in air forms 0.80 g of copper oxide. What is the simplest formula of copper oxide?   **(2 marks)**

(A_r: O = 16; Cu = 64)

12. EXTENDED Calculate the simplest formulae of the compounds formed in the following reactions:

a) 2.3 g of sodium reacting with 8.0 g of bromine $\qquad$ **(2 marks)**

b) 0.6 g of carbon reacting with oxygen to make 2.2 g of a compound $\qquad$ **(2 marks)**

c) 11.12 g of iron reacting with chlorine to make 32.20 g of a compound. **(2 marks)**

$(A_r: C = 12; O = 16; Na = 23; Cl = 35.5; Fe = 56; Br = 80)$

13. EXTENDED Titanium chloride contains 25% titanium and 75% chlorine by mass. Work out the simplest formula of titanium chloride. $(A_r: Ti = 48; Cl = 35.5)$ **(3 marks)**

14. EXTENDED What mass of barium sulfate can be produced from 50 cm³ of 0.2 mol/dm³ barium chloride solution and excess sodium sulfate solution?

(3 marks)

$(A_r: O = 16; S = 32; Ba = 137)$

$BaCl_2(aq) + Na_2SO_4(aq) \rightarrow BaSO_4(s) + 2NaCl(aq)$

15. EXTENDED Iron(III) oxide is reduced to iron by carbon monoxide.

$(A_r: C = 12; O = 16; Fe = 56)$

$Fe_2O_3(s) + 3CO(g) \rightarrow 2Fe(s) + 3CO_2(g)$

a) Calculate the mass of iron that could be obtained by the reduction of 800 tonnes of iron(III) oxide. **(3 marks)**

b) What volume of carbon dioxide, measured at room temperature and pressure, would be obtained by the reduction of 320 g of iron(III) oxide? **(3 marks)**

16. EXTENDED Write ionic equations for the following reactions:

a) calcium ions and carbonate ions form calcium carbonate $\qquad$ **(2 marks)**

b) iron(III) ions and hydroxide ions form iron(III) hydroxide $\qquad$ **(2 marks)**

c) silver(I) ions and bromide ions form silver(I) bromide. $\qquad$ **(2 marks)**

Modern physical chemistry originated in the 19th century. It is not as clearly defined a category as organic chemistry, but it is still a useful description of this branch of science. Physical chemistry focuses on chemical processes at the 'macro level' (where properties can be observed) more than at the 'micro level' (too small to see) of individual atoms, molecules and ions. However, observed physical properties can still be explained in terms of what the atoms, molecules or ions are doing.

In this section you will explore the chemical reactions that can be caused by using electricity, a process known as electrolysis. You will then investigate some chemical reactions that produce significant amounts of heat energy, as well as some strange ones that seem to absorb energy and make everything cooler. The speed or rate of chemical reactions will also be explored, together with chemists' strategies to try to control them. You will learn about redox reactions, which are reactions involving reduction and oxidation, as well as about acids, bases and salts. Finally, you will look at some of the simple analytical techniques that can be used to identify ions and gases.

STARTING POINTS

1. How many non-renewable fuels can you name? What products do they form when they burn?

2. Give an example of a very rapid, almost instantaneous, chemical reaction. Now give an example of a very slow one.

3. Explain how you can easily distinguish between an acid and an alkali.

4. What is a catalyst? Name two examples where catalysts are used in everyday life.

5. Acids react with alkalis in neutralisation reactions. What is meant by neutralisation?

SECTION CONTENTS

a) Electricity and chemistry

b) Energy changes in chemical reactions

c) Chemical reactions

d) Acids, bases and salts

2
Physical chemistry

△ Physical chemistry deals with properties that can be observed.

Electricity and chemistry

△ Fig. 2.1 Industrial electroplating is a form of electrolysis.

INTRODUCTION

Most elements in nature are found combined with other elements as compounds. These compounds must be broken down to obtain the elements that they contain. One of the most efficient and economical ways to break down some compounds is using electricity in a process called electrolysis. Simple electrolysis experiments can be performed in the laboratory, and electrolysis is also used in large-scale industrial processes to produce important chemicals like aluminium and chlorine.

This topic deals with the underlying principles of electrolysis as well as some of the experiments that can be performed in the laboratory and some of the important industrial processes involving electrolysis.

KNOWLEDGE CHECK

✓ Know the different arrangements of the particles in solids, liquids and gases.
✓ Understand the terms 'conductor' and 'insulator'.
✓ Understand the differences between ionic and covalent bonding.

LEARNING OBJECTIVES

✓ Be able to define *electrolysis* as the breakdown of an ionic compound, either molten or in aqueous solution, by the passage of electricity.
✓ Be able to use the terms inert electrode, electrolyte, anode and cathode.
✓ Be able to describe the electrode products in the electrolysis of:
  – molten lead(II) bromide
  – concentrated aqueous sodium chloride
  – dilute sulfuric acid.
✓ Be able to describe electroplating with copper.
✓ **EXTENDED** Be able to state that metals or hydrogen are formed at the negative electrode (cathode) and that non-metals (other than hydrogen) are formed at the positive electrode (anode).
✓ **EXTENDED** Be able to relate the products of electrolysis to the electrolyte and electrodes in specific examples (including copper(II) sulfate using carbon or copper electrodes).
✓ **EXTENDED** Be able to describe electrolysis in terms of the ions present and reactions at the electrodes, in terms of gain of electrons by cations and loss of electrons by anions to form atoms.

✓ **EXTENDED** Be able to predict the products of electrolysis of a specified molten binary compound.

✓ **EXTENDED** Be able to construct ionic half-equations for the formation of elements at the cathode.

✓ **EXTENDED** Be able to describe in outline the manufacture of aluminium from pure aluminium oxide in molten cryolite.

✓ **EXTENDED** Be able to describe in outline the manufacture of chlorine, hydrogen and sodium hydroxide from concentrated aqueous sodium chloride.

ELECTROLYTES AND NON-ELECTROLYTES

Compounds that can conduct electricity are called **electrolytes** – they undergo a reaction called **electrolysis**. Experiments can be carried out using a simple electrical **cell**, as shown in Fig. 2.2.

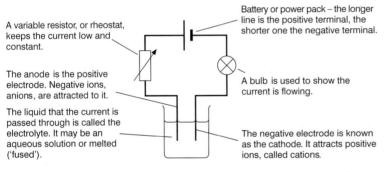

A variable resistor, or rheostat, keeps the current low and constant.

Battery or power pack – the longer line is the positive terminal, the shorter one the negative terminal.

The anode is the positive electrode. Negative ions, anions, are attracted to it.

A bulb is used to show the current is flowing.

The liquid that the current is passed through is called the electrolyte. It may be an aqueous solution or melted ('fused').

The negative electrode is known as the cathode. It attracts positive ions, called cations.

△ Fig. 2.2 A simple electrolysis cell.

When the solution in the beaker is an electrolyte, a complete circuit will form and the bulb will light. The electric current that flows is caused by electrons moving in the electrodes and wires of the circuit, and by ions moving in the solution. If a current does not flow then the beaker must contain a non-electrolyte. Because of this, a simple circuit like this can be used to distinguish between electrolytes and non-electrolytes.

CONDITIONS FOR ELECTROLYSIS

The substance being electrolysed (the electrolyte) must contain ions, and these ions must be free to move. In other words, the substance must be either molten or dissolved in water.

A direct current (d.c.) voltage must be used. The **electrode** connected to the positive terminal of the power supply is known as the **anode**. The electrode connected to the negative terminal is known as the **cathode**. The electrical circuit can be drawn as shown in Fig. 2.3.

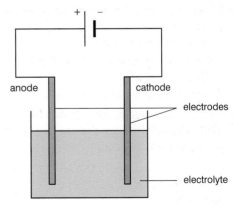

anode   cathode

electrodes

electrolyte

△ Fig. 2.3 A typical electrical circuit used in electrolysis.

QUESTIONS

1. What is meant by the term *electrolysis*?

2. What is the name given to the positive electrode?

3. What two conditions must exist for a substance to be an electrolyte and allow an electric current to pass through it?

SCIENCE LINK

PHYSICS – ELECTRIC CIRCUITS

- The rules for electric circuits – that there must be a complete circuit, there must be an energy source, there must be mobile charge carriers ('charged particles') – apply both to circuits involving electrolysis and to circuits with bulbs and batteries.

- The charge carriers may be different – ions in molten materials or in solutions, compared to electrons in wires – but the measurements of electric current and potential difference are defined in exactly the same way.

- Ion formation through the gain or loss of electrons is another idea that is common to both areas.

ELECTROLYSIS OF MOLTEN LEAD(II) BROMIDE

When an electric current passes through an electrolyte, new substances are formed. The examples below show how you can work out what products will form.

Lead(II) bromide ($PbBr_2$) is ionically bonded and contains Pb^{2+} ions and Br^- ions. When the solid is melted and a voltage is applied, the ions are able to move. The positive lead ions move to the negative electrode (the cathode), and the negative bromide ions move to the positive electrode (the anode). The electrodes are usually made of carbon, which is inert, and do not undergo any **chemical change** during the electrolysis. The products of the electrolysis are lead and bromine. Silvery deposits of lead form near the bottom of the dish, and brown bromine vapour near the anode.

EXTENDED

At the cathode (negative electrode), the lead ions accept electrons to form lead atoms:

$Pb^{2+}(l) + 2e^- \rightarrow Pb(l)$

At the anode (positive electrode), the bromide ions give up electrons to form bromine atoms, and then bromine molecules:

$$2Br^-(l) \rightarrow Br_2(g) + 2e^-$$

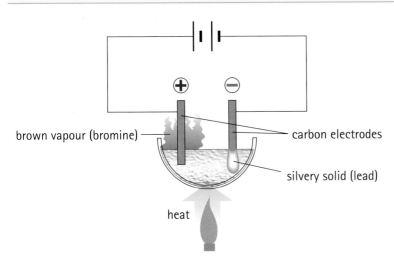

△ Fig. 2.4 Electrolysis of molten lead(II) bromide.

Note: the two equations above are known as half-equations. Unlike normal chemical equations, they do not show the whole chemical change – just the change occurring at an electrode. In the half-equations above, you will see that the numbers of electrons accepted and released are the same. The electric current is produced by this flow of electrons around the external circuit.

END OF EXTENDED

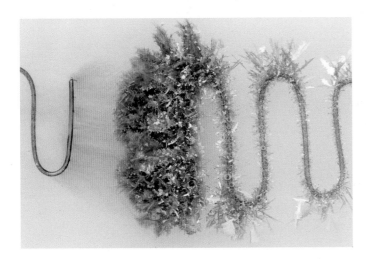

△ Fig. 2.5 Electrolysis of tin bromide solution – tin ions go to the cathode; bromide ions go to the anode.

ELECTROLYSIS OF SODIUM CHLORIDE SOLUTION

When concentrated sodium chloride solution is electrolysed, hydrogen ions (from the water solvent) form hydrogen molecules at the cathode and chloride ions form chlorine molecules at the anode.

This experiment can be performed using a cell as shown in Fig. 2.2. Again, inert carbon electrodes are used.

EXTENDED

When the ionic compound sodium chloride dissolves in water, the sodium and chloride ions separate and are free to move independently. In addition, the water provides a small quantity of hydrogen (H^+) and hydroxide (OH^-) ions:

$$NaCl(aq) \rightarrow Na^+(aq) + Cl^-(aq)$$

$$H_2O(l) \rightleftharpoons H^+(aq) + OH^-(aq)$$

This process is known as **dissociation**. The water breaks up and forms ions. In fact, the ions also combine to form water – the reaction goes both ways: it is a **reversible** reaction. Although there are very few ions present, if they are removed they will be immediately replaced. Therefore, whenever you consider the electrolysis of an aqueous solution you must always include the H^+ and OH^- ions.

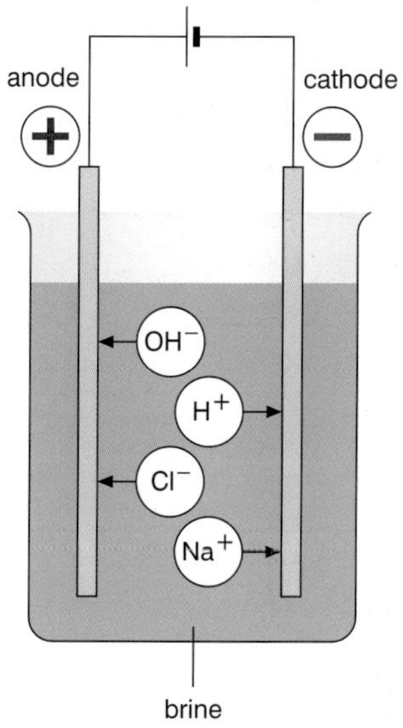

△ Fig. 2.6 The electrolysis of sodium chloride solution (brine).

- At the cathode (negative electrode):

two ions, Na^+ and H^+, move to the cathode but only H^+ ions are discharged. The sodium ions remain as ions, but the solution turns alkaline because the loss of hydrogen ions leaves a surplus of hydroxide ions.

$$2H^+(aq) + 2e^- \rightarrow H_2(g)$$

The hydrogen ions accept electrons and form hydrogen molecules.

- At the anode (positive electrode):

two ions, Cl^- and OH^-, move to the anode. Either ion could be discharged depending on the concentration of the solution. If the solution is very dilute, OH^- ions are discharged; if the solution is concentrated, Cl^- ions are discharged. At intermediate concentrations both ions are likely to be discharged, giving a mixture of products.

$$4OH^-(aq) \rightarrow 2H_2O(l) + O_2(g) + 4e^-$$

The hydroxide ions give up electrons and form oxygen molecules.

$$2Cl^-(aq) \rightarrow Cl_2(g) + 2e^-$$

The chloride ions give up electrons and form chlorine molecules.

Bubbling or effervescence is seen at each of the two electrodes, and the products of the electrolysis are hydrogen and oxygen and/or chlorine.

END OF EXTENDED

REMEMBER

When the sodium chloride solution is concentrated, the main product at the anode is chlorine, which forms as a pale green gas.

When the sodium chloride solution is dilute, the main product at the anode is oxygen, which forms as a colourless gas.

Whatever the concentration of the sodium chloride solution, hydrogen forms as a colourless gas at the cathode.

When dilute sodium chloride solution is electrolysed, the solution becomes increasingly alkaline as sodium hydroxide is formed.

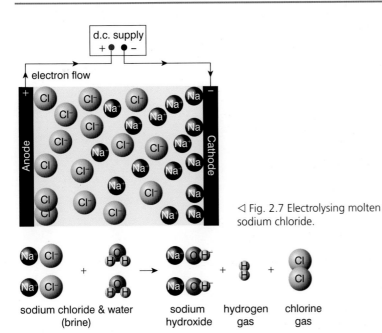

◁ Fig. 2.7 Electrolysing molten sodium chloride.

sodium chloride & water (brine) → sodium hydroxide + hydrogen gas + chlorine gas

△ Fig. 2.8 Electrolysing brine. At which electrode is hydrogen formed?

ELECTROLYSIS OF COPPER(II) SULFATE SOLUTION
Using carbon electrodes

When copper(II) sulfate solution is electrolysed using inert carbon electrodes, the products of the electrolysis are copper and oxygen. The copper forms as a red-brown coating on the carbon cathode and bubbles of a colourless gas, oxygen, are seen next to the anode. The solution will become paler blue as the copper ions are discharged.

The following changes occur.

• At the cathode (negative electrode):

two ions, Cu^{2+} and H^+, move to the cathode and Cu^{2+} ions are discharged.

$Cu^{2+}(aq) + 2e^- \rightarrow Cu(s)$

The copper ions accept electrons and form copper atoms.

• At the anode (positive electrode):

two ions, SO_4^{2-} and OH^-, move to the anode and OH^- ions are discharged.

$4OH^-(aq) \rightarrow 2H_2O(l) + O_2(g) + 4e^-$

The hydroxide ions give up electrons and form oxygen molecules.

As the ions are discharged the electrolyte will increasingly contain sulfuric acid (H^+ ions and SO_4^{2-} ions).

Using copper electrodes

When the electrolysis is repeated with copper electrodes, copper is deposited as a red/brown coating at the cathode but there is a difference in the reaction that takes place at the anode.

• At the cathode (negative electrode):

Cu^{2+} ions gain two electrons and are discharged. Copper atoms are formed and the mass of the electrode increases.

$Cu^{2+}(aq) + 2e^- \rightarrow Cu(s)$

• At the anode (positive electrode):

copper atoms lose two electrons and Cu^{2+} ions are formed. The anode slowly dissolves and loses mass.

$$Cu(s) \rightarrow Cu^{2+}(aq) + 2e^-$$

The concentration of the Cu^{2+} ions in the solution remains constant because the rate of production of Cu^{2+} ions at the anode is *exactly balanced* by the rate of removal of Cu^{2+} ions at the cathode. This reaction is important in the refining of copper. Copper is extracted from its ore by reduction with carbon, but the copper produced is not pure enough for many of its uses, such as in electrical cables. It can be purified using electrolysis.

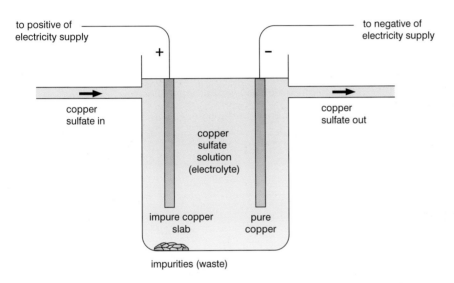

△ Fig. 2.9 Copper is purified by electrolysis.

The impure copper is made at the anode in a cell with copper(II) sulfate solution as the electrolyte. The cathode is made of a thin piece of pure copper. At the anode the copper atoms form copper ions and impurities fall to the bottom of the tank. The copper ions are then deposited as pure copper on the cathode. The cathode can be replaced by another thin piece of copper once sufficient copper has been deposited.

END OF EXTENDED

PREDICTING THE PRODUCTS OF ELECTROLYSIS

Predicting the products of the electrolysis of simple molten ionic compounds is relatively straightforward. The metal forms at the cathode and the non-metal forms at the anode. For example, the electrolysis of molten aluminium oxide forms aluminium (at the cathode) and oxygen (at the anode).

In the case of aqueous solutions, there is potentially a number of different products. At the cathode, the product is either the metal or hydrogen. From the **reactivity series** of metals shown in Fig. 2.10, the rule is: only metals below hydrogen in the series are deposited as the metal on the cathode; metals above hydrogen produce hydrogen gas instead.

For example, if magnesium chloride solution is electrolysed, hydrogen, not magnesium, is formed at the cathode.

At the anode, the main product often depends on the concentration of the solution. For example, if concentrated hydrochloric acid is electrolysed, chlorine is the main product at the anode; if dilute hydrochloric acid is electrolysed instead, oxygen is likely to be the main product.

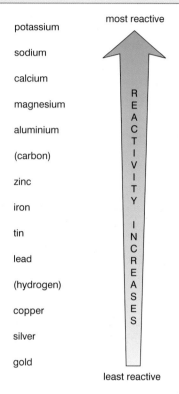

△ Fig. 2.10 Reactivity of metals.

In electrolysis, negative ions give up electrons and usually form molecules (such as Cl_2, Br_2). Positive ions accept electrons and usually form metallic atoms (such as Cu, Al) or hydrogen gas.

The loss of electrons is **oxidation** (of the non-metal ions), the gain of electrons is **reduction** (of the metal ions).

QUESTIONS

1. a) What is an *inert* electrode?

b) Give an example of a substance that is often used as an inert electrode.

2. What products are formed when the following molten solids are electrolysed?

a) lead(II) chloride

b) magnesium oxide

c) aluminium oxide.

3. EXTENDED What are the products at the cathode when the following solutions are electrolysed?

a) sodium bromide solution

b) zinc chloride solution

c) silver nitrate solution.

4. EXTENDED **a)** Write a half-equation showing how oxide ions (O^{2-}) are discharged as oxygen gas.

b) At which electrode would this change take place?

Electroplating

Electroplating involves using electrolysis to coat an object with a thin film of metal. Often this is done for economic reasons, with a fairly cheap metal like steel or nickel being coated with more expensive metals like silver, gold or chromium. Expensive-looking 'silver' knives and forks sometimes have the letters EPNS stamped on them. EPNS stands for **E**lectro-**P**lated **N**ickel **S**ilver. The item is made from nickel with a thin coating of silver added by electrolysis.

Electroplating can also be used to modify the chemical reactivity of the object plated. One example of this is steel cans for food containers plated inside with a thin layer of tin. Tin itself is too soft and expensive to use for the whole can, but it is fairly unreactive and prevents the food from causing the steel to rust.

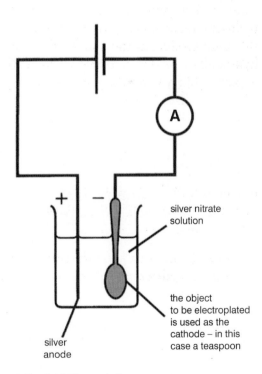

silver nitrate solution

the object to be electroplated is used as the cathode – in this case a teaspoon

silver anode

△ Fig. 2.11 Electroplating.

To summarise: electroplating is a good way of improving the appearance of metals and preventing their corrosion.

Developing investigative skills

Fig. 2.12 shows the apparatus that can be used to electrolyse dilute sulfuric acid. (Note: dilute sulfuric acid may cause harm in eyes or a cut.)

Using and organising techniques, apparatus and materials

❶ Inert electrodes were used. Suggest what the electrodes were made of.

❷ Was the hydrogen formed at the anode or the cathode?

❸ What name is given to solutions, such as sulfuric acid, that allow an electric current to flow through them?

Observing, measuring and recording

❹ Oxygen was collected at the left-hand electrode. How would you expect the volume of oxygen collected to compare with the volume of hydrogen collected at the right-hand electrode?

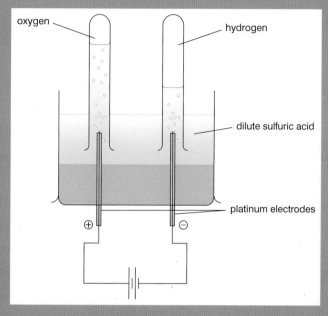

△ Fig. 2.12 Electrolysis of dilute sulfuric acid.

Interpreting observations and data

❺ EXTENDED What ions are present in a solution of sulfuric acid?

❻ EXTENDED Write a half-equation showing the formation of the hydrogen at the right-hand electrode.

EXTENDED

In this example of silver plating, the following reactions occur.

• At the anode (positive electrode):

each silver atom loses an electron and forms a silver ion

$Ag(s) \rightarrow Ag^+(aq) + e^-$

• At the cathode (negative electrode):

each silver ion accepts an electron and forms a silver atom

$Ag^+(aq) + e^- \rightarrow Ag(s)$

The increase in mass at the cathode is equal to the decrease in mass at the anode. Therefore the concentration of the silver ions in the silver nitrate electrolyte remains constant.

END OF EXTENDED

QUESTIONS

1. Electrolysis of aqueous solutions can be used in electroplating. The metal to be plated needs to made as the negative electrode (cathode) in a solution containing ions of the plating metal. The positive electrode (anode) is made of the pure plating metal. Electroplating can be set up on a small scale in a school laboratory.

   A student wanted to copper plate a ring. She was provided with a beaker (100 cm³), the ring, copper(II) sulfate solution, a copper strip, a set of leads with crocodile clips and a battery.

   a) Draw a labelled diagram to show how this could be done.

   b) **EXTENDED** Write the ionic half-equations to show what occurs at each electrode.

EXTENDED

EXTRACTING ALUMINIUM

Aluminium is extracted from the ore bauxite. Aluminium oxide is extracted from bauxite by purification. It is insoluble in water and has an extremely high melting point (2045 °C), therefore it is dissolved in molten cryolite at about 950 °C (this saves considerably on energy costs). This allows the ions to move when an electric current is passed through it. The anodes are made from carbon and the cathode is the carbon-lined steel case.

• At the cathode aluminium is formed:

$Al^{3+}(l) + 3e^- \rightarrow Al(l)$

• At the anode oxygen is formed:

$2O^{2-}(l) \rightarrow O_2(g) + 4e^-$

The overall equation is:

$$2Al_2O_3(l) \rightarrow 4Al(l) + 3O_2(g)$$

The oxygen reacts with the carbon anodes to form carbon dioxide, which escapes. Because of this the rods need to be replaced constantly.

$$C(s) + O_2(g) \rightarrow CO_2(g)$$

The process uses a great deal of electricity and is not cost-efficient unless the electricity is cheap. Aluminium is often extracted in countries with well-developed hydroelectric power.

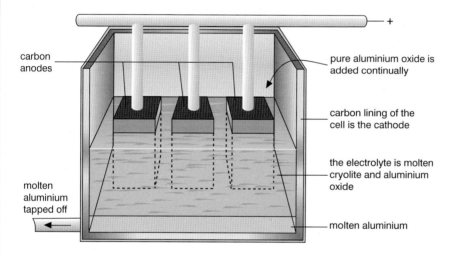

carbon anodes

pure aluminium oxide is added continually

carbon lining of the cell is the cathode

the electrolyte is molten cryolite and aluminium oxide

molten aluminium tapped off

molten aluminium

$\triangle$ Fig. 2.13 Extracting aluminium is expensive. Molten cryolite is used to produce an electrolyte that has a lower melting point than that of pure aluminium oxide.

REMEMBER

Remember that the aluminium ions are reduced by the addition of electrons to form aluminium atoms. The oxide ions are oxidised because they lose electrons to form oxygen molecules.

THE USES OF ALUMINIUM

The uses of aluminium are linked directly to its properties.

Uses of aluminium	Properties making aluminium suitable for the use
Packaging – drinks cans, foil wrapping, foil containers	Non-toxic Impermeable – no aroma or loss of flavour Resistant to corrosion
Transport – aeroplanes	High strength-to-weight ratio Low density Resistant to corrosion (Note: alloys are often used because they are stronger than pure aluminium)
Overhead electrical cables	High electrical conductivity; low density
As a building material	Easily shaped Low corrosion High strength-to-weight ratio
For kitchen utensils	Shiny appearance; non-corrosive

△ Table 2.1 Uses of aluminium.

QUESTIONS

1. In the extraction of aluminium using electrolysis:

   a) Why is cryolite used?

   b) At which electrode do the aluminium ions form aluminium atoms?

   c) Write a half-equation for the formation of aluminium atoms from aluminium ions.

   d) Are the aluminium ions oxidised or reduced as they form aluminium atoms? Explain your answer.

   e) Why is it necessary to replace the carbon electrodes regularly?

2. What properties of aluminium make it a suitable material for constructing an aeroplane?

END OF EXTENDED

SCIENCE IN CONTEXT

FACTS ABOUT ALUMINIUM

1. Aluminium is the most abundant metal in the Earth's crust, and the third most abundant element overall, after oxygen and silicon. It makes up about 8% by weight of the Earth's solid surface. Aluminium metal is too reactive to occur in nature. Instead, it is found combined in over 270 different minerals. The main ore of aluminium is bauxite. Bauxite is mined extensively to meet the demand for aluminium: Australia produced 62 million tonnes of bauxite in 2005.

2. The gemstones ruby and sapphire are crystals of aluminium oxide coloured by chromium or iron compounds.

3. The cost of electricity represents about 20% to 40% of the total cost of producing aluminium, depending on the location of the smelter. Smelters tend to be situated where electric power is both plentiful and inexpensive, such as in the United Arab Emirates where there are excess natural gas supplies, and Iceland and Norway with energy generated from renewable sources such as hydroelectric power. Aluminium production consumes roughly 5% of the electricity generated in the USA.

4. The corrosion resistance of aluminium is due to a thin surface layer of aluminium oxide that forms when the metal is exposed to air, effectively preventing further oxidation.

5. Aluminium is 100% recyclable without any loss of its natural qualities. Recycling involves melting the scrap, which requires only 5% of the energy used to produce aluminium from its ore, although a significant part (up to 15% of the input material) is lost as dross (an ash-like oxide). However, the dross can undergo a further process to extract more aluminium.

△ Fig. 2.14 Worldwide we use 6 billion aluminium cans each year, about 200 000 tonnes of aluminium.

MANUFACTURING SODIUM HYDROXIDE, HYDROGEN AND CHLORINE

Sodium hydroxide and chlorine are manufactured by the electrolysis of concentrated sodium chloride solution (brine) in a diaphragm cell. This process is the basis of what is known as the chlor-alkali industry.

During the electrolysis three products are made: chlorine, sodium hydroxide and hydrogen. It is very important to keep these products separate, and this is why the diaphragm cell is used.

REMEMBER

The fact that there are four ions involved in sodium chloride solution, yet in electrolysis only two ions are converted to atoms or molecules, is called *preferential discharge*.

You will need to remember the two ions that are discharged, and that oxidation and reduction are involved:

$2Cl^-(aq) \rightarrow Cl_2(g) + 2e^-$ = oxidation of Cl^-

$2H^+(aq) + 2e^- \rightarrow H_2(g)$ = reduction of H^+

When sodium chloride dissolves in water, its ions separate:

$NaCl(aq) \rightarrow Na^+(aq) + Cl^-(aq)$

There are also two ions from the water:

$H_2O(l) \rightleftharpoons H^+(aq) + OH^-(aq)$

In the process of electrolysis, ions are converted to atoms or molecules. In the case of brine:

• $Na^+(aq)$ and $H^+(aq)$ are attracted to the cathode.
• $Cl^-(aq)$ and $OH^-(aq)$ are attracted to the anode.

At the cathode (−)	At the anode (+)
Sodium is more reactive than hydrogen, so only the hydrogen ions are changed to form a molecule:	Both OH^- and Cl^- are attracted to the anode, but only the chloride ions are changed to form a molecule:
$2H^+(aq) + 2e^- \rightarrow H_2(g)$	$2Cl^-(aq) \rightarrow Cl_2(g) + 2e^-$

△ Table 2.2 What happens when brine is electrolysed.

The remaining solution contains the ions $Na^+(aq)$ and $OH^-(aq)$, so it is sodium hydroxide solution, $NaOH(aq)$.

Summary

At the cathode: hydrogen gas

At the anode: chlorine gas

The solution: sodium hydroxide.

Both chlorine and sodium hydroxide are vitally important chemicals in the manufacture of other industrial products and millions of tonnes of them are used every year.

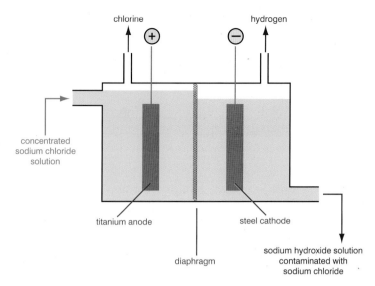

△ Fig. 2.15 The diaphragm cell.

REMEMBER

You should know that the reason for keeping the chlorine and sodium hydroxide apart in the diaphragm cell is because they react together to form sodium chlorate(I), NaOCl (used as a bleach).

△ Fig. 2.16 Uses of sodium hydroxide.   △ Fig. 2.17 Uses of chlorine.

QUESTIONS

1. a) What ions are present in an aqueous solution of sodium chloride?

  b) Which two of these ions will be attracted to the cathode? What factor determines which of these ions will be discharged?

  c) Write a half-equation to show the discharge of this ion at the cathode.

2. List the major uses of sodium hydroxide.

END OF EXTENDED

End of topic checklist

Key terms

anode, cathode, cell, chemical change, dissociation, electrode, electrolysis, electrolyte, inert electrode, oxidation, reduction, reversible reaction

During your study of this topic you should have learned:

○ That electrolysis is the breakdown of an ionic compound, molten or in aqueous solution, by the passage of electricity.

○ How to use the terms inert electrode, electrolyte, anode and cathode.

○ How to describe the electrode products in the electrolysis, using inert electrodes of platinum or carbon, of:

- molten lead(II) bromide
- concentrated aqueous sodium chloride
- dilute sulfuric acid.

○ How to describe electroplating with copper.

○ **EXTENDED** That metals or hydrogen are formed at the negative electrode (cathode) and that non-metals (other than hydrogen) are formed at the positive electrode (anode).

○ **EXTENDED** How to relate the products of electrolysis to the electrolyte and electrodes used in the following examples:

- molten lead(II) bromide
- concentrated aqueous sodium chloride
- dilute sulfuric acid
- aqueous copper(II) sulfate using carbon and copper electrodes.

○ **EXTENDED** How to describe electrolysis in terms of the ions present and reactions at the electrodes in the above examples.

○ **EXTENDED** How to predict the products of electrolysis of a specified molten binary compound.

○ **EXTENDED** How to construct ionic half-equations for reactions at the cathode.

○ **EXTENDED** How to describe, in outline, the manufacture of:

- aluminium from pure aluminium oxide in molten cryolite
- chlorine, hydrogen and sodium hydroxide from concentrated aqueous sodium chloride.

End of topic questions

Note: The marks given for these questions indicate the level of detail required in the answers. In the examination, the number of marks given to questions like these may be different.

1. Explain the following terms:

   a) *electrolysis*   (1 mark)

   b) *electrolyte*   (1 mark)

   c) *electrode*   (1 mark)

   d) *anode*   (1 mark)

   e) *cathode.*   (1 mark)

2. Zinc bromide, $ZnBr_2$, is an ionic solid. Why does the solid not conduct electricity?   (2 marks)

3. Copy and complete the following table which shows the products formed when molten electrolytes undergo electrolysis.   (4 marks)

Electrolyte	Product at the anode	Product at the cathode
Silver bromide		
Lead(II) chloride		
Aluminium oxide		
	Iodine	Magnesium

4. Sodium chloride, NaCl, is ionic. What are the products at the anode and cathode in the electrolysis of:

   a) molten sodium chloride?   (2 marks)

   b) concentrated aqueous sodium chloride?   (2 marks)

5. An iron fork is to be silver plated.

   a) Which electrode would be the iron fork?   (1 mark)

   b) What would be used as the other electrode?   (1 mark)

6. **EXTENDED** Write half-equations for the following reactions:

   a) the formation of aluminium atoms from aluminium ions   (2 marks)

   b) the formation of sodium atoms from sodium ions   (2 marks)

   c) the formation of oxygen gas from oxide ions   (2 marks)

   d) the formation of bromine gas from bromide ions   (2 marks)

   e) the formation of oxygen gas and water from hydroxide ions.   (2 marks)

7. **EXTENDED** Aluminium is extracted from aluminium oxide (Al_2O_3) by electrolysis. Aluminium oxide contains Al^{3+} and O^{2-} ions. The aluminium oxide is dissolved in molten cryolite.

   a) Why is the electrolysis carried out in a solution of aluminium oxide rather than solid aluminium oxide?   (2 marks)

   b) Write a half-equation to show how O^{2-} ions are converted into oxygen gas.   (2 marks)

   c) The carbon electrodes used in the electrolysis need to be constantly replaced. Explain why this is necessary.   (2 marks)

   d) Write a half-equation to show the formation of aluminium at the cathode.   (2 marks)

   e) The extraction of aluminium often takes place in areas with easy access to hydroelectric power. Suggest a reason for this.   (2 marks)

8. **EXTENDED** Sodium hydroxide and chlorine are manufactured by the electrolysis of concentrated sodium chloride solution.

   a) **i)** At which electrode is the chlorine gas formed?   (1 mark)

   ii) Write a half-equation, including state symbols, for the formation of chlorine.   (2 marks)

   b) **i)** What gas is formed at the other electrode?   (1 mark)

   ii) Write a half-equation, including state symbols, for the formation of this gas.   (2 marks)

   c) Where does the sodium hydroxide form?   (2 marks)

Energy changes in chemical reactions

△ Fig. 2.18 Fireworks are carefully controlled chemical reactions.

INTRODUCTION

When chemicals react together, the reactions cause energy changes. This is obvious when a fuel is burned and heat energy is released into the surroundings. Heat changes in other reactions may be less dramatic but they still take place. A knowledge of chemical bonding can really help to understand how these energy changes occur.

KNOWLEDGE CHECK

✓ Know that atoms in molecules are held together by covalent bonds.
✓ Know that many common fuels are organic compounds called alkanes.
✓ Be able to write and interpret balanced chemical equations.

LEARNING OBJECTIVES

✓ Be able to describe the meaning of exothermic and endothermic reactions.
✓ **EXTENDED** Be able to interpret energy level diagrams showing exothermic and endothermic reactions and the activation energy of a reaction.
✓ **EXTENDED** Be able to describe bond breaking as endothermic, and bond forming as exothermic.
✓ **EXTENDED** Be able to draw and label energy level diagrams for exothermic and endothermic reactions using data provided.

ENERGY CHANGES IN CHEMICAL REACTIONS

In most reactions, energy is transferred to the surroundings and the temperature goes up. These reactions are **exothermic**. Some examples of exothermic reactions are **combustion**, respiration and neutralisation. In a minority of cases, energy is absorbed from the surroundings as a reaction takes place and the temperature goes down. These reactions are **endothermic**. Some examples of endothermic reactions are photosynthesis and thermal decomposition.

For example, when magnesium ribbon is added to dilute hydrochloric acid, the temperature of the acid increases – the reaction is exothermic. In contrast, when sodium hydrogencarbonate is added to hydrochloric acid, the temperature of the acid decreases – the reaction is endothermic.

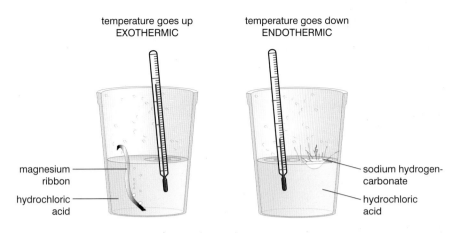

temperature goes up
EXOTHERMIC

temperature goes down
ENDOTHERMIC

magnesium ribbon

hydrochloric acid

sodium hydrogen-carbonate

hydrochloric acid

△ Fig. 2.19 Measuring energy changes in reactions.

Energy changes in reactions like these can be measured using a polystyrene cup (an insulator) as a calorimeter. If a lid is added to the cup, very little energy is transferred to the air and reasonably accurate results can be obtained.

QUESTIONS

1. What is an *exothermic* reaction?

2. What is an *endothermic* reaction?

3. Why do polystyrene cups make good calorimeters for measuring energy changes in some chemical reactions?

ENTHALPY CHANGE

The heat energy in chemical reactions is called enthalpy.
An **enthalpy change** is given the symbol ΔH. The enthalpy change for a particular reaction is shown at the end of the balanced equation. The units are kJ/mol.

EXTENDED

ENERGY PROFILES AND ΔH

Energy level diagrams show the enthalpy difference between the reactants and the products.

In an exothermic reaction, the energy content of the reactants is greater than the energy content of the products. Energy is being lost to the surroundings. ΔH is negative.	In an endothermic reaction, the energy content of the products is greater than the energy content of the reactants. Energy is being absorbed from the surroundings. ΔH is positive.

All ΔH values should have a + or − sign in front of them to show if they are endothermic or exothermic.

Activation energy is the *minimum* amount of energy required for a reaction to occur. Fig. 2.20 shows the activation energy of a reaction.

The energy profile can now be completed as shown. The reaction for this profile is exothermic, with ΔH negative.

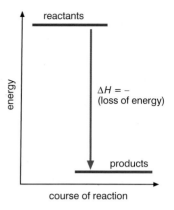

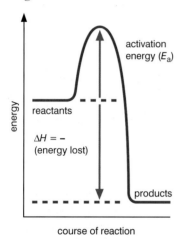

△ Fig. 2.20 Energy profile.

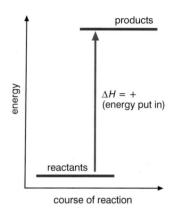

△ Fig. 2.21 Energy level diagrams for exothermic and endothermic reactions.

QUESTIONS

1. **EXTENDED** The enthalpy change for a particular reaction is positive. Is the reaction endothermic or exothermic?

2. **EXTENDED** On an energy profile, what is the name given to the minimum amount of energy required for a reaction to occur?

3. **EXTENDED** Draw and label energy level diagrams for each of the reactions shown in the table below:

Reaction	Activation Energy (kJ/mol)	Enthalpy Change (kJ/mol)
A	120	−90
B	80	+10

BIOLOGY – CHARACTERISTICS OF LIVING ORGANISMS

- The key chemical reactions in living things, photosynthesis and respiration, have energy transfer as their central purpose.

- In photosynthesis, the energy transfer is to allow the energy to be stored.

- In respiration, energy is released so that it can be used to power further changes.

- The effects of energy transfers (often unwanted) from, for example, combustion, can also have important effects on ecosystems.

PHYSICS – ENERGY RESOURCES

- The storage and transfer of energy play a key part in many physical processes, for example releasing energy from petrol in order for a car to gain kinetic energy.

- Energy resources on a global scale, for the generating of heat and electricity, are a key feature of modern life.

Developing investigative skills

Two students used a polystyrene cup to compare the energy changes in two reactions:

- magnesium with hydrochloric acid
- sodium hydrogencarbonate with hydrochloric acid.

They added 50 cm³ of 0.5 M hydrochloric acid to a polystyrene cup and measured its temperature. They then added a known mass of magnesium ribbon to the acid. They stirred the reaction mixture with a glass stirring rod until the reaction was complete and then took the final temperature. They then repeated the procedure using sodium hydrogencarbonate. Their results are shown in the table.

Reaction	Mass of solid used (g)	Initial temperature of the acid (°C)	Final temperature of the acid (°C)	Temperature change (°C)
Magnesium + hydrochloric acid	0.1	22	35	
Sodium hydrogencarbonate + hydrochloric acid	2.5	22	18	

Using and organising techniques, apparatus and materials

❶ What apparatus do you think was used to measure the volumes of hydrochloric acid?

❷ Why did the students stir the reaction mixtures until the reaction was complete and the final temperature was taken?

Observing, measuring and recording
❸ What would you expect to observe when magnesium ribbon is added to dilute hydrochloric acid?

Interpreting observations and data
❹ Work out the temperature change in each reaction.
❺ Work out the temperature change per gram of solid in each reaction.
❻ In each case is the reaction exothermic or endothermic?
❼ Draw a simple energy level diagram to represent the reaction between magnesium and hydrochloric acid.

Evaluating methods
❽ Energy is often lost from the polystyrene cup, making the temperature change lower than it should be. Suggest one way this error could be reduced.

WHERE DOES THE ENERGY COME FROM?

The reaction that occurs when a fuel is burning can be considered to take place in two stages. In the first stage the covalent bonds between the atoms in the fuel molecules and the oxygen molecules are broken. In the second stage the atoms combine and new covalent bonds are formed. For example, in the combustion of propane:

propane	+	oxygen	→	carbon dioxide	+	water
$C_3H_8(g)$	+	$5O_2(g)$	→	$3CO_2(g)$	+	$4H_2O(l)$

$\Delta H = -2202$ kJ/mol

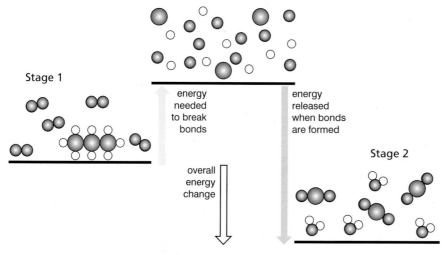

Stage 1

energy needed to break bonds

energy released when bonds are formed

Stage 2

overall energy change

Δ Fig. 2.22 Energy changes in an exothermic reaction.

Stage 1: Energy is needed (absorbed from the surroundings) to break the bonds. This process is endothermic.

Stage 2: Energy is released (transferred to the surroundings) as the new bonds form. This process is exothermic.

The overall reaction is exothermic because forming the new bonds releases more energy than is needed initially to break the old bonds. Fig. 2.23 is a simplified energy level diagram showing the exothermic nature of the reaction.

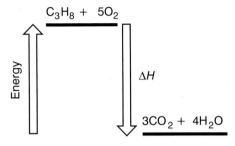

$C_3H_8 + 5O_2$

ΔH

$3CO_2 + 4H_2O$

△ Fig. 2.23 A simplified energy level diagram for the reaction.

The larger the alkane molecule, the more the energy is released on combustion. This is because although more bonds must be broken in the first stage of the reaction, more bonds are formed in the second stage.

Alkane		Molar enthalpy of combustion (kJ/mol)
Methane	CH_4	−882
Ethane	C_2H_6	−1542
Propane	C_3H_8	−2202
Butane	C_4H_{10}	−2877
Pentane	C_5H_{12}	−3487
Hexane	C_6H_{14}	−4141

△ Table 2.3 Molar enthalpy of combustion of alkanes.

REMEMBER

In an exothermic reaction, the energy released on forming new bonds is greater than that needed to break the old bonds.
In an endothermic reaction, more energy is needed to break the old bonds than is released when new bonds are formed. The energy changes in endothermic reactions are usually relatively small.

The enthalpy figures given in Table 2.3 for the alkanes are calculated when 1 mole of each alkane is completely burned in a plentiful supply of oxygen to form carbon dioxide and water. The increase in energy from one alkane to the next is almost constant due to the extra CH_2 unit in the molecule.

END OF EXTENDED

1. **EXTENDED** What does the sign of ΔH indicate about a reaction?

2. **EXTENDED** Is energy needed or released when bonds are broken?

3. **EXTENDED** In an endothermic reaction is more or less energy needed to break the old bonds than is recovered when new bonds are formed?

SCIENCE IN CONTEXT

HOW COMMON ARE ENDOTHERMIC REACTIONS?

Almost all chemical reactions in which simple compounds or elements react to make new compounds are exothermic. One exception is the formation of nitrogen oxide (NO) from nitrogen and oxygen. Overall, energy is needed to create this compound, with less energy being released on forming bonds than was needed to break the bonds of the reactants. Nitrogen oxide is often formed in lightning storms. The lightning provides enough energy to split the nitrogen and oxygen molecules before the atoms combine to form nitrogen oxide:

△ Fig. 2.24 These plants are making food by photosynthesis, an endothermic reaction.

$$N_2(g) + O_2(g) \rightarrow 2NO(g) \quad \Delta H \text{ positive}$$

Another exception is **photosynthesis**. Plants use energy from sunlight to convert carbon dioxide and water into glucose and oxygen:

$$6CO_2(g) + 6H_2O(l) \rightarrow C_6H_{12}O_6(aq) + 6O_2(g) \quad \Delta H \text{ positive}$$

'Cold packs', which you can buy in some countries, can be used to help you keep cool. Usually you have to bend a pack to break a partition inside and allow two substances to mix. The pack will then stay cold for an hour or longer. However, it may not be an endothermic reaction that is working in the cold pack. Dissolving chemicals like urea or ammonium nitrate in water also causes the temperature of water to fall, but dissolving is a **physical change**, not a chemical change. Whether it is an endothermic reaction or not is the manufacturer's secret.

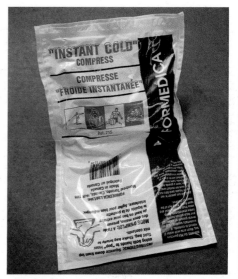

△ Fig. 2.25 A cold pack.

End of topic checklist

Key terms

activation energy, combustion, endothermic, enthalpy change, exothermic, photosynthesis, physical change

During your study of this topic you should have learned:

◯ How to describe the meaning of exothermic and endothermic reactions.

◯ **EXTENDED** How to describe bond breaking as endothermic and bond forming as exothermic.

◯ **EXTENDED** How to draw and label energy level diagrams for exothermic and endothermic reactions using data provided.

◯ **EXTENDED** How to interpret energy level diagrams showing exothermic and endothermic reactions and the activation energy of a reaction.

End of topic questions

Note: The marks given for these questions indicate the level of detail required in the answers. In the examination, the number of marks given to questions like these may be different.

1. Explain each of the following:

    a) A polystyrene cup is used when measuring energy changes in simple reactions, such as adding magnesium ribbon to an acid. **(2 marks)**

    b) When sodium hydrogencarbonate is added to a solution of an acid the temperature of the acid falls. **(1 mark)**

2. EXTENDED Calcium oxide reacts with water as shown in the equation:

$$CaO(s) + H_2O(l) \rightarrow Ca(OH)_2(s)$$

An energy level diagram for this reaction is shown below.

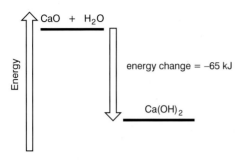

What does the energy level diagram tell us about the type of energy change that takes place in this reaction? **(1 mark)**

3. EXTENDED Chlorine (Cl_2) and hydrogen (H_2) react together to make hydrogen chloride (HCl). The equation can be written as:

$$H–H + Cl–Cl \rightarrow H–Cl + H–Cl$$

When this reaction occurs, energy is transferred to the surroundings. Explain this in terms of the energy transfer processes taking place when bonds are broken and when bonds are made. **(2 marks)**

Chemical reactions

INTRODUCTION

Some chemical reactions take place extremely quickly. For example, when petrol is ignited it combines with oxygen almost instantaneously. Reactions like these have a *high rate*. Other reactions are much slower, for example when an iron bar rusts in the air; reactions like these have a *low rate*. Chemical reactions can be controlled and made to be quicker or slower. This can be very important in situations like food production, either by slowing down or increasing the rate at which food ripens, or in the chemical industry where the rate of a reaction can be adjusted to an optimum level.

△ Fig. 2.26 Petrol igniting.

KNOWLEDGE CHECK

✓ Know the arrangement, movement and energy of the particles in the three states of matter: solid, liquid and gas.
✓ Be able to interpret balanced chemical equations.
✓ Know about ions and ion charges.
✓ **EXTENDED** Understand how the course of a reaction can be shown in an energy level diagram.
✓ **EXTENDED** Know about half-equations.

LEARNING OBJECTIVES

✓ Be able to describe practical methods for investigating the rate of a reaction that produces a gas.
✓ Be able to interpret data obtained from experiments concerned with rate of reaction.
✓ Be able to describe the effect of concentration, particle size, catalysts and temperature on the rate of reactions.
✓ Be able to describe how concentration, temperature and surface area create a danger of explosive combustion with fine powders (for example flour mills) and gases (for example methane in mines).
✓ **EXTENDED** Be able to suggest suitable apparatus, given information, for experiments, including collection of gases and measurement of rates of reaction.
✓ **EXTENDED** Be able to describe and explain the effect of concentration in terms of frequency of collisions between reacting particles.
✓ **EXTENDED** Be able to describe and explain the effect of changing temperature in terms of the frequency of collisions between reacting particles and more colliding particles possessing the minimum energy (activation energy) to react.

- ✓ Know the definitions of *oxidation* and *reduction* in terms of oxygen loss or gain.
- ✓ Know that oxidation states are used to name ions, for example iron(II), iron(III) and copper(II).
- ✓ **EXTENDED** Know the definition of *redox* in terms of electron transfer and be able to identify such reactions from given information.
- ✓ **EXTENDED** Know that an *oxidising agent* is a substance which oxidises another substance during a *redox* reaction and a *reducing agent* is a substance which reduces another substance during a *redox* reaction.

RATE OF A REACTION

A quick reaction takes place in a short time. It has a high **rate of reaction**. As the time taken for a reaction to be completed increases, the rate of the reaction decreases. In other words:

Speed	Rate	Completion time
Quick or fast	High	Short
Slow	Low	Long

Δ Table 2.4 Speed, rate and time.

COLLISION THEORY

For a chemical reaction to occur, the reacting particles (atoms, molecules or ions) must collide. The energy involved in the collision must be enough to break the chemical bonds in the reacting particles – or the particles will just bounce off one another.

A collision that has enough energy to result in a chemical reaction is an **effective collision**.

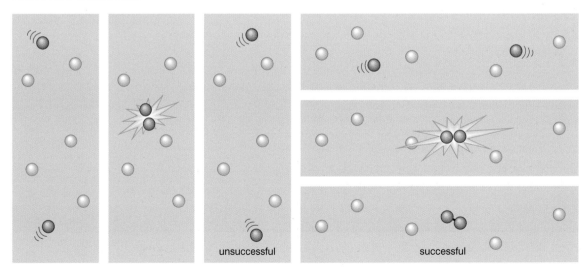

unsuccessful   successful

Δ Fig. 2.27 Particles must collide with sufficient energy to make an effective collision.

Some chemical reactions occur extremely quickly (for example, the explosive reaction between petrol and oxygen in a car engine) and some more slowly (for example, iron rusts over days or weeks). This is because they have different **activation energies**. Activation energy acts as a barrier to a reaction. It is the minimum amount of energy required in a collision for a reaction to occur. As a general rule, the bigger the activation energy, the slower the reaction will be at a particular temperature.

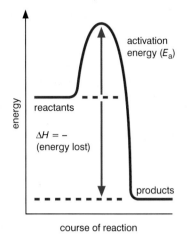

△ Fig. 2.28 Reaction profile.

END OF EXTENDED

QUESTIONS

1. **EXTENDED** In the collision theory, what two things must happen for two particles to react?

2. **EXTENDED** What is an *effective* collision?

3. **EXTENDED** Describe, using a diagram, what is meant by the term *activation energy*.

MONITORING THE RATE OF A REACTION

The rate of a reaction changes as the reaction proceeds. There are some easy ways of monitoring this change.

When marble (calcium carbonate) reacts with hydrochloric acid, the following reaction starts straight away:

calcium carbonate + hydrochloric acid → calcium chloride + carbon dioxide + water

$CaCO_3(s)$ + $2HCl(aq)$ → $CaCl_2(aq)$ + $CO_2(g)$ + $H_2O(l)$

The reaction can be monitored as it proceeds either by measuring the volume of gas being formed or by measuring the change in mass of the reaction flask.

The volume of gas produced in this reaction can be measured using the apparatus shown in Fig. 2.29. The hydrochloric acid is put into the conical flask, the marble chips are added, the bung is quickly fixed into the neck of the flask and the stopclock is started.

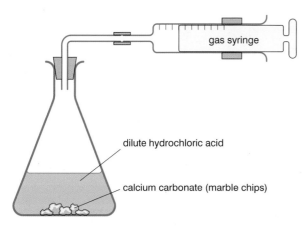

gas syringe

dilute hydrochloric acid

calcium carbonate (marble chips)

Δ Fig. 2.29 Monitoring the rate of a reaction.

The reaction will start immediately, effervescence (bubbling) will occur in the flask as the carbon dioxide gas is produced and the plunger on the syringe will start to move. Measuring the volume of gas in the syringe every 10 seconds will indicate how the total amount of gas produced changes as the reaction proceeds. The change in the rate of the reaction with time can be shown on a graph of the results (see Fig. 2.31).

EXTENDED

To measure the change in mass in the same reaction, the apparatus shown in Fig. 2.30 can be used. The hydrochloric acid is put into the conical flask, the marble chips are added, the cotton wool plug is put in the neck of the flask and the stopclock is started. The mass of the flask and contents is measured as soon as the plug is inserted and then every 10 seconds as the reaction occurs. The mass will decrease as carbon dioxide gas escapes from the flask.

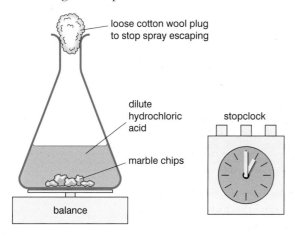

loose cotton wool plug to stop spray escaping

dilute hydrochloric acid

stopclock

marble chips

balance

Δ Fig. 2.30 Measuring the change in mass.

As before, drawing a graph of the results shows the change in the rate of the reaction over time.

Graphs of the results from both experiments have almost identical shapes. The rate of the reaction decreases as the reaction proceeds.

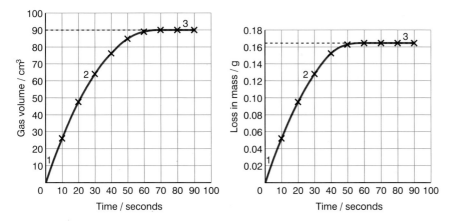

△ Fig. 2.31 Volume of carbon dioxide produced or loss in mass.

Loss in mass during the reaction

The rate of the reaction at any point can be calculated from the gradient of the curve. The shapes of the graphs can be divided into three regions.

1. At this point, the curve is the steepest (has the highest gradient) and the reaction has its highest rate. The maximum number of reacting particles are present and the number of effective collisions per second is at its greatest.

2. The curve is not as steep (has a lower gradient) at this point and the rate of the reaction is lower. Fewer reacting particles are present and so the number of effective collisions per second is lower.

3. The curve is horizontal (gradient is zero) and the reaction is complete. At least one of the reactants has been completely used up and so no further collisions can occur between the two reactants.

END OF EXTENDED

REMEMBER

In experiments like these it is helpful to have a good understanding of the types of **variables** involved. The factor you are investigating is called the **independent variable** – when investigating how the reaction between marble and hydrochloric acid changes over time, time is the independent variable. A **dependent variable** is changed by the independent variable – in the marble and hydrochloric acid reaction, the volume of carbon dioxide produced is the dependent variable. Other variables involved are **control variables** and are not allowed to change to ensure a 'fair test'. So temperature could be a control variable in the reaction between marble and hydrochloric acid.

In chemical reactions it is very rare that exact (as predicted by the equation) quantities of reactants are used. In the marble and hydrochloric acid reaction all the marble may be used up (it is called the *limiting reactant*) but not all the hydrochloric acid; some is left when the reaction has stopped (it is *in excess*).

QUESTIONS

1. What piece of apparatus can accurately measure the volume of gas produced in a reaction?

2. **EXTENDED** On a volume versus time graph, what does a horizontal line show?

3. **EXTENDED** When comparing two reactions, will the slower or quicker reaction have a steeper volume/time gradient at the beginning?

WHAT CAN CHANGE THE RATE OF A REACTION?

There are four key factors that can change the rate of a reaction:

- Concentration (of a solution)
- Temperature
- Particle size (of a solid)
- A catalyst.

EXTENDED

A simple **collision theory** can be used to explain how these factors affect the rate of a reaction. Two important parts of the theory are:

- The reacting particles must collide with each other.
- There must be sufficient energy in the collision to overcome the activation energy.

END OF EXTENDED

Concentration

Increasing the concentration of a reactant will increase the rate of reaction. When a piece of magnesium ribbon is added to a solution of hydrochloric acid, the following reaction occurs:

magnesium	+	hydrochloric acid	$\rightarrow$	magnesium chloride	+	hydrogen
$Mg(s)$	+	$2HCl(aq)$	$\rightarrow$	$MgCl_2(aq)$	+	$H_2(g)$

As the magnesium and acid come into contact, there is effervescence ('bubbling') and hydrogen gas is given off. Two experiments were performed using the same length of magnesium ribbon, but different concentrations of acid. In experiment 1 the hydrochloric acid used was

2.0 mol/dm³, in experiment 2 the acid was 0.5 mol/dm³. The graph in Fig. 2.32 shows the results of the two experiments.

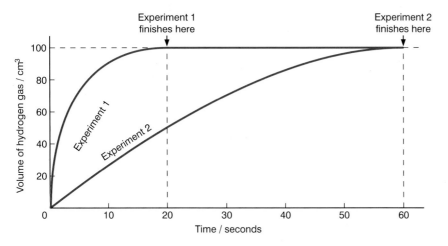

△ Fig. 2.32 Volume of hydrogen produced in the reaction between magnesium and hydrochloric acid.

In experiment 1 the curve is steeper (has a higher gradient) than in experiment 2. In experiment 1 the reaction is complete after 20 seconds, whereas in experiment 2 it takes 60 seconds. The initial rate of the reaction is higher with 2.0 mol/dm³ hydrochloric acid than with 0.5 mol/dm³ hydrochloric acid.

EXTENDED

In the 2.0 mol/dm³ hydrochloric acid solution there are more hydrogen ions in a given volume, a higher concentration of hydrogen ions, and so there will be a lot more effective collisions per second with the surface of the magnesium ribbon than in the 0.5 mol/dm³ hydrochloric acid.

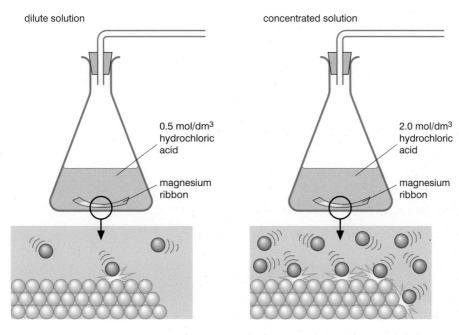

△ Fig. 2.33 Using dilute and concentrated solutions in a reaction.

Developing investigative skills

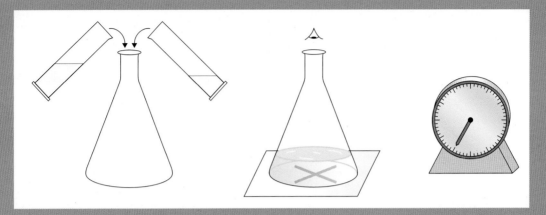

△ Fig. 2.34 Experiment with sodium thiosulfate solution and hydrochloric acid.

A student was investigating the reaction between sodium thiosulfate solution and hydrochloric acid. As the reaction takes place, a precipitate of sulfur forms in the solution and makes it change from colourless (and clear) to pale yellow (and opaque). The time it takes for a certain amount of sulfur to form can be used as a measure of the rate of the reaction.

The student used 1.0 mol/dm³ sodium thiosulfate solution and made up different concentrations of the solution by using the volumes of the solution and water shown in the table that follows.

She then drew a cross in pencil on a piece of paper.

She then added 5 cm³ of dilute hydrochloric acid to the solution in one of the flasks, the stopclock was started, the mixture was quickly stirred or swirled and then the conical flask was put on top of the pencilled cross.

The student looked through the conical flask to the cross and stopped the stopclock as soon as the cross could no longer be seen.

She then repeated the process with the other four solutions. Her results are shown in the table:

Volume of sodium thiosulfate solution (cm³)	50	40	30	20	10
Volume of water (cm³)	0	10	20	30	40
Volume of hydrochloric acid (cm³)	5	5	5	5	5
Time for the cross to be obscured (s)	14	18	23	36	67

Using and organising techniques, apparatus and materials

❶ Why was the total volume in the flask always 55 cm³?

❷ Why was the stopclock started when the acid was added and not when the flask was put on the pencilled cross?

❸ What apparatus would you use to measure the volume of sodium thiosulfate solution?

END OF EXTENDED

TEMPERATURE

Increasing the temperature of the reactants will increase the rate of a reaction.

EXTENDED

Warming a substance transfers kinetic energy to its particles. More kinetic energy means that the particles move faster. Because they are moving faster there will be more collisions each second. The increased energy of the collisions also means that the proportion of collisions that are effective will increase. A reaction was carried out at two different temperatures – first at 20 °C and then at 30 °C.

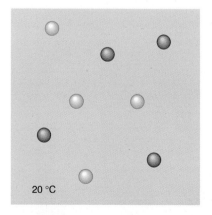
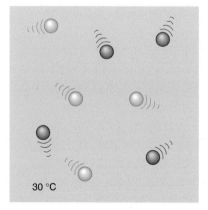

Δ Fig. 2.35 Effect of increasing temperature on particles.

Increasing the temperature of the reaction between some marble chips and hydrochloric acid will not increase the final amount of carbon dioxide produced. The same amount of gas will be produced in a shorter time. The rates of the two reactions are different but the final loss in mass is the same.

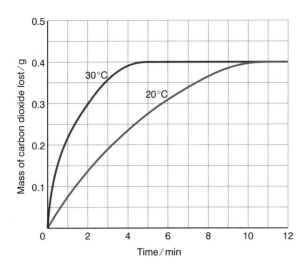

△ Fig. 2.36 The effect of temperature on the reaction between hydrochloric acid and marble chips.

END OF EXTENDED

QUESTIONS

1. **EXTENDED** What units are used to measure the concentration of solutions?

2. **EXTENDED** In terms of particles colliding, why does increasing the concentration of a solution increase the rate of reaction?

3. **EXTENDED** Give two reasons why increasing temperature increases the rate of reaction.

SCIENCE IN CONTEXT

THE EXPLOSIVE TRUTH ABOUT FLOUR MILLS

The surface area of particles really does affect the rate of some reactions!

Baking bread is a common and important activity, but making the flour that goes into the bread can be a dangerous business. Ever since a serious explosion at a flour mill near Minneapolis in the USA in 1878 killed 18 people, the milling industry has tried to reduce the risk of flour particles igniting into 'flour bombs'. In fact flour dust is thought to be more explosive than coal dust! Similar explosions have occurred in other factories when dust has exploded.

The key components to a flour or dust explosion are very small particles suspended in a plentiful supply of air, in a confined space and with a source

△ Fig. 2.37 Dropping milk powder on a flame.

of ignition. In factories the source of ignition doesn't have to be something obvious such as a discarded cigarette or match; it could be a spark from an electric motor or other electrical device, or even a light switch. In the case of the 1878 flour mill explosion, the cause of the explosion was thought to be a spark from an ageing electric motor.

In the laboratory or at home, if you put a match to some flour you might be able to get it to burn, but it certainly won't explode – the flour needs to be suspended in the air as very small particles that are close enough together so that if one flour particle ignites it starts a rapid chain reaction with other particles and then an explosion. So don't underestimate the importance of particle size on the rate of some reactions.

PARTICLE SIZE

Decreasing the particle size (or increasing the **surface area**) of a solid reactant will increase the rate of a reaction.

EXTENDED

A reaction can only take place if the reacting particles collide. This means that the reaction takes place at the surface of a solid. The particles within the solid cannot react until those on the surface have reacted and moved away.

END OF EXTENDED

Powdered calcium carbonate has a smaller particle size (or much larger surface area) than the same mass of marble chips. A lump of coal will burn slowly in the air, whereas coal dust can react explosively. This is a hazard in coal mines where coal dust can react explosively with air. In addition, as well as the danger of explosive mixtures of coal dust and air, the build-up of methane gas can also form an explosive mixture with the air.

Δ Fig. 2.38 Powdered carbon has a much larger surface area than the same mass in larger lumps.

CATALYSTS

A **catalyst** is a substance that alters the rate of a chemical reaction and is chemically unchanged at the end of the reaction. An **enzyme** is a biological catalyst, for example amylase, which is found in saliva.

Note: Enzymes are involved in the fermentation of glucose. Enzymes are present in yeast and these increase the rate at which glucose is converted into ethanol and carbon dioxide. The reaction rate increases as the yeast multiplies – but as the concentration of ethanol increases, the rate decreases because the ethanol begins to kill or denature the enzymes.

Most catalysts work by providing an alternative 'pathway' for the reaction – one that has a lower activation energy. The lower activation energy means that more of the collisions between particles will be effective.

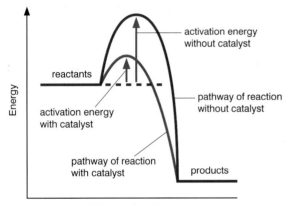

△ Fig. 2.39 The catalyst provides a lower energy route from reactants to products.

One example of the effect of a catalyst on a reaction is the use of manganese(IV) oxide in the decomposition of hydrogen peroxide. Hydrogen peroxide decomposes at room temperature into water and oxygen. The rate of this reaction is considerably increased by adding manganese(IV) oxide. As a gas is produced, the rate of the reaction can be monitored by collecting the gas in a gas syringe.

$$2H_2O_2(aq) \rightarrow 2H_2O(l) + O_2(g)$$

Catalysts are often used in industry to manufacture important chemicals. Table 2.5 shows some important industrial catalysts.

△ Fig. 2.40 The effect of manganese dioxide catalyst on the decomposition of hydrogen peroxide.

Industrial process	Catalyst used
Manufacture of ethanol	Phosphoric acid
Cracking long-chain alkanes	Silica or alumina
Manufacture of ammonia	Iron
Manufacture of sulfuric acid	Vanadium(V) oxide

△ Table 2.5 Uses of catalysts.

REMEMBER

Enzymes are often very specific to a particular reaction. They have an 'active site' which is just the right shape for the reacting particles to fit into. Molecules with other structures and shapes cannot do this. Metals, such as iron used in the manufacture of ammonia, work in the same sort of way that enzymes do. The surface of the iron allows molecules of nitrogen and hydrogen to get 'trapped'. They then collide more frequently in the confined space and effective collisions become more likely.

END OF EXTENDED

QUESTIONS

1. What is a *catalyst*?

2. What is a biological catalyst usually called?

BIOLOGY – ENZYMES

- The factors that affect how quickly a chemical reaction happens link directly to the role of enzymes in the maintenance of body processes.

- Describing how the energy of the particles changes at higher temperatures also allows us to explain why enzymes will not work above a certain temperature.

PHYSICS – SIMPLE KINETIC MODEL

- Explaining why the different factors affect the rate of a chemical reaction uses the same particle model that gives us the simple structure of solids, liquids and gases.

- Thinking about the forces between the particles and the energy involved in the interactions between particles leads to a common explanation in terms of particle speed and kinetic energy.

REDOX

Oxidation reactions are very familiar in everyday life – like the rusting of iron and bleaching, which is effective because bleach is a powerful oxidising agent. Whenever anything burns, an oxidation reaction takes place between the fuel and oxygen in the air. Reduction reactions may seem less familiar, but oxidation and reduction go hand in hand – if an element or compound in a chemical reaction is oxidised, then another element or compound in the same reaction must be reduced. So even when a bonfire is burning furiously and using oxygen from the air, reduction is taking place at the same time!

△ Fig. 2.41 Oxidation and reduction are both taking place in this bonfire.

OXIDATION, REDUCTION AND REDOX

When oxygen is added to an element or a compound, the process is called **oxidation**:

$$2Cu(s) + O_2(g) \rightarrow 2CuO(s)$$

The copper has been oxidised.

Removing oxygen from a compound is called **reduction**:

$$CuO(s) + Zn(s) \rightarrow ZnO(s) + Cu(s)$$

The copper(II) oxide has been *reduced*.

If we look more carefully at this last reaction, we see the zinc has changed to zinc oxide: that is, it has been oxidised at the same time as the copper(II) oxide has been reduced.

This is one example of reduction and oxidation taking place at the same time, in the same reaction. These are called **redox** reactions.

EXTENDED

There is another way to look at redox reactions if we consider the reaction in a different way:

$CuO(s)$	+	$Zn(s)$	$\rightarrow$	$ZnO(s)$	+	$Cu(s)$
ionic compound		element		ionic compound		element

Rewrite it:

$$Cu^{2+} + O^{2-} + Zn \rightarrow Zn^{2+} + O^{2-} + Cu$$

Remove the oxygen ions because they are on both sides of the equation (the O^{2-} ion is unchanged and so is a spectator ion):

$Cu^{2+}(s) + Zn(s) \rightarrow Zn^{2+}(s) + Cu(s)$

Split the equation into two half-equations and add electrons to balance them:

$Cu^{2+} + 2e^- \rightarrow Cu$

that is: CuO to Cu = reduction

$Zn \rightarrow Zn^{2+} + 2e^-$

that is: Zn to ZnO = oxidation

In this reaction the copper(II) oxide has been reduced by the zinc. The zinc is a **reducing agent**.

The zinc itself has been oxidised by the copper(II) oxide. The copper(II) oxide is an **oxidising agent**.

You now have a new definition using electrons instead of oxygen:

• Oxidation is loss of electrons.
• Reduction is gain of electrons.

Remember this as OIL-RIG: *Oxidation Is Loss – Reduction Is Gain*.

END OF EXTENDED

OXIDATION STATES

When you learned to write chemical formulae, you were introduced to the use of Roman numerals for metals that had more than one ion – for example, iron as Fe^{2+} or Fe^{3+}:

• Iron(II) oxide = FeO
• Iron(III) oxide = Fe_2O_3

The II and III are called **oxidation states**.

• Fe^{2+} has an oxidation state of +2.
• Fe^{3+} has an oxidation state of +3.
• Oxygen has an oxidation state of –2.

You take the ion charge and reverse it, so an ion of 3– has oxidation number –3.

The oxidation state of elements is always 0 (zero).

An oxidation state describes how many electrons an atom loses or gains when it forms a chemical bond.

If you look at the equation for the reaction between Cu^{2+} and Zn again, you will see that we can use oxidation states:

$Cu^{2+} + 2e^- \rightarrow Cu$ reduction

+2   0

$Zn \rightarrow Zn^{2+} + 2e^-$ oxidation

0   +2

This gives another definition for oxidation/reduction:

• Oxidation happens when oxidation states increase.

• Reduction happens when oxidation states decrease.

Changes in oxidation state

Solid potassium manganate(VII) comes in the form of dark purple crystals.

Manganese is in the oxidation state +7 (the 'VII' in the name) and is the cause of the purple colour.

Potassium manganate(VII) crystals dissolve in water to produce a dark purple solution, which is a powerful oxidising agent. When potassium manganate(VII) is used, the manganate(VII) ion is reduced to the manganese(II) ion, which is almost colourless:

◁ Fig. 2.42 When manganate(VII) ions are reduced colourless Mn^{2+} ions are formed.

$MnO_4^-(aq) \rightarrow Mn^{2+}(aq)$

+7   +2

purple   colourless

When the manganate(VII) ions are reduced, the colour changes from purple to colourless.

Another example of colour changes linked to changes in oxidation states is given by potassium iodide, KI, which is a white solid dissolving in water to form a colourless solution.

In some reactions the iodide ion, I⁻, is oxidised to iodine (there is an increase in oxidation state), which has a dark orange colour in solution:

$2I^-(aq) \longrightarrow I_2(aq) + 2e^-$

2(–1)   2(0)

colourless   orange

Fumes of iodine are produced when potassium iodide is oxidised by concentrated sulfuric acid.

END OF EXTENDED

SCIENCE IN CONTEXT — PHOTOCHROMIC GLASS

Some people who wear glasses prefer those with photochromic lenses, which darken when exposed to bright light. These glasses eliminate the need for sunglasses – they can reduce up to 80% of the light transmitted through the lenses to the eyes. The basis of this change in colour in response to light can be explained in terms of oxidation reduction or redox reactions.

△ Fig. 2.43 A photochromic reaction was produced when the right lens of these glasses was exposed to bright light.

Glass is ordinarily transparent to visible light. In photochromic lenses, silver chloride (AgCl) and copper(I) chloride (CuCl) crystals are added during the manufacturing of the glass. These crystals become uniformly embedded in the glass.

One characteristic of silver chloride is that it is affected by light. The following reactions occur:

$Cl^- \rightarrow Cl + e^-$ = oxidation

$Ag^+ + e^- \rightarrow Ag$ = reduction

The chloride ions are oxidised to produce chlorine atoms and the silver ions are reduced to silver atoms. The silver atoms cluster together and block the transmission of light, causing the lenses to darken. This process occurs almost instantaneously.

The photochromic process would not be useful unless it were reversible. The presence of copper(I) chloride reverses the darkening process in the following way. When the lenses are removed from bright light, the following reactions occur:

$$Cl + Cu^+ \rightarrow Cu^{2+} + Cl^-$$

The chlorine atoms formed by the exposure to light are reduced by the copper(I) ions forming chloride ions (Cl^-). The copper(I) ions are oxidised to copper(II) ions. The copper(II) ions then oxidise the silver atoms:

$$Cu^{2+} + Ag \rightarrow Cu^+ + Ag^+$$

The result of these reactions is that the lenses become transparent again as the silver atoms are converted back to silver ions.

QUESTIONS

1. Define the term *reduction*.

2. What is the oxidation state of the metal ion in each of the following compounds?

   a) copper(II) oxide

   b) iron(III) chloride

   c) potassium manganate(VII).

3. **EXTENDED** In the following half-equation, has the Cu^{2+} ion been oxidised or reduced? Explain your answer.

$$Cu^{2+}(aq) + e^- \rightarrow Cu^+(aq)$$

4. **EXTENDED** In the following half-equation, has the chromium (Cr) atom been oxidised or reduced? Explain your answer.

$$Cr(s) \rightarrow Cr^{3+}(aq) + 3e^-$$

End of topic checklist

Key terms

activation energy, catalyst, collision theory, control variable, dependent variable, effective collision, enzyme, independent variable, oxidation, oxidising agent, rate of reaction, redox, reducing agent, reduction, surface area

During your study of this topic you should have learned:

○ How to describe practical methods for investigating the rate of a reaction that produces a gas.

○ How to interpret data obtained from experiments concerned with rate of reaction.

○ How to describe the effect of concentration, particle size, catalysts and temperature on the rate of reactions.

○ How concentration, temperature and surface area create a danger of explosive combustion with fine powders (for example flour mills) and gases (for example methane in mines).

○ **EXTENDED** How to suggest suitable apparatus, given information, for experiments, including collection of gases and measurement of rates of reaction.

○ **EXTENDED** How to describe and explain the effect of concentration in terms of frequency of collisions between reacting particles.

○ **EXTENDED** How to describe and explain the effect of changing temperature in terms of the frequency of collisions between reacting particles and more colliding particles possessing the minimum energy (activation energy) to react.

○ The definitions of *oxidation* and *reduction* in terms of oxygen loss or gain.

○ That oxidation states are used to name ions – for example iron(II), iron(III), copper(II), manganate(VII).

○ **EXTENDED** The definition of *redox* in terms of electron transfer.

○ **EXTENDED** That an *oxidising agent* is a substance that oxidises another substance during a *redox* reaction.

○ **EXTENDED** That a *reducing agent* is a substance that reduces another substance during a *redox* reaction.

○ **EXTENDED** How to identify oxidising agents and reducing agents from simple equations.

End of topic questions

Note: The marks given for these questions indicate the level of detail required in the answers. In the examination, the number of marks given to questions like these may be different.

1. This question is about the reaction between magnesium and hydrochloric acid.

   a) Draw and label a diagram of the apparatus that could be used to monitor the rate of the reaction by measuring the volume of hydrogen produced.   **(2 marks)**

   b) How will the following changes affect the rate of the reaction?

   i) Using powdered magnesium rather than magnesium ribbon.   **(1 mark)**

   ii) Using a less concentrated solution of hydrochloric acid.   **(1 mark)**

   iii) Lowering the temperature of the hydrochloric acid.   **(1 mark)**

2. Explain why there is a risk of an explosion in a flour mill.   **(2 marks)**

3. EXTENDED For a chemical reaction to occur, the reacting particles must collide. Why don't all collisions between the particles of the reactants lead to a chemical reaction?   **(2 marks)**

4. EXTENDED The diagrams below show the activation energies of two different reactions A and B.

   a) What is the *activation energy* of a reaction?   **(1 mark)**

   b) Which reaction is likely to have the higher rate of reaction at a particular temperature? Explain your answer.   **(2 marks)**

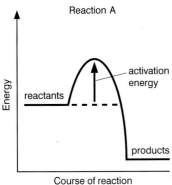

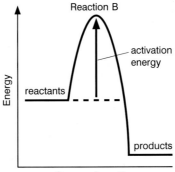

5. EXTENDED Look at the table of results obtained when dilute hydrochloric acid is added to marble chips.

Time (seconds)	0	10	20	30	40	50	60	70	80	90
Volume of gas (cm³)	0	20	36	49	58	65	69	70	70	70

a) What is the name of the gas produced in this reaction? **(1 mark)**

b) Write a balanced equation, including state symbols, for the reaction. **(2 marks)**

c) Draw a graph of volume of gas (*y*-axis) against time (*x*-axis).

   Label it 'Graph 1'. **(3 marks)**

d) Use the results to calculate the volume of gas produced:

   i) in the first 10 seconds **(1 mark)**

   ii) between 10 and 20 seconds **(1 mark)**

   iii) between 20 and 30 seconds **(1 mark)**

   iv) between 80 and 90 seconds. **(1 mark)**

e) Explain why the rate of the reaction changes as the reaction takes place. **(2 marks)**

f) Use the collision theory to explain the change in the rate of reaction. **(2 marks)**

g) The reaction was repeated using the same volume and concentration of hydrochloric acid with the same mass of marble, but as a powder instead of chips. Draw another curve on your graph paper, using the same axes as before (label as Graph 2), to show how the original results will change. **(3 marks)**

h) The reaction was repeated, but this time using the original mass of new marble chips and the same volume of hydrochloric acid, but with the acid only half as concentrated as originally. Draw another curve on your graph paper, using the same axes as before (label as Graph 3), to show how the original results will change. **(3 marks)**

6. The following equation shows a redox reaction:

$Mg(s) + ZnO(s) \rightarrow MgO(s) + Zn(s)$

a) What has been oxidised in the reaction? **(1 mark)**

b) What has been reduced in the reaction? **(1 mark)**

c) **EXTENDED** What is the oxidising agent? **(1 mark)**

d) **EXTENDED** What is the reducing agent? **(1 mark)**

7. **EXTENDED** The relationship between lead atoms and lead ions is shown in the following half-equation:

$Pb(s) \rightarrow Pb^{2+}(s) + 2e^-$

In this reaction, has the lead atom been oxidised or reduced?
Explain your answer. **(2 marks)**

8. **EXTENDED** The reaction between copper and chlorine produces copper(II) chloride.

$Cu(s) + Cl_2(g) \rightarrow CuCl_2(s)$

a) What is the oxidation state of copper as an element? **(1 mark)**

b) What is the oxidation state of the copper in copper(II) chloride? **(1 mark)**

c) Is this reaction a redox reaction? Explain your answer. **(2 marks)**

Acids, bases and salts

INTRODUCTION

Acids are commonly used in everyday life. Many of them, such as hydrochloric and sulfuric acids, are extremely toxic and corrosive. About 20 million tonnes of hydrochloric acid are manufactured worldwide each year. Some of this is used to make important chemicals such as PVC (polyvinyl chloride) plastic. Alkalis and bases are less common in everyday use, yet about 60 million tonnes of sodium hydroxide are produced worldwide each year and used in the manufacture of paper and **soap**. Sodium hydroxide is harmful and corrosive. Common salt, sodium chloride, is an example of a salt.

Δ Fig. 2.44 Sodium hydroxide.

KNOWLEDGE CHECK

✓ Know the names of some common acids, including hydrochloric acid and sulfuric acid.
✓ Know that vegetable dyes can be used as indicators to identify acids and alkalis.
✓ Understand the nature of the chemical bonding in ionic compounds.
✓ Be familiar with the terms anion and cation.
✓ Know some of the characteristics of Group I and Group VII elements.
✓ Know the order of the common metals that are included in the reactivity series.

LEARNING OBJECTIVES

✓ Be able to describe the characteristic properties of acids.
✓ Be able to describe the characteristic properties of bases.
✓ Be able to describe neutrality and relative acidity and alkalinity in terms of pH.
✓ Be able to describe and explain the importance of controlling acidity in soil.
✓ **EXTENDED** Know the definitions of acids and bases in terms of proton transfer in aqueous solutions.
✓ Be able to classify oxides as either acidic or basic, related to metallic and non-metallic character.
✓ **EXTENDED** Be able to classify other oxides as neutral or amphoteric.
✓ Be able to describe the preparation, separation and purification of salts.

✓ **EXTENDED** Be able to suggest a method of making a given salt from a suitable starting material, given appropriate information.

✓ Be able to describe the tests for the aqueous cations of ammonium, calcium, copper(II), iron(II), iron(III) and zinc using aqueous sodium hydroxide and aqueous ammonia.

✓ Be able to use a flame test to identify lithium, sodium, potassium and copper(II) cations.

✓ Be able to describe the tests for the anions carbonate, chloride, bromide, nitrate and sulfate.

✓ Be able to describe the tests for the gases ammonia, carbon dioxide, chlorine, hydrogen and oxygen.

AQUEOUS SOLUTIONS

When any substance dissolves in water, it forms an aqueous solution, shown by the state symbol (aq). Aqueous solutions can be acidic, alkaline or neutral. A neutral solution is neither acidic or alkaline.

Indicators are used to tell if a solution is acidic, alkaline or neutral. They can be used either as liquids or in paper form, and they turn different colours with different solutions. There are different indicators that can be used.

The most common indicator is **litmus**. Its colours are shown in the table:

Colour of litmus	Type of solution
Red	Acidic
Blue	Alkaline

△ Table 2.6 Litmus.

Universal indicator can show how strongly acidic or how strongly alkaline a solution is because it has more colours than litmus. Each colour is linked to a number ranging from 0 (most strongly acidic solution) to 14 (most strongly alkaline solution). A neutral substance has a pH of 7. This range is called the **pH scale** and is related to the concentration of hydrogen ions ($H^+(aq)$).

Concentration of hydrogen ions compared to distilled water			Examples of solutions and their respective pH
1/10 000 000	14	Liquid drain cleaner, caustic soda	
1/1 000 000	13	Bleaches, oven cleaner	
1/100 000	12	Soapy water	
1/10 000	11	Household ammonia (11.9)	
1/1 000	10	Milk of magnesia (10.5)	
1/100	9	Toothpaste (9.9)	
1/10	8	Baking soda (8.4), seawater, eggs	
0	7	Pure water (7)	
10	6	Urine (6), milk (6.6)	
100	5	Acid rain (5.6), black coffee (5)	
1 000	4	Tomato juice (4.1)	
10 000	3	Grapefruit and orange juice, soft drink	
100 000	2	Lemon juice (2.3), vinegar (2.9)	
1 000 000	1	Hydrochloric acid secreted from the stomach lining (1)	
10 000 000	0	Battery acid	

Δ Fig. 2.45 The pH scale.

Phenolphthalein indicator is colourless in acid solution but turns pink in alkaline solution.

Methyl orange indicator is pink in acid solution and yellow in alkaline solution.

WHAT ARE ACIDS?

Acids are substances that contain replaceable hydrogen atoms. These hydrogen atoms are replaced in chemical reactions by metal atoms, forming a compound known as a salt. Acids have pHs in the range 0–7.

Acid name	Acid formula
Hydrochloric acid	HCl
Nitric acid	HNO_3
Sulfuric acid	H_2SO_4
Phosphoric acid	H_3PO_4

Δ Table 2.7 Common acids.

Acids only show their acidic properties when water is present. This is because in water acids form hydrogen ions, $H^+(aq)$ (which are also protons), and it is these ions that create acidic properties. An acid is therefore a proton donor. For example:

$$HCl(aq) \rightarrow H^+(aq) + Cl^-(aq)$$

The typical reactions of acids include:
- Acid + metal makes a salt and hydrogen gas.
- Acid + carbonate makes a salt, carbon dioxide and water.
- Acid + base makes a salt and water.

WHAT ARE BASES AND ALKALIS?
The oxides and hydroxides of metals are called **bases**.

If the oxide or hydroxide of a metal dissolves in water, it is also called an **alkali**. For example:

sodium + oxygen → sodium oxide

$$4Na(s) + O_2(g) \rightarrow 2Na_2O(s)$$

sodium oxide + water → sodium hydroxide

$$Na_2O(s) + H_2O(l) \rightarrow 2NaOH(aq)$$

Sodium oxide is a base because it is the oxide of the metal sodium. In addition, it reacts with water to make the alkali sodium hydroxide. Alkalis have pHs in the range 7–14 (but not 7.0).

The typical reactions of bases include:
- Base + acid makes a salt and water.
- Base + an ammonium compound makes ammonia gas.

In their reactions with acids, in the presence of water, bases and alkalis accept protons (H^+ ions). Alkalis only show their alkaline properties when water is present. This is because in water the alkali forms hydroxide ions, $OH^-(aq)$, which can then react with $H^+(aq)$ ions from an acid to make water.

REMEMBER

Acids are proton (H^+) donors in water.

Bases are proton (H^+) acceptors in water.

END OF EXTENDED

QUESTIONS

1. Two solutions are tested with universal indicator paper. Solution A has a pH of 8 and solution B has a pH of 14. What does this tell you about the two solutions?

2. Methyl orange is added to a solution and the solution turns pink. What does this tell you about the solution?

3. Calcium oxide is an example of a base. How do we know this?

THE IMPORTANCE OF CONTROLLING ACIDITY IN SOIL

If soil is too acidic, then it can be neutralised using quicklime. Quicklime is made from limestone, which is quarried from limestone rocks. It is heated in lime kilns at 1200 °C to make calcium oxide or quicklime:

1200 °C ↑

limestone → quicklime + carbon dioxide

$$CaCO_3(s) \rightarrow CaO(s) + CO_2(g)$$

When quicklime is added to water, it makes calcium hydroxide, which is an alkali and so can neutralise the acidic soil:

quicklime + water → slaked lime

$$CaO(s) + H_2O(l) \rightarrow Ca(OH)_2(s)$$

Different plants grow better in different types of soil. The pH of a soil is an important factor in the growth of different plants – some plants prefer slightly acidic conditions and others slightly alkaline conditions.

Adding fertilisers to soil can also affect the pH and so the soil may have to be treated by adding acids or alkalis. The pH of soil can be measured by taking a small sample, putting it in a test tube with distilled water and adding indicator solution or using indicator paper. The pH can be found from a pH chart.

TYPES OF OXIDES

The **oxides** of elements can often be made by heating the element in air or oxygen. For example, the metal magnesium burns in oxygen to form magnesium oxide:

magnesium + oxygen → magnesium oxide

$2Mg(s)$ + $O_2(g)$ → $2MgO(s)$

Magnesium oxide forms as a white solid. When distilled water is added to the ash and the mixture is tested with universal indicator, the pH is greater than 7 – the oxide has formed an alkaline solution.

△ Fig. 2.46 Magnesium burning in oxygen.

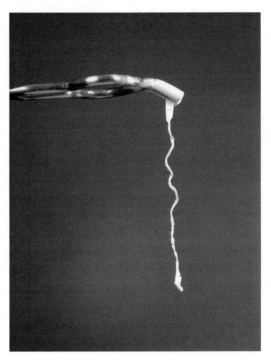

△ Fig. 2.47 Magnesium oxide is a white solid.

When sulfur is burned in oxygen, sulfur dioxide gas is formed:

sulfur + oxygen → sulfur dioxide

$S(s)$ + $O_2(g)$ → $SO_2(g)$

When sulfur dioxide is dissolved in water and then tested with universal indicator solution, the pH is less than 7 – the oxide has formed an acidic solution.

The oxides of most elements can be classified as **basic oxides** or **acidic oxides**. Some elements form neutral oxides. For example, water is a neutral oxide. Basic oxides that dissolve in water are called alkalis.

Oxides that do not dissolve in water cannot be identified using the pH of their solutions. For insoluble oxides, the test is seeing if they will react with hydrochloric acid, HCl (these would be basic oxides), or sodium hydroxide solution, NaOH (these would be acidic oxides). Oxides that do not react with hydrochloric acid or sodium hydroxide are neutral oxides.

Most metal oxides are basic oxides, such as CaO, MgO, BaO, Na_2O.

Basic oxides react with acids (neutralisation):

acid   +   base   →   a salt   +   water

$2HCl(aq)$ + $MgO(s)$ → $MgCl_2(aq)$ + $H_2O(l)$

Most non-metal oxides are acidic, for example:

NO_2, SO_2, SO_3, CO_2, P_2O_5

Acidic oxides react with bases (neutralisation) and dissolve in water to form acids, for example sulfuric acid (H_2SO_4):

$SO_3(g) + H_2O(l) \rightarrow H_2SO_4(aq)$

Oxide	Type of oxide	pH of solution	Other reactions of the oxide
Metal oxide	Basic	More than 7 (alkaline)	Reacts with an acid to make a salt + water
Non-metal oxide	Acidic	Less than 7 (acidic)	Reacts with a base to make a salt + water

△ Table 2.8 Acidic and basic oxides.

EXTENDED

Amphoteric oxides are the oxides of less reactive metals, for example Al_2O_3, ZnO and PbO. They can behave as both acidic oxides *and* basic oxides, so react with both bases and acids.

Neutral oxides do not react with acids or alkalis. Examples of neutral oxides are water, H_2O, nitrogen monoxide, NO, nitrous oxide, N_2O, and carbon monoxide, CO.

END OF EXTENDED

QUESTIONS

1. Is potassium oxide a basic oxide or an acidic oxide? Explain your answer.

2. **EXTENDED** What is the difference between a basic oxide and an amphoteric oxide?

WHAT ARE SALTS?

Acids contain replaceable hydrogen atoms. When metal atoms take their place, a compound called a **salt** is formed. The names of salts have two parts, as shown in Fig. 2.48.

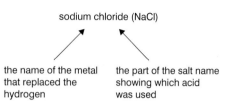

sodium chloride (NaCl)

the name of the metal that replaced the hydrogen

the part of the salt name showing which acid was used

△ Fig. 2.48 Salt – sodium chloride.

Table 2.9 shows the four most common acids and their salt names.

Acid	Salt name
Hydrochloric (HCl)	Chloride (Cl⁻)
Nitric (HNO_3)	Nitrate (NO_3^-)
Sulfuric (H_2SO_4)	Sulfate (SO_4^{2-})
Phosphoric (H_3PO_4)	Phosphate (PO_4^{3-})

△ Table 2.9 Common acids and their salt names.

△ Fig. 2.49 Sodium chloride crystals.

△ Fig. 2.50 Copper(II) sulfate crystals.

Salts are ionic compounds. The names of these compounds are created by taking the first part of the name from the metal ion, which is a positive ion (cation), and the second part of the name from the acid, which is a negative ion (anion). For example:

copper(II) sulfate: Cu^{2+} and $SO_4^{2-} \rightarrow CuSO_4$

    cation   anion   salt

Salts are often found in the form of crystals. Crystals of many salts contain **water of crystallisation**, which is responsible for their crystal shape. Water of crystallisation is shown in the chemical formula of a salt. For example:

copper(II) sulfate crystals: $CuSO_4.5H_2O$

iron(II) sulfate crystals: $FeSO_4.7H_2O$

Salts that do not contain water of crystallisation are **anhydrous**.

MAKING SALTS

There are five common methods for making salts. Four of these make soluble salts and one makes insoluble salts.

The solubility of salts in water

Here are the general rules that describe the solubility of common types of salts in water:

- All common sodium, potassium and ammonium salts are soluble.
- All nitrates are soluble.
- Common chlorides, bromides and iodides are soluble – except those of silver chloride, silver bromide and silver iodide.
- Common sulfates are soluble – except those of barium, lead and calcium.
- Common carbonates are insoluble – except those of sodium, potassium and ammonium.

Making soluble salts

1.

| acid | + | alkali | → | a salt | + | water |

For example:

| HCl(aq) | + | NaOH(aq) | → | NaCl(aq) | + | $H_2O(l)$ |

2.

| acid | + | base | → | a salt | + | water |

For example:

| $H_2SO_4(aq)$ | + | CuO(s) | → | $CuSO_4(aq)$ | + | $H_2O(l)$ |

3.

acid   +   carbonate → a salt   +   water + carbon dioxide

For example:

$$2HNO_3(aq) + CuCO_3(s) \rightarrow Cu(NO_3)_2(aq) + H_2O(l) + CO_2(g)$$

4.

acid   +   metal → a salt   +   hydrogen

For example:

$$2HCl(aq) + Mg(s) \rightarrow MgCl_2(aq) + H_2(g)$$

Here is a shortcut for remembering the four general equations above.
Remember the initials of the reactants:

A (acid) + A (alkali)

A (acid) + B (base)

A (acid) + C (carbonate)

A (acid) + M (metal)

The symbol '(aq)' after the formula of the salt shows that it is a soluble
salt.

Neutralisation describes the reactions of acids with alkalis and bases.
When acids react with alkalis, the reaction is between H^+ ions and
OH^- ions to make water, as in:

$$H^+(aq) + OH^-(aq) \rightarrow H_2O(l)$$

Reactions of acids with alkalis are used in the experimental procedure
of **titration**, in which solutions react together to give the end-point
shown by an indicator. Calculations can then be performed to find the
concentration of the acid or the alkali.

In the laboratory

Of the four methods for making soluble salts, shown by the symbol
(aq), only one uses two solutions:

1. acid(aq) + alkali(aq) → a salt(aq) + water(l)

The other three methods involve adding a solid(s) to a solution(aq):

2. acid(aq) + base(s) → a salt(aq) + water(l)

3. acid(aq) + carbonate(s) → a salt(aq) + water(l) + carbon dioxide(g)

4. acid(aq) + metal(s) → a salt(aq) + hydrogen(g)

Method 1 involves the titration method.
An indicator is used to show when exact quantities of acid and alkali have been mixed. The procedure is then repeated using the same exact volumes of acid and alkali, but without the indicator. The resulting solution is evaporated to the point of crystallisation, then left to cool and the salt to crystallise.

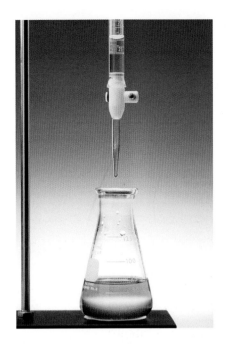

▷ Fig. 2.51 Using the neutralisation method for a titration.

EXTENDED

REMEMBER

You should know that because acids in water form $H^+(aq)$ ions and alkalis form $OH^-(aq)$ ions, the neutralisation reaction of acids with alkalis can be summarised as:

$$H^+(aq) \quad + \quad OH^-(aq) \quad \rightarrow \quad H_2O(l)$$

All neutralisation reactions can be represented by this equation, whatever the acid or alkali used.

END OF EXTENDED

The general procedure used for each of the methods 2, 3 and 4 is the same:

- The solid (base, carbonate or metal) is added to the acid with stirring until no more solid will react. Heating may be necessary.
- The mixture is filtered to remove unreacted solid and the solution is collected as the **filtrate** in an evaporating dish.
- The solution is evaporated to the point of crystallisation and is then left to cool and the salt to crystallise.

The process is summarised in Fig. 2.52:

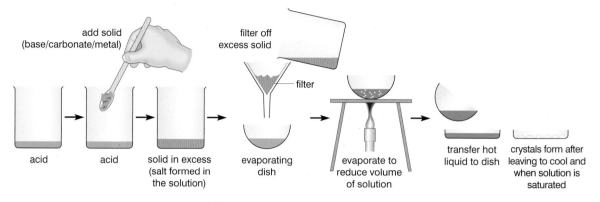

△ Fig. 2.52 Making soluble salts from solids.

QUESTIONS

1. What is a *salt*?

2. Which acid would you use to make a sample of sodium sulfate?

3. Would you expect potassium chloride to be soluble or insoluble in water? Explain your answer.

4. What is the name of the salt formed when calcium carbonate reacts with nitric acid?

5. What does the word *neutralisation* mean?

6. Which ion do all acids form in solution?

7. Which ion do all alkalis form in solution?

EXTENDED

Making insoluble salts

If two solutions of **soluble** salts are mixed together to form two new salts, and one of the products is **insoluble**, the insoluble salt forms a precipitate – a solid made in solution. This process is called **precipitation**. The general equation is:

soluble salt   +   soluble salt   →   insoluble salt   +   soluble salt
                                        (precipitate)

For example:

$Na_2CO_3(aq)$ + $CuSO_4(aq)$ → $CuCO_3(s)$ + $Na_2SO_4(aq)$

The state symbols show the salts in solution as (aq) and the precipitate – the insoluble salt – as (s).

In the laboratory

The practical method involves making a precipitate of an insoluble salt by mixing solutions of two soluble salts.

The procedure is as follows:

1. The two solutions of soluble salts are mixed together and a precipitate forms.

2. The precipitate is separated by filtration.

3. The precipitate is then washed with a little cold water and allowed to dry.

The process is summarised in Fig. 2.53.

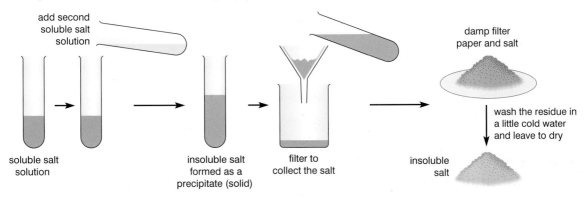

△ Fig. 2.53 Making an insoluble salt.

QUESTIONS

1. What is a *precipitation* reaction?

2. When preparing an insoluble salt what process is used to separate the insoluble salt from any soluble salts?

3. Why is the insoluble salt washed with a little cold water before it is left to dry?

END OF EXTENDED

SOME INTERESTING FACTS ABOUT ACIDS AND ALKALIS

1. Pure sulfuric acid is a clear, oily, highly corrosive liquid. It was well known to Islamic, Greek and Roman scholars in the ancient world, when it was called 'oil of vitriol'. Although pure sulfuric acid does not occur naturally on Earth because of its attraction for water, dilute sulfuric acid is found in acid rain and in the upper atmosphere of the planet Venus. It has a wide range of industrial uses from making fertilisers, dyes, paper and

△ Fig. 2.54 A wasp.

pharmaceuticals to batteries, steel and iron. Sulfuric acid is not toxic but it is highly reactive with water, in a strongly exothermic reaction. It can cause severe burns. The acid must be stored in glass containers (never plastic or metal) and handled with extreme care.

2. Hydrochloric acid, although classified as toxic and corrosive, is part of the gastric acid in the stomach and is involved in digestion. Excess acid in the stomach can cause indigestion but 'anti-acid' (alkali) medications can be taken to neutralise this.

3. Perhaps the strongest acid is a mixture of nitric acid and hydrochloric acid, known as 'aqua regia' because it reacts with the 'royal' metals. Unlike other acids, it reacts with very unreactive metals such as gold and platinum. However, some metals like titanium and silver are not affected.

4. Formic acid (now called methanoic acid) is in the venom of ant and bee stings. Such stings can be relieved by (or neutralised with) an alkali such as sodium bicarbonate (sodium hydrogencarbonate). Wasp stings, however, contain an alkali and so need to be neutralised by a weak acid such as vinegar.

The differences can be remembered using:

Bee – **B**icarb

Wasp (W looks like two **V**s) – **V**inegar

Developing investigative skills

A student wanted to make a sample of copper(II) sulfate crystals, $CuSO_4.5H_2O$. She used the following steps in her method.

She put on eye protection and warmed 50 cm³ of dilute sulfuric acid in a 250 cm³ beaker and then copper(II) oxide was added a spatula at a time, stirring the reaction mixture with a glass rod.

When no more copper(II) oxide would react, she filtered the mixture and collected the copper(II) sulfate solution in an evaporating basin.

She then heated the solution in the evaporating basin until she could see crystals starting to form and then allowed it to cool.

After several hours, blue crystals of copper(II) sulfate had formed. She drained off any remaining liquid and dried the crystals between filter papers.

Using and organising techniques, apparatus and materials

❶ Copper(II) sulfate crystals are 'hydrated'. Explain what this means.

❷ Draw a diagram showing the apparatus the student could have used to filter the mixture in step 2.

❸ What is the general name given to a liquid that passes through a filter paper?

❹ How could the student have tested for the crystallisation point while heating the filtrate?

Observing, measuring and recording

❺ What is the colour of copper(II) oxide?

❻ What would be the colour of the solution the student evaporated?

Evaluating methods

❼ While heating the solution in the evaporating dish the student noticed some very pale blue powder around the edges of the evaporating basin. What do you think this powder was and how do you think it had formed?

❽ Write a fully balanced equation for the reaction.

IDENTIFICATION OF IONS AND GASES

It is important to be able to analyse different substances and identify the different elements or components. The techniques used today are fairly sophisticated but many of them are based on simple laboratory tests. With improved understanding of the beneficial and harmful properties of chemical substances, it has become more and more important to identify metals and non-metals in chemical processes and in the environment.

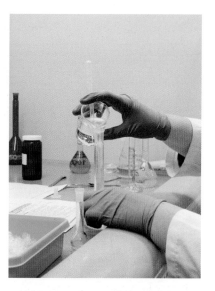

△ Fig. 2.55 A chemist performs a chemical test on a substance in her pharmaceutical laboratory.

Identifying metal ions (cations)

Ions of metals are **cations** – positive ions – and are found in ionic compounds. There are two ways of identifying metal cations:

• *either* from solids of the compound
• *or* from solutions of the compound.

Flame tests

In a flame test, a piece of nichrome wire is dipped into concentrated hydrochloric acid, then into the solid compound, and then into a blue Bunsen flame. The colour seen in the flame identifies the metal ion in the compound.

Name of ion	Formula of ion	Colour seen in flame
lithium	Li^+	bright red
sodium	Na^+	golden yellow/orange
potassium	K^+	lilac (light purple)
copper	Cu^{2+}	green

△ Table 2.10 Colours of ions in a flame.

△ Fig. 2.56 The colour of the flame can be used to identify the metal ions present.

Tests on solutions in water

Metal ions are found in ionic compounds, so most of them will dissolve in water to form solutions. These solutions can be tested with sodium hydroxide solution to identify the aqueous cation.

Name of ion in solution	Formula	Result
Calcium	$Ca^{2+}(aq)$	White precipitate formed; remains, even when excess sodium hydroxide solution added
Copper(II)	$Cu^{2+}(aq)$	Light-blue precipitate formed; insoluble in excess sodium hydroxide solution
Iron(II)	$Fe^{2+}(aq)$	Green precipitate formed; insoluble in excess sodium hydroxide solution; after a few minutes starts to change to reddish-brown colour
Iron(III)	$Fe^{3+}(aq)$	Reddish-brown precipitate formed; insoluble in excess sodium hydroxide solution
Zinc	$Zn^{2+}(aq)$	White precipitate formed; dissolves in excess sodium hydroxide solution

△ Table 2.11 Tests for identifying cations by adding sodium hydroxide solution to excess.

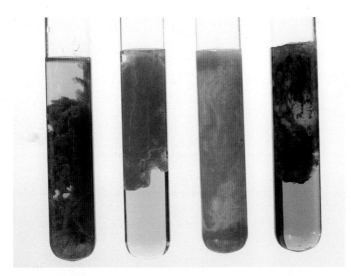

△ Fig. 2.57 Colourful hydroxide precipitates.

Note:

Similar results can be obtained if these reactions are performed using ammonia solution instead of sodium hydroxide solution. However, there is a noticeable difference in the case of copper(II) ions. At first, as with sodium hydroxide solution, a pale-blue precipitate is formed, but then as excess ammonia solution is added the precipitate dissolves to form a royal-blue solution.

The reactions in the table can be represented by ionic equations. For example:

$Ca^{2+}(aq) \quad + \quad 2OH^-(aq) \quad \rightarrow \quad Ca(OH)_2(s)$

white precipitate

$Cu^{2+}(aq) \quad + \quad 2OH^-(aq) \quad \rightarrow \quad Cu(OH)_2(s)$

light-blue precipitate

$Fe^{3+}(aq) \quad + \quad 3OH^-(aq) \quad \rightarrow \quad Fe(OH)_3(s)$

reddish-brown precipitate

QUESTIONS

1. a) What would you observe if you added sodium hydroxide solution to a solution of calcium chloride?

   b) In what way would the observations be different if zinc chloride solution were used instead of calcium chloride solution?

2. What test can be used to distinguish between Fe^{2+} and Fe^{3+} ions? What is the result of the test with each ion?

Identifying ammonium ions, NH_4^+

The test for the ammonium ion is shown in Fig. 2.58.

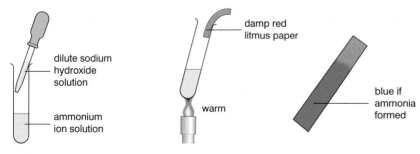

△ Fig. 2.58 Test for the ammonium ion NH_4^+.

The suspected ammonium compound is dissolved in water in a test tube and a few drops of dilute sodium hydroxide are added. The mixture is then warmed over a Bunsen burner and some damp red litmus paper (or universal indicator paper) is placed in the mouth of the test tube. A colour change in the indicator to blue (alkaline) shows that an ammonium compound is present.

Identifying anions

Negative ions (**anions**) can be tested as solids or in solution.

Testing for anions in solids or solutions

The following test for anions in solids applies only to **carbonates**.

Dilute hydrochloric acid is added to the solid, and any gas produced is passed through limewater. If the limewater goes cloudy/milky, the solid contains a carbonate.

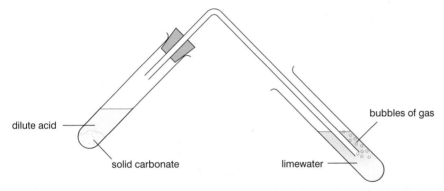

dilute acid

solid carbonate

bubbles of gas

limewater

△ Fig. 2.59 Testing for anions in solids.

This reaction is as follows:

acid + carbonate → a salt + water + carbon dioxide

$2HCl(aq) + Na_2CO_3(s) \rightarrow 2NaCl(aq) + H_2O(l) + CO_2(g)$

$2HCl(aq) + ZnCO_3(s) \rightarrow ZnCl_2(aq) + H_2O(l) + CO_2(g)$

EXTENDED

The reaction between an acid and a carbonate can be represented by the following ionic equation:

$CO_3^{2-}(s) + 2H^+(aq) \rightarrow CO_2(g) + H_2O(l)$

END OF EXTENDED

Many ionic compounds are soluble in water, and so they form solutions that contain anions.

The tests and results used to identify some other common anions are shown in the table.

Name of ion	Formula	Test	Result
Chloride	$Cl^-(aq)$	To a solution of the halide ions add: 1. Dilute nitric acid 2. Silver nitrate solution	White precipitate (of AgCl)
Bromide	$Br^-(aq)$		Cream precipitate (of AgBr)
Iodide	$I^-(aq)$		Yellow precipitate (of AgI)
Sulfate	$SO_4^{2-}(aq)$	Add: 1. Dilute hydrochloric acid 2. Barium chloride solution	White precipitate (of $BaSO_4$)
Nitrate	$NO_3^-(s)$	1. Add sodium hydroxide solution and warm 2. Add aluminium powder 3. Test any gas produced with damp red litmus paper	Red litmus paper goes blue (ammonia gas is produced)

△ Table 2.12 Tests for anions.

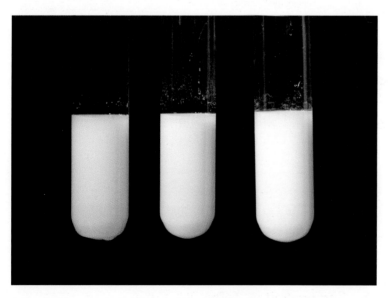

△ Fig. 2.60 Test for the halide ions. Left: chloride, white precipitate.
Centre: bromide, pale-cream precipitate. Right: iodide, pale-yellow precipitate.
(Note: knowledge of the iodide test is not required in the examination.)

These reactions can be represented by ionic equations:

$$Ag^+(aq) \quad + \quad Cl^-(aq) \quad \rightarrow \quad AgCl(s)$$

white precipitate

$$Ag^+(aq) \quad + \quad Br^-(aq) \quad \rightarrow \quad AgBr(s)$$

cream precipitate

$$Ag^+(aq) \quad + \quad I^-(aq) \quad \rightarrow \quad AgI(s)$$

yellow precipitate

$$Ba^{2+}(aq) \quad + \quad SO_4^{2-}(aq) \quad \rightarrow \quad BaSO_4(s)$$

white precipitate

END OF EXTENDED

QUESTIONS

1. Describe how you would test for an ammonium compound. Give the result of the test.

2. When a carbonate is reacted with dilute hydrochloric acid, a gas is given off.

   a) What is the name of the gas?

   b) What is the test for the gas? Give the result of the test.

3. Sodium hydroxide solution is added to solution X and a reddish-brown precipitate is formed. What metal ion was present in solution X?

4. A mixture of dilute nitric acid and silver nitrate solution is added to solution Y in a test tube. A white precipitate forms. What anion is present in solution Y?

5. EXTENDED Metallic ions in solution can be identified using sodium hydroxide solution.

   Sodium hydroxide is useful because it forms coloured precipitates with many metallic ions although it will form white precipitates with others.

a) Copy and complete the table with the names of two cations that form white precipitates and three cations that give coloured precipitates.

Name of cation	Colour of precipitate

b) Halide ions can be identified using nitric acid and silver nitrate. Give a general ionic equation to show the formation of the precipitate of the halide ion.

c) When testing for sulfate ions, why is it important to add dilute hydrochloric acid before adding barium chloride?

6. A forensic scientist has been provided with a small sample of a blue compound which is suspected to be copper(II) sulfate, and a white compound that is suspected to be sodium carbonate. Devise a series of tests that could be followed to identify the ions. Indicate in your plan the expected results if the samples are to be positively identified.

Identifying gases

Many chemical reactions produce a gas as one of the products. Identifying the gas is often a step towards identifying the compound that produced it in the reaction.

Gas	Formula	Test	Result of test
Hydrogen	H_2	Put in a lighted splint (a flame)	'Pop' or 'squeaky pop' heard (flame usually goes out)
Oxygen	O_2	Put in a glowing splint	Splint relights, producing a flame
Carbon dioxide	CO_2	Pass gas through limewater	Limewater goes cloudy/milky
Chlorine	Cl_2	Put in a piece of damp blue litmus paper or universal indicator paper	Paper goes red then white (bleached)
Ammonia	NH_3	Put in a piece of damp red litmus or universal indicator paper	A strong smell is produced and the indicator paper goes blue

△ Table 2.13 Tests for gases.

Carbon dioxide: cloudiness with limewater is caused by insoluble calcium carbonate. If carbon dioxide continues to be passed through, the cloudiness disappears: $CaCO_3(s)$ is changed to soluble calcium hydrogencarbonate, $Ca(HCO_3)_2(aq)$.

Chlorine: the gas is acidic, but also a bleaching agent.

Ammonia: the only basic gas.

QUESTIONS

1. What is the name of a gas that is alkaline?
2. What is the name of a gas that supports combustion?
3. What is the name of a gas that acts as a bleach?

SCIENCE LINK

BIOLOGY – CHARACTERISTICS OF LIVING THINGS, HUMAN EFFECTS ON ECOSYSTEMS

- A number of plants grow flowers of different colours, depending on whether they are growing in acidic soil or alkaline soil – this property forms the basis of many indicators used in chemistry, such as litmus.

- A knowledge of acids and bases is important in understanding the effects of acid rain and some other environmental effects – it is also important in trying to reduce any damaging consequences.

PHYSICS – PROPERTIES OF WAVES

- Flame tests can be used to identify a number of elements.

- The different types of atom produce light of different wavelengths when they are heated – each type of atom produces a characteristic set of colours (a spectrum), rather like a fingerprint for elements!

End of topic checklist

Key terms

acid, alkali, amphoteric oxide, anhydrous, anion, base, carbonate, cation, filtrate, indicator, insoluble, litmus, neutralisation, oxide, pH scale, precipitation, salt, soap, soluble, titration, universal indicator, water of crystallisation

During your study of this topic you should have learned:

○ How to describe the characteristic properties of acids including their effect on litmus paper and their reactions with metals, bases and carbonates.

○ How to describe the characteristic properties of bases including their effect on litmus paper and their reactions with acids and ammonium salts.

○ How to describe neutrality and relative acidity and alkalinity in terms of pH measured using universal indicator.

○ How to describe and explain the importance of controlling acidity in soil.

○ **EXTENDED** The definitions of acids and bases in terms of proton transfer in aqueous solutions.

○ How to classify oxides as either acidic or basic, related to metallic and non-metallic character.

○ **EXTENDED** How to classify other oxides as neutral or amphoteric.

○ How to describe the preparation, separation and purification of salts as prepared by the following reactions:
  ● acid + metal
  ● acid + base
  ● acid + carbonate
  ● acid + alkali.

○ **EXTENDED** How to describe the preparation of insoluble salts by precipitation.

○ **EXTENDED** How to suggest a method of making a given salt from a suitable starting material, given appropriate information.

○ How to carry out tests for the aqueous cations ammonium, calcium, copper(II), iron(II), iron(III) and zinc using aqueous sodium hydroxide and aqueous ammonia.

○ How to use a flame test to identify lithium, sodium, potassium and copper(II).

○ How to carry out tests for the anions:
- carbonate by reaction with dilute acid and then limewater
- chloride and bromide by reaction under acidic conditions with aqueous silver nitrate
- nitrate by reduction with aluminium
- sulfate by reaction under acidic conditions with aqueous barium ions.

○ How to carry out tests for gases:
- ammonia using damp red litmus paper
- carbon dioxide using limewater
- chlorine using damp litmus paper
- hydrogen using a lighted splint
- oxygen using a glowing splint.

End of topic questions

Note: The marks given for these questions indicate the level of detail required in the answers. In the examination, the number of marks given to questions like these may be different.

1. a) What is an *indicator*? (1 mark)

b) What is an *acid*? (1 mark)

c) What is an *alkali*? (1 mark)

d) What is the name of the process when an acid reacts with an alkali to form water? (1 mark)

2. Calcium chloride can be made from calcium oxide and dilute hydrochloric acid.

a) What type of chemical is calcium oxide? (1 mark)

b) What type of chemical is calcium chloride? (1 mark)

c) Is calcium chloride soluble or insoluble in water? (1 mark)

d) Describe the different stages in the preparation of calcium chloride crystals. (4 marks)

e) Write a fully balanced equation, including symbols, for the reaction. (2 marks)

3. **EXTENDED** Barium sulfate is an insoluble salt and can be made using a precipitation reaction.

a) What acid can be used to make barium sulfate? **(1 mark)**

b) What other chemical could be used to make barium sulfate? **(1 mark)**

c) Describe the different stages in the preparation of a dry sample of barium sulfate. **(3 marks)**

d) Write a fully balanced equation, including state symbols, for the reaction. **(2 marks)**

4. **EXTENDED** Copy and complete the following equations and include state symbols:

a) $2KOH(aq) + H_2SO_4(aq) \rightarrow$ _____ + _____ **(2 marks)**

b) $2HCl(aq) + MgO(s) \rightarrow$ _____ + _____ **(2 marks)**

c) $2HNO_3(aq) + BaCO_3(s) \rightarrow$ _____ + _____ + _____ **(2 marks)**

d) $2HCl(aq) + Zn(s) \rightarrow$ _____ + _____ **(2 marks)**

e) $ZnCl_2(aq) + K_2CO_3(aq) \rightarrow$ _____ + _____ **(2 marks)**

5. What ions are likely to be present in the compounds X, Y and Z?

a) Solution X forms a pale-blue precipitate when sodium hydroxide solution is added. **(1 mark)**

b) Solution Y forms no precipitate when sodium hydroxide solution is added, but produces a strong-smelling, alkaline gas when the mixture is heated. **(1 mark)**

c) Solution Z forms an orange-brown precipitate when sodium hydroxide solution is added. **(1 mark)**

6. Copy and complete the table about the identification of gases. **(3 marks)**

Gas	Test	Observations
Chlorine	Damp universal indicator paper	
	Bubble through limewater	White precipitate or suspension forms
Hydrogen		Burns with a 'pop'

7. A white powder is labelled 'lithium carbonate'. What test could you do to prove it was a carbonate? **(2 marks)**

8. How would you test a solid to identify the presence of each of the ions shown below?

    a) the sulfate ion, SO_4^{2-} **(3 marks)**

    b) the iodide ion, I^- **(3 marks)**

    c) the nitrate ion, NO_3^-.   **(3 marks)**

9. **EXTENDED** Write ionic equations for the following reactions:

    a) between copper(II) sulfate and sodium hydroxide solution   **(2 marks)**

    b) between sodium carbonate and dilute hydrochloric acid.   **(2 marks)**

This section concentrates on a 'branch' of chemistry known as inorganic chemistry. As the title suggests, it focuses on the chemical elements, of which there are over 100. This may seem rather a lot, but the good news is that you will not study all 100 elements! However, because the chemical elements are arranged in a particular pattern, known as the Periodic Table, learning about one element often provides a very good idea of how other elements may behave. So it should be possible to learn about the chemistry of about 45 elements from studying this section.

The section starts with the Periodic Table. You will learn about how the elements are arranged into groups and periods. You will then study a group of metals and a group of non-metals, followed by the transition metals and noble gases. The topic on metals highlights differences in the reactivity of metals and how this influences the methods used to extract them from their ores. A topic on air and water allows a consideration of the environmental impact of living in an industrial world. Finally, this study of the elements and some of their compounds provides an opportunity to look at sulfur and some important compounds, carbonates.

STARTING POINTS

1. What is an element – how would you define the term?

2. What does the proton number of an atom tell you about its structure?

3. In terms of electronic structures, what is the difference between a metal and a non-metal?

4. You will be learning about the Periodic Table of elements. Look at the Periodic Table and make a list of the things that you notice about it.

5. You will be learning about the composition of gases in the air. What is the most abundant gas in the air?

6. Make a list of about six to eight metals that you have come across. Which metal in your list do you think is the most reactive? Which metal do you think is the least reactive? Explain your choices.

SECTION CONTENTS

a) The Periodic Table

b) Metals

c) Air and water

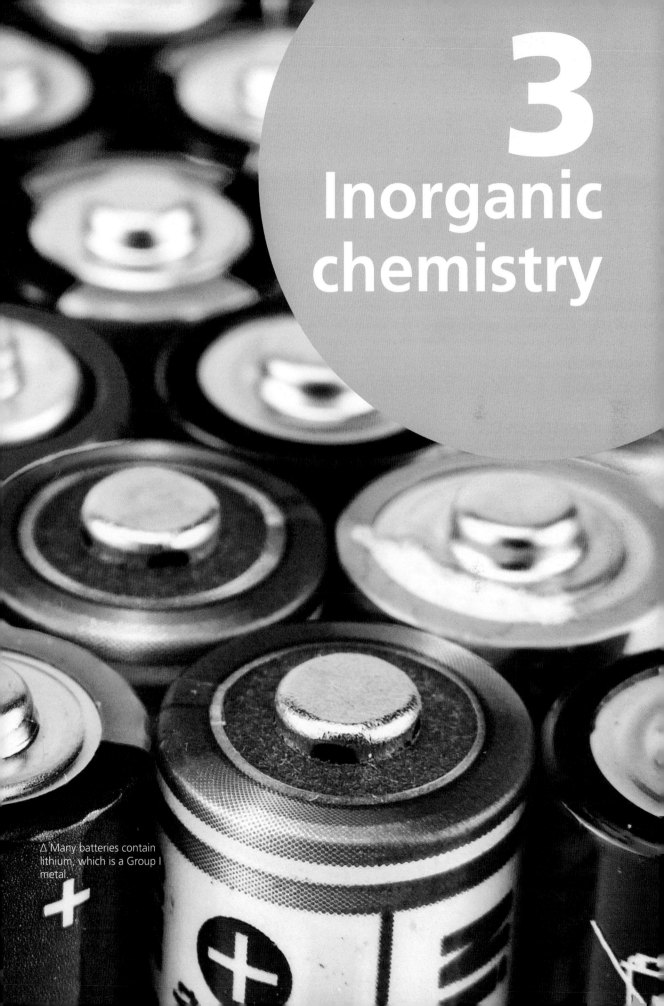

3
Inorganic chemistry

△ Many batteries contain lithium, which is a Group I metal.

The Periodic Table

INTRODUCTION

With over 100 different elements in existence, it's very important to have some way of ordering them. The **Periodic Table** puts elements with similar properties into columns, with a gradual change in properties moving from left to right along the rows. This topic looks at some of the basic features of the Periodic Table. Later topics will look in more detail at particular groups and arrangements of the elements.

△ Fig. 3.1 This ordering of elements was first published in 1871 by the Russian chemist Dmitri Mendeleev.

KNOWLEDGE CHECK

✓ Understand that all matter is made up of elements.
✓ Know that the proton number of an element gives the number of protons (and electrons) in an atom of the element.
✓ Know that electrons are arranged in shells around the nucleus of the atom.
✓ Know that metal oxides are basic and those that dissolve in water form alkalis.

LEARNING OBJECTIVES

✓ Be able to describe the Periodic Table as a method of classifying elements and recognise its use in predicting properties of elements.
✓ Be able to describe the change from metallic to non-metallic character across a period.
✓ **EXTENDED** Be able to describe the relationship between group number, number of outer shell electrons and metallic/non-metallic character.
✓ Be able to describe lithium, sodium and potassium in Group I as a collection of relatively soft metals showing trends in melting point, density and reaction with water.
✓ **EXTENDED** Be able to predict the properties of other elements in Group I, given data where appropriate.
✓ Be able to describe chlorine, bromine and iodine in Group VII as a collection of diatomic non-metals showing trends in colour and in physical state.
✓ **EXTENDED** Be able to predict the properties of other elements in Group VII, given data where appropriate.
✓ **EXTENDED** Be able to state the reaction of chlorine, bromine and iodine with other halide ions.

✓ **EXTENDED** Be able to identify trends in other groups, given information about the elements concerned.
✓ Be able to describe the transition elements as a collection of metals with high densities, high melting points and forming coloured compounds.
✓ Know that transition elements and their compounds are often used as catalysts.
✓ Be able to describe the noble gases as being unreactive, monatomic gases and explain this in terms of electronic structure.
✓ Be able to describe the uses of the noble gases in providing an inert atmosphere, such as argon in lamps and helium in balloons.

THE PERIODIC TABLE

As new elements were discovered in the 19th century, chemists tried to organise them into patterns based on the similarities in their properties. The English chemist John Newlands was the first to classify elements according to their properties and produced his classification system before Mendeleev produced his. When the structure of the atom was better known, elements were arranged in order of increasing proton number, and then the patterns started to make more sense. (Proton number is the number of protons in an atom.)

More than 110 elements have now been identified, and each has its own properties and reactions. In the **Periodic Table**, elements with similar properties and reactions are shown close together.

The Periodic Table arranges the elements in order of increasing proton number. They are then arranged in periods and groups.

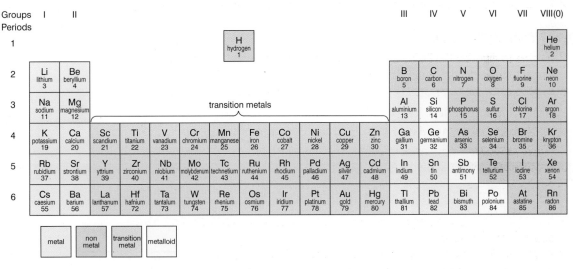

Δ Fig. 3.2 The Periodic Table.

Horizontal rows of elements are arranged in increasing proton number from left to right. Rows correspond to **periods**, which are numbered from 1 to 7.

Moving across a period, each successive atom of the elements gains one proton and one electron (in the same outer shell/orbit).

You can see how this works in Fig. 3.3.

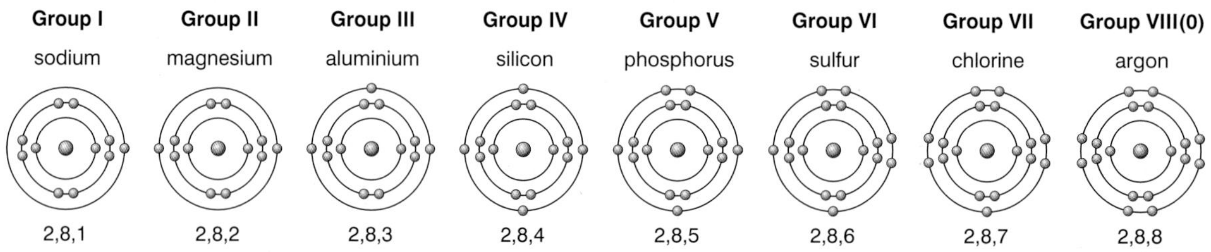

Group I	Group II	Group III	Group IV	Group V	Group VI	Group VII	Group VIII(0)
sodium	magnesium	aluminium	silicon	phosphorus	sulfur	chlorine	argon
2,8,1	2,8,2	2,8,3	2,8,4	2,8,5	2,8,6	2,8,7	2,8,8

△ Fig. 3.3 Moving across a period shows the atomic structure of each element.

Moving across a period like Period 3 (sodium to argon), the following trends take place:

- Metals on the left going to non-metals on the right.
- Group I elements are the most reactive metal group, and as you go to the right the reactivity of the groups decreases. Group IV elements are the least reactive.
- Continuing right from Group IV, the reactivity increases until Group VII, the most reactive of the non-metal groups.

Groups

Vertical columns contain elements with the proton number increasing down the column – they are called **groups**. They are numbered from I to VIII (Group VIII is sometimes referred to as Group 0).

Groups are referred to as 'families' of elements because they have similar characteristics, just like families – the alkali metals (Group I), the alkaline earth metals (Group II) and the halogens (Group VII).

REMEMBER

It is important to understand the relationship between group number, number of outer electrons, and metallic and non-metallic character across periods.

QUESTIONS

1. Find the element calcium in the Periodic Table. Answer these questions about calcium:

   a) What is its proton number?

   b) What information does the proton number give about the structure of a calcium atom?

c) Which group of the Periodic Table is calcium in?

d) Which period of the Periodic Table is calcium in?

e) Is calcium a metal or a non-metal?

2. What is the family name for the Group VII elements?

3. Are the Group VII elements metals or non-metals?

CHARGES ON IONS AND THE PERIODIC TABLE

We can explain why elements in the same group have similar reactions in terms of the electron structures of their atoms. Elements with the same number of electrons in their outer shells have similar chemical properties. The relationship between the group number and the number of electrons in the outer electron shell is shown in Table 3.1.

Group number	I	II	III	IV	V	VI	VII	VIII(0)
Electrons in the outer electron shell	1	2	3	4	5	6	7	2 or 8

△ Table 3.1 Relationship between group number and number of electrons in outer shell.

The ion formed by an element can be worked out from the element's position in the Periodic Table. The elements in Group IV and Group VIII (0) generally do not form ions.

Group number	I	II	III	IV	V	VI	VII	VIII (0)
Ion charge	1+	2+	3+	Typically no ions	3–	2–	1–	No ions
Metallic or non-metallic	Metallic			Non-metallic, **metalloid** and metallic	Non-metallic (except for some metalloids)			

△ Table 3.2 Groups and their ions.

REACTIVITIES OF ELEMENTS

Going from the top to the bottom of a group in the Periodic Table, metals become more reactive, but non-metals become less reactive. As the metal atom gets bigger, the outer electrons get further away from the nucleus and can be removed more easily to form positive ions. So the larger metal atoms can react more easily with other elements and form compounds.

The reverse is true for a group of non-metal atoms: the smaller the atom, the easier it is to accept electrons and form ions. So the smaller non-metal atoms react more easily with other elements to form compounds.

Group VIII(0) elements, known as the noble gases, are very unreactive. They already have full outer electron shells (eight electrons in the outer shell) and so rarely react with other elements to form compounds.

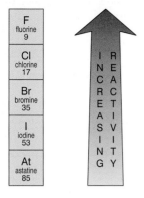

△ Fig. 3.4 The Group VII elements (non-metal) become more reactive further up the group.

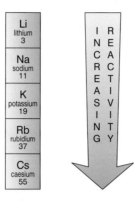

△ Fig. 3.5 Group I elements (metals) become more reactive further down the group.

END OF EXTENDED

QUESTIONS

1. How many electrons does an aluminium atom have in its outer shell?

2. What ion charge does oxygen have?

3. Which is the most reactive element in Group VII?

4. Which is the most reactive element in Group II?

SCIENCE IN CONTEXT   THE FIRST PERIODIC TABLE

In 1871 the Russian chemist Dmitri Mendeleev published his work on the Periodic Table. It included the 66 elements that were known at the time. Interestingly, Mendeleev left gaps in his arrangement when the next element in his order did not seem to fit. He predicted that there should be elements in the gaps but that they had yet to be discovered. One such element is gallium (discovered in 1875), which Mendeleev predicted would be between aluminium and indium.

By June 2011 there were 118 known elements, but only 91 of these occurred naturally – the others had been made artificially. Some of these artificial elements can now be detected in small quantities in the environment – for example the element americium (Am, proton number 95), which is used in smoke detectors.

Metals are positioned on the left-hand side and in the middle of the Periodic Table. Therefore the Group I elements are metals, but rather different from the metals in everyday use. In fact, when you see how the Group I metals react with air and water, it is hard to think how they could be used outside the laboratory. This very high reactivity makes them interesting to study. Our focus is on the first three elements in the group: lithium, sodium and potassium. Rubidium, caesium and francium are not available in schools because they are too reactive.

Group I elements

All Group I elements react with water to produce an alkaline solution. This makes them recognisable as a 'family' of elements, often called the **alkali metals**.

△ Fig. 3.6 Potassium reacting with water.

These very reactive metals all have only one electron in their outer electron shell. This electron is easily given away when the metal reacts with non-metals. The more electrons a metal atom has to lose in a reaction, the more energy is needed to start the reaction. This is why the Group II elements are less reactive – they have to lose two electrons when they react.

EXTENDED

Reactivity increases down the group because as the atom gets bigger the outer electron is further away from the nucleus and so can be removed more easily, as the atoms react to form positive ions.

END OF EXTENDED

PROPERTIES OF GROUP I METALS
The properties of Group I metals are as follows:

- Soft to cut.
- Shiny when cut, but quickly tarnish in the air.
- Very low melting points compared with most metals – melting points decrease down the group.
- Very low densities compared with most metals. Lithium, sodium and potassium float on water. Densities increase down the group.
- React very easily with air, water and elements such as chlorine. The alkali metals are so reactive that they are stored in oil to prevent reaction with air and water. Reactivity increases down the group.

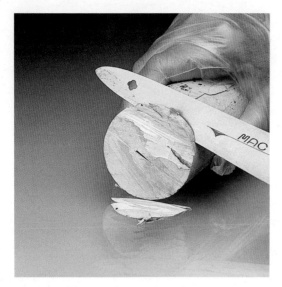

△ Fig. 3.7 The freshly cut surface of sodium.

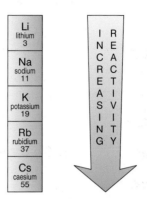

△ Fig. 3.8 Group I elements become more reactive as you go down the group.

QUESTIONS

1. Why are the Group I elements known as the *alkali metals*?

2. How many electrons do the Group I elements atoms have in their outer shell?

3. The Group I metals are unusual metals. Give one property they have that is different from most other metals.

4. **EXTENDED** Predict how the melting point of rubidium will compare to that of sodium. Explain your answer.

5. **EXTENDED** Why is potassium more reactive than lithium?

Reaction	Observations	Equations
Air or oxygen oil / metal	The metals burn easily and their compounds colour flames: lithium – red sodium – orange/yellow potassium – lilac A white solid oxide is formed	lithium + oxygen → lithium oxide $4Li(s) + O_2(g) \rightarrow 2Li_2O(s)$ sodium + oxygen → sodium oxide $4Na(s) + O_2(g) \rightarrow 2Na_2O(s)$ potassium + oxygen → potassium oxide $4K(s) + O_2(g) \rightarrow 2K_2O(s)$
Water	The metals react vigorously They float on the surface, moving around rapidly With both sodium and potassium, the heat of the reaction melts the metal so it forms a sphere; bubbles of gas are given off and the metal 'disappears' With the more reactive metals (such as potassium) the hydrogen gas produced burns The resulting solution is alkaline	lithium + water → lithium hydroxide + hydrogen $2Li(s) + 2H_2O(l) \rightarrow 2LiOH(aq) + H_2(g)$ sodium + water → sodium hydroxide + hydrogen $2Na(s) + 2H_2O(l) \rightarrow 2NaOH(aq) + H_2(g)$ potassium + water → potassium hydroxide + hydrogen $2K(s) + 2H_2O(l) \rightarrow 2KOH(aq) + H_2(g)$
Chlorine chlorine / sodium	The metals react easily, burning in the chlorine to form a white solid, the metal chloride	lithium + chlorine → lithium chloride $2Li(s) + Cl_2(g) \rightarrow 2LiCl(s)$ sodium + chlorine → sodium chloride $2Na(s) + Cl_2(g) \rightarrow 2NaCl(s)$ potassium + chlorine → potassium chloride $2K(s) + Cl_2(g) \rightarrow 2KCl(s)$

△ Table 3.3 Reactions of Group I metals.

Compounds of the Group I metals

The compounds of Group I metals are usually colourless crystals or white solids and always have ionic bonding. Most of them are soluble in water. Some examples are sodium chloride ($NaCl$) and potassium nitrate (KNO_3).

The compounds of the alkali metals are widely used:

- Lithium carbonate – as a hardener in glass and ceramics.
- Lithium hydroxide – removes carbon dioxide in air-conditioning systems.
- Sodium chloride – table salt.
- Sodium carbonate – a water softener.
- Sodium hydroxide – used in paper manufacture.
- Monosodium glutamate – a flavour enhancer.
- Sodium sulfite – a preservative.
- Potassium nitrate – a fertiliser; also used in explosives.

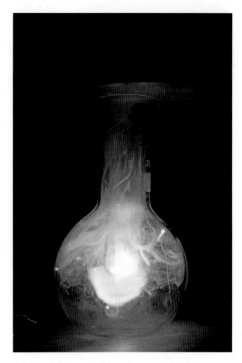

△ Fig. 3.9 Sodium burning in chlorine.

QUESTIONS

1. Sodium burns in oxygen to make sodium oxide. What colour would you expect sodium oxide to be?

2. What gas is produced when potassium reacts with water? What is the name of the solution formed in this reaction?

3. Are the compounds of the Group I metals usually soluble or insoluble in water?

It is important to understand the structure of the Periodic Table and how it relates to the properties and reactions of the elements. These questions link electronic structure with the reactivity trends of the different elements in the Periodic Table.

4. **EXTENDED** These questions are based on Group I of the Periodic Table.

   a) What do you understand by a *group* in the Periodic Table?

   b) Name the first three metals of Group I.

   c) Why do the elements in this group have similar chemical properties?

   d) Group I elements are very reactive. Suggest reasons for this.

FACTS ABOUT THE GROUP I METALS

1. Lithium is found in large quantities (estimated at 230 billion tonnes) in compounds in seawater.

2. Sodium is found in many minerals and is the sixth most abundant element overall in the Earth's crust (amounting to 2.6% by weight).

3. Potassium is also found in many minerals and is the seventh most abundant element in the Earth's crust (amounting to 1.5% by weight).

4. Rubidium was discovered by Bunsen (of Bunsen burner fame) in 1861. It is more abundant than copper, about the same as zinc and is found in very small quantities in a large number of minerals. Because of this low concentration in mineral deposits, only 2 to 4 tonnes of rubidium are produced each year worldwide.

5. Caesium is more abundant than tin, mercury and silver. However, its very high reactivity makes it very difficult to extract from mineral deposits.

6. Francium was discovered as recently as 1939 as a product of the radioactive decay of an isotope of actinium.

Δ Fig. 3.10 Lithium is used in all of these batteries.

Group VII elements are located on the right-hand side of the Periodic Table with the other non-metals. They look very different from each other, so it may seem strange that they are in the same group. However, their chemical properties are very similar, and all of them are highly reactive. This topic focuses on chlorine, bromine and iodine. Fluorine is a highly reactive gas and astatine is a radioactive black solid with a very short half-life (so will exist in only very small quantities).

Group VII elements

The Group VII elements are sometimes referred to as the **halogen** elements or halogens.

'Halogen' means 'salt-maker' – halogens react with most metals to make salts.

Halogen atoms have seven electrons in their outermost electron shell, so they need to gain only one electron to obtain a full outer shell. This is what makes them very reactive. They react with metals, gaining an electron and forming a singly charged negative ion.

△ Fig. 3.11 At room temperature and atmospheric pressure, chlorine is a pale green gas, bromine a red-brown liquid and iodine is a black solid.

EXTENDED

The reactivity of the elements *decreases down the group* because as the atom gets bigger, an eighth electron will be further from the attractive force of the nucleus. This makes it harder for the atom to gain this electron.

END OF EXTENDED

The properties of the Group VII elements are as follows.

- Fluorine is a pale-yellow gas; chlorine is a pale-green gas; bromine is a red-brown liquid; iodine is a black, shiny solid.
- All the atoms have seven electrons in their outermost electron shell.
- All exist as diatomic molecules – each molecule contains two atoms. For example – F_2, Cl_2, Br_2, I_2.
- Halogens react with water and react with metals to form salts. Iodine has very low solubility and little reaction with water.
- They undergo **displacement reactions**.

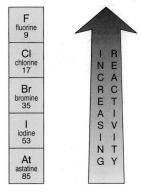

△ Fig. 3.12 Increasing reactivity goes up Group VII.

Reaction	Observations	Equations
Water chlorine gas / water	The halogens dissolve in water and also react with it, forming solutions that behave as bleaches Chlorine solution is pale yellow Bromine solution is orange Iodine solution is yellow/brown	chlorine + water → hydrochloric acid + chloric(I) acid $Cl_2(g) + H_2O(l) \rightarrow HCl(aq) + HClO(aq)$
Metals chlorine / sodium	The halogens form salts with all metals. For example, gold leaf will catch fire in chlorine without heating With a metal such as iron, brown fumes of iron(III) chloride form	iron + chlorine → iron(III) chloride $2Fe(s) + 3Cl_2(g) \rightarrow 2FeCl_3(s)$ Fluorine forms salts called fluorides Chlorine forms salts called chlorides Bromine forms salts called bromides Iodine forms salts called iodides
Displacement chlorine gas sodium iodide solution / iodine being formed	A more reactive halogen will displace a less reactive halogen from a solution of a salt Chlorine displaces bromine from sodium bromide solution. The colourless solution (sodium bromide) turns orange when chlorine is added due to the formation of bromine Chlorine displaces iodine from sodium iodide solution. The colourless solution (sodium iodide) turns brown when chlorine is added due to the formation of iodine	chlorine + sodium bromide → sodium chloride + bromine $Cl_2(g) + 2NaBr(aq) \rightarrow 2NaCl(aq) + Br_2(aq)$ chlorine + sodium iodide → sodium chloride + iodine $Cl_2(g) + 2NaI(aq) \rightarrow 2NaCl(aq) + I_2(aq)$

△ Table 3.4 Properties of the Group VII elements.

The displacement reactions between halogens and solutions of halide ions (shown above) are examples of redox reactions – that is, oxidation and reduction reactions. The Na+ ions are 'spectator' ions and play no part in the reaction, so if the reaction between chlorine and sodium bromide solution is written with them removed, the equation becomes:

$$Cl_2(aq) + 2Br^-(aq) \rightarrow 2Cl^-(aq) + Br_2(aq)$$

This reaction can be written as two half-equations showing how electrons are involved:

$$Cl_2(aq) + 2e^- \rightarrow 2Cl^-(aq)$$

The chlorine has gained electrons – it has been reduced.

$$2Br^-(aq) \rightarrow Br_2(aq) + 2e^-$$

The bromide ions have lost electrons – they have been oxidised.

In this reaction the chlorine is an oxidising agent – it oxidises the bromide ions and is itself reduced. The bromide ions are reducing agents – they reduce the chlorine and are themselves oxidised.

END OF EXTENDED

QUESTIONS

1. How many electrons do the Group VII element atoms have in their outer shell?

2. Why are the Group VII elements particularly reactive when compared to other non-metals?

3. Chlorine exists as diatomic molecules. Explain what this means.

4. **EXTENDED** Astatine is an element in Group VII. Predict whether you would expect it to be a solid, liquid or gas at room temperature. Explain your answer.

5. **EXTENDED** What is meant by a 'displacement reaction' involving the Group VII elements?

6. **EXTENDED** Why are displacement reactions also redox reactions?

Developing investigative skills

A student was provided with three aqueous solutions containing chlorine, bromine and iodine. She added a few drops of cyclohexane to each solution in separate test tubes and then stirred each with a clean glass rod. Cyclohexane does not mix with water, it floats on top of aqueous solutions. When each cyclohexane layer separated from the solution, she recorded the colours of the cyclohexane layers in the table:

Solution in water	Colour of the cyclohexane layer
chlorine	colourless
bromine	orange
iodine	violet

She cleaned out the tubes and then performed a series of test tube reactions as indicated in the table below. In each case she mixed small quantities of solution A with twice the volume of solution B, added 10 drops of cyclohexane and then stirred the mixture with a clean glass rod. Once the cyclohexane layer had separated, she recorded her results.

Solution A	Solution B	Colour of cyclohexane layer
aqueous chlorine	sodium bromide	orange
aqueous chlorine	sodium iodide	violet
aqueous bromine	sodium chloride	orange
aqueous bromine	sodium iodide	violet
aqueous iodine	sodium chloride	violet
aqueous iodine	sodium bromide	orange

Using and organising techniques, apparatus and materials

❶ Cyclohexane is highly flammable and the chlorine and bromine solutions are both irritants. What precautions should the student have taken when doing this experiment?

Interpreting observations and data

❷ What can you deduce about the relative reactivity of chlorine, bromine and iodine from the *first two* results in the second table?

❸ Write an equation for the reaction indicated by result 4 in the second table.

Evaluating methods

❹ The student made a mistake in recording one of her results. Which one? Explain how you know.

Uses of halogens

Halogens and their compounds have a wide range of uses:

- Fluorides – in toothpaste help prevent tooth decay.
- Fluorine compounds – making plastics like Teflon (the non-stick surface on pans).
- Chlorofluorocarbons – propellants in aerosols and refrigerants (now being replaced because of their damaging effect on the ozone layer).
- Chlorine – purifying water.
- Chlorine compounds – household bleaches.
- Hydrochloric acid – widely used in industry.
- Bromine compounds – making pesticides.
- Silver bromide – the light-sensitive film coating on photographic film.
- Iodine solution – an antiseptic.

SCIENCE IN CONTEXT — FLUORINE

Fluorine is the most reactive non-metal in the Periodic Table. It reacts with most other elements except helium, neon and argon. These reactions are often sudden or explosive. Even radon, a very unreactive noble gas, burns with a bright flame in a jet of fluorine gas. All metals react with fluorine to form fluorides. The reactions of fluorine with Group I metals are explosive.

Early scientists tried to make fluorine from hydrofluoric acid (HF(aq)) but this proved to be highly dangerous, killing or blinding several scientists who attempted it. They became known as the 'fluorine martyrs'. Today fluorine is manufactured by the electrolysis of the mineral fluorite, which is calcium fluoride.

Fluorine is not an element to play with. You will certainly not see it in your laboratory!

QUESTIONS

1. Why is chlorine used in the treatment of drinking water in many countries?

2. Which halogen element has medical uses as an antiseptic?

3. Fluorine is used to make a plastic material with the common name of 'Teflon'. What is Teflon used for?

You should be familiar with the elements of Group VII, the halogens. These are coloured, non-metallic elements of varying reactivity. Although they are potentially harmful, their properties make them very useful. Use your knowledge of atomic structure, bonding and reaction types to answer the questions below.

4. EXTENDED Chlorine is a pale green gas which can be obtained by the electrolysis of an aqueous solution of sodium chloride. Chlorine can be used to kill bacteria and is used in the manufacture of bleach.

   a) The electronic structure of a chlorine atom is 2,8,7. Draw simple diagrams to show the arrangement of the outer electrons in a diatomic molecule of Cl_2 and a chloride ion, Cl^-.

   b) In the electrolysis of an aqueous solution of sodium chloride, the positive anode attracts the OH^- ions and Cl^- ions to form chlorine molecules. Copy and complete the equation below and explain why this is oxidation.

   _____$Cl^-(aq) \rightarrow$ _____$(g) + 2e^-$

   c) Sodium hydroxide and chlorine react at room temperature to form bleach, sodium chlorate (I), which is used in domestic cleaning agents. Copy and complete and balance the equation shown.

sodium hydroxide + chlorine → sodium chloride + sodium chlorate(I) + water

_____ + $Cl_2(aq)$ → _____ + $NaClO(aq)$ + $H_2O(l)$

   d) Chlorine will displace bromine from a solution of potassium bromide to form bromine and potassium chloride. Explain why this reaction takes place and describe what you would observe if chlorine water was added to a solution of potassium bromide in a test tube.

5. EXTENDED Fluorine is a pale yellow gas and is the most reactive of the chemical elements. It is so reactive that glass, metals and even water burn with a bright flame in a jet of fluorine gas. Fluorides, however, are often added to toothpaste and, controversially, to some water supplies to prevent dental decay.

   a) Give a reason why fluorine is so reactive.

   b) Write an ionic half-equation that shows the conversion of fluorine to fluoride ions.

   c) Potassium fluoride is a compound that may be found in toothpaste. Explain why fluorine cannot be displaced from this compound using either chlorine or iodine.

**PHYSICS – SIMPLE KINETIC MODEL, ATOMIC
PHYSICS**

- The Periodic Table lists the 'cast of characters' from which all materials are made.

- The patterns in the Periodic Table give us clues to how different materials behave – for example, the similarities between the metals as good conductors.

- The numbers associated with the elements (atomic number and mass number) allow us to calculate the masses of chemicals that will react (and how much energy will be released or taken in) as well as allowing us to describe the deeper patterns of the structure of the atom itself.

- The patterns in the Periodic Table also give clues as to why some elements are radioactive.

TRANSITION ELEMENTS

The **transition metals** are grouped in the centre of the Periodic Table and include iron, copper, zinc and chromium.

All the transition metals have more than one electron in their outer electron shell. They are much less reactive than Group I and Group II metals and so are more 'everyday' metals. They have much higher melting points and densities. They react much more slowly with water and with oxygen.

They are widely used as construction metals (particularly iron through steel).

One of the typical properties of transition metals and their compounds is their ability to act as **catalysts** and speed up the rate of a chemical reaction by providing an alternative pathway with a lower activation energy – for example vanadium(V) oxide in the contact process and iron in the Haber process.

Δ Fig. 3.13 This incandescent lightbulb contains unreactive argon instead of air.

Property	Group I metal	Transition metal
Melting point	Low	High
Density	Low	High
Colour of compounds	White	Mainly coloured
Reactions with water/air	Vigorous	Slow or no reaction
Reactions with an acid	Violent (dangerous)	Slow or no reaction

△ Table 3.5 Properties of the Group I metals and the transition metals.

The compounds of the transition metals are usually coloured. Copper compounds are usually blue or green; iron compounds tend to be either green or brown.

EXTENDED

When sodium hydroxide solution is added to a solution of a transition metal compound, a precipitate of the metal hydroxide is formed. The colour of the precipitate helps to identify the metal. For example:

copper(II) sulfate + sodium hydroxide → copper(II) hydroxide + sodium sulfate

$CuSO_4(aq)$ + $2NaOH(aq)$ → $Cu(OH)_2(s)$ + $Na_2SO_4(aq)$

This can be written as an ionic equation:

$Cu^{2+}(aq) + 2OH^-(aq) \rightarrow Cu(OH)_2(s)$

Colour of metal hydroxide	Likely metal present
Blue	Copper(II) Cu^{2+}
Green	Nickel(II) Ni^{2+}
Green turning to brown	Iron(II) Fe^{2+}
Orange/brown	Iron(III) Fe^{3+}

△ Table 3.6 Transition metal hydroxides and their colours.

END OF EXTENDED

1. Would you expect a reaction to happen between copper and water?

2. Chromium forms a compound called chromium(III) oxide. What does the number in the name indicate?

3. **EXTENDED** a) Write a fully balanced equation for the reaction between iron(II) sulfate solution and sodium hydroxide solution.

   b) What will be the colour of the precipitate formed?

NOBLE GASES

This is actually a group of *very* unreactive non-metals. They used to be called the inert gases as it was thought that they didn't react with anything. But scientists later managed to produce fluorine compounds of some of the **noble gases**. As far as your school laboratory work is concerned, however, they are completely unreactive.

Name	Symbol
Helium	He
Neon	Ne
Argon	Ar
Krypton	Kr
Xenon	Xe
Radon	Rn

△ Table 3.7 The noble gases.

The unreactivity of the noble gases can be explained in terms of their electronic structures. The atoms all have complete outer electron shells or eight electrons in their outer shell. They don't need to lose electrons (as metals do), or gain electrons (as most non-metals do).

Similarities of the noble gases
- Full outer electron shells
- Very unreactive
- Gases
- Exist as single atoms – they are **monatomic** (He, Ne, Ar, Kr, Xe, Rn).

How are the noble gases used?
- Helium – in balloons
- Neon – in red tube lights
- Argon – in lamps and lightbulbs.

End of topic checklist

Key terms

alkali metal, catalyst, displacement reaction, group, halogens, metalloid, monatomic, noble gas, period, Periodic Table, transition metal

During your study of this topic you should have learned:

○ How to describe the Periodic Table as a method of classifying elements and its use to predict properties of elements.

○ How to describe the change from metallic to non-metallic character across a period.

○ **EXTENDED** How to describe the relationship between group number, number of outer shell electrons and metallic/non-metallic character.

○ How to describe lithium, sodium and potassium in Group I as a collection of relatively soft metals showing trends in melting point, density and reaction with water.

○ **EXTENDED** How to predict the properties of other elements in Group I, given data where appropriate.

○ How to describe chlorine, bromine and iodine in Group VII as a collection of diatomic non-metals showing trends in colour and in physical state.

○ **EXTENDED** How to predict the properties of other elements in Group VII, given data where appropriate.

○ **EXTENDED** The reactions of chlorine, bromine and iodine with other halide ions.

○ **EXTENDED** How to identify trends in other groups, given information about the elements concerned.

○ How to describe the transition elements as a collection of metals with high densities, high melting points and forming coloured compounds.

○ That transition elements and their compounds are often used as catalysts.

○ That the noble gases are unreactive, monatomic gases.

○ How to describe the uses of the noble gases in providing an inert atmosphere, such as argon in lamps and helium in balloons.

End of topic questions

Note: The marks given for these questions indicate the level of detail required in the answers. In the examination, the number of marks given to questions like these may be different.

1. Look at the diagram representing the Periodic Table. The letters stand for elements.

	a																
													b				
			c														d
e																f	

   a) Which element is in Group IV?   (1 mark)

   b) Which element is in the second period?   (1 mark)

   c) Which element is a noble gas?   (1 mark)

   d) Which element is a transition metal?   (1 mark)

   e) Which elements are non-metals?   (1 mark)

   f) Which element is most likely to be a gas?   (1 mark)

2. What are the electron arrangements in the following atoms?

   a) sodium (proton number = 11)   (1 mark)

   b) silicon (proton number = 14)   (1 mark)

   c) fluorine (proton number = 9).   (1 mark)

3. How does the metallic and non-metallic nature of the elements change across Period 3 of the Periodic Table?   (1 mark)

4. Why do elements in the same group have similar chemical properties?   (1 mark)

5. What ions would you expect the following atoms to form?

   a) sodium   (1 mark)

   b) chlorine.   (1 mark)

6. In the Periodic Table, what is the trend in reactivity:

   a) down a group of metals? (1 mark)

   b) down a group of non-metals? (1 mark)

7. Explain why the noble gases in Group 0 are very unreactive. (2 marks)

8. This question is about the Group I elements lithium, sodium and potassium.

   a) Which is the most reactive of these elements? (1 mark)

   b) Why are the elements stored in oil? (1 mark)

   c) Which element is the easiest to cut? (1 mark)

   d) Why do the elements tarnish quickly when they are cut? (1 mark)

   e) Why does sodium float when added to water? (1 mark)

9. Why are the Group I elements known as the 'alkali metals'? (2 marks)

10. Write word equations and balanced equations for the following reactions:

   a) lithium and oxygen (3 marks)

   b) potassium and water (3 marks)

   c) potassium and chlorine. (3 marks)

11. **EXTENDED** This question is about rubidium (symbol Rb), which is a less common Group I element.

   a) What state of matter would you expect rubidium to be in at room temperature and pressure? (1 mark)

   b) When rubidium is added to water:

      i) which gas is formed? (1 mark)

      ii) what chemical compound would be formed in solution? What result would you predict if universal indicator was added to the solution? (2 marks)

   c) Would you expect rubidium to be more or less reactive than potassium? Explain your answer. (2 marks)

12. **EXTENDED** Explain why potassium is more reactive than sodium. (3 marks)

13. This question is about the Group VII elements: chlorine, bromine and iodine.

a) Which is the most reactive of these elements? **(1 mark)**

b) Which of the elements exists as a liquid at room temperature and pressure? **(1 mark)**

c) Which of the elements exists as a solid at room temperature and pressure? **(1 mark)**

d) What is the appearance of bromine? **(1 mark)**

14. Explain the following statements:

a) The Group VII elements are the most reactive non-metals. **(2 marks)**

b) The most reactive halogen is at the top of its group. **(2 marks)**

15. Write word and balanced equations for the following reactions:

a) sodium and chlorine **(3 marks)**

b) magnesium and bromine **(3 marks)**

c) hydrogen and fluorine. **(3 marks)**

16. EXTENDED Aqueous bromine reacts with sodium iodide solution.

a) What type of chemical reaction is this? **(1 mark)**

b) Write a balanced equation for the reaction. **(2 marks)**

c) The reaction involves oxidation and reduction.

i) What is *oxidation*? What has been oxidised in this reaction? **(2 marks)**

ii) What is *reduction*? What has been reduced in this reaction? **(2 marks)**

17. This question is about the transition metals.

a) Give two differences in the physical properties of the transition metals compared with the alkali metals. **(2 marks)**

b) Transition metals are used as catalysts. What is a *catalyst*? **(1 mark)**

c) Suggest why the alkali metals are more reactive than the transition metals. **(2 marks)**

18. Look at the table of observations.

Compound tested	Colour of compound	Effect of adding sodium hydroxide solution to a solution of the compound
A	White	No change
B	Blue	Blue precipitate formed
C	White	White precipitate formed

a) Which of the compounds, A, B or C, contains a transition metal?
   Explain your answer. **(1 mark)**

b) Which transition metal do you think it is? **(1 mark)**

c) EXTENDED Compound B is a metal sulfate. Write a balanced equation for the reaction between a solution of this transition metal compound and sodium hydroxide solution. **(2 marks)**

19. Explain why the noble gases are so unreactive. **(2 marks)**

20. The noble gases are *monatomic*. What does this mean? **(1 mark)**

21. Although the noble gases are generally very unreactive, reactions do occur with very reactive elements such as fluorine. Which of the noble gases are more likely to react – helium at the top of the group or xenon near the bottom of the group? **(1 mark)**

Metals

INTRODUCTION

Metals are very important in our everyday lives and many have very similar physical properties. Some metals are highly reactive, like the Group I metals on the left-hand side of the Periodic Table. Other metals are much less reactive, such as the transition metals in the middle of the Periodic Table. Knowing the order of the reactivity of metals can help chemists make very accurate predictions about how the metals will react with different substances and also what individual metals can be used for.

△ Fig. 3.14 What sort of properties should the metals used in the construction of this helicopter have?

KNOWLEDGE CHECK

✓ Know where metals are found in the Periodic Table.
✓ Know that metals have different reactivities.
✓ Know some of the uses of everyday metals.

LEARNING OBJECTIVES

✓ Be able to describe the general physical properties of metals.
✓ **EXTENDED** Be able to describe metallic bonding as a lattice of positive ions in a 'sea of electrons' and use this to describe the electrical conductivity and malleability of metals.
✓ Be able to describe alloys, such as brass, as mixtures of a metal with other elements.
✓ Be able to explain in terms of their properties why alloys are used instead of pure metals.
✓ **EXTENDED** Be able to describe how the properties of iron are changed by the controlled use of additives to form steel alloys.
✓ **EXTENDED** Be able to identify representations of alloys from diagrams of structure.
✓ Know the order of reactivity of metals – potassium, sodium, calcium, magnesium, aluminium, (carbon), zinc, iron, (hydrogen) and copper – by reference to the reactions, if any, of the metals with water or steam, or dilute hydrochloric acid.
✓ Know which metal oxides can be reduced by carbon.
✓ **EXTENDED** Be able to describe the reactivity series as being related to the tendency of a metal to form its positive ion illustrated by its reaction, if any, with the aqueous ions or the oxides of other metals.
✓ Be able to deduce an order of reactivity from a given set of experimental results.
✓ Be able to describe the use of carbon in the extraction of some metals from their ores.
✓ **EXTENDED** Be able to describe the essential reactions in the extraction of iron from haematite.
✓ Know that aluminium is extracted from the ore bauxite by electrolysis.
✓ Be able to describe metal ores as a finite resource and hence the need to recycle metals.

✓ **EXTENDED** Be able to relate the method of extraction of a metal from its ore to its position in the reactivity series.

✓ Know that aluminium is used in the manufacture of aircraft because of its strength and low density.

✓ Know that aluminium is used to make food containers because of its resistance to corrosion.

✓ **EXTENDED** Be able to describe and explain the apparent unreactivity of aluminium in terms of the oxide layer which adheres to the metal.

✓ Know that mild steel is used to make car bodies and machinery and that stainless steel is used to make chemical plant and cutlery.

✓ **EXTENDED** Know that zinc can be used for galvanising and for making brass.

PROPERTIES OF METALS

Most metals have similar physical properties.

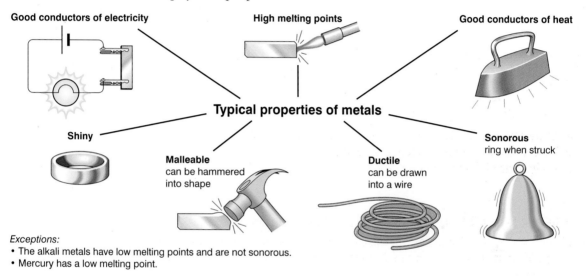

Good conductors of electricity

High melting points

Good conductors of heat

Typical properties of metals

Shiny

Malleable
can be hammered
into shape

Ductile
can be drawn
into a wire

Sonorous
ring when struck

Exceptions:
• The alkali metals have low melting points and are not sonorous.
• Mercury has a low melting point.

Δ Fig. 3.15 Properties of metals.

EXTENDED

The structure of metals

Metals are giant structures with high melting and boiling points.

Metal atoms give up one or more of their electrons to form positive ions called **cations**. The electrons they give up form a 'sea of electrons' surrounding the positive metal ions, and the negative electrons are attracted to the positive ions holding the structure together.

The electrons are free to move through the whole structure. The electrons are **delocalised**, meaning they are not fixed in one position.

The properties of metals

Metals are shiny, **malleable** (can be hammered into a sheet), **ductile** (can be drawn or pulled into a wire), good **conductors** of electricity and good conductors of heat.

Metals are good conductors because their delocalised electrons are free to move through the structure. When a metal is in an electric circuit, electrons can move toward the positive terminal and the negative terminal can supply electrons to the metal.

Metals are malleable and ductile because metallic bonds are not as rigid as the bonds in diamond, for example, although they are still very strong. So the ions in the metal can move around into different positions when the metal is hammered or worked.

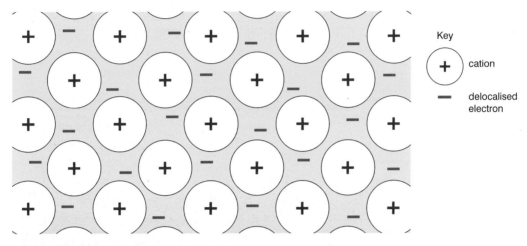

Key

+ cation

— delocalised electron

Δ Fig. 3.16 Cations and delocalised electrons in a metal.

END OF EXTENDED

Alloys

An **alloy** is a mixture of a metal with one or more other elements.

The reason for producing alloys is to 'improve' the properties of a metal. Table 3.8 shows some examples.

Alloy	Property improved
Steel	Hardness/tensile strength
Bronze	Hardness
Solder	Lower melting point
Cupronickel	Cheaper than silver (used for coins)
Stainless steel	Resistance to corrosion
Brass	Easier to shape and stamp into shape

Δ Table 3.8 Alloys and their properties.

◁ Fig. 3.17 Alloys are used to make coins.

The structure of alloys

The structure of pure metallic elements is usually shown as in Fig. 3.18.

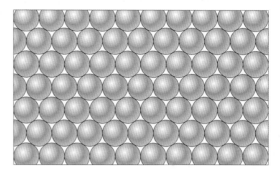

△ Fig. 3.18 Particles in a solid.

This is a simplified picture but, surprisingly, such a structure is very weak. If there is the slightest difference between the planes of atoms, the metal will break at that point.

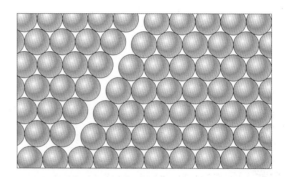

△ Fig. 3.19 The gaps show a weak point of a metal.

The more irregular (jumbled-up) the metal atoms are, the stronger the metal is. This is why alloy structures are stronger: because of the elements added.

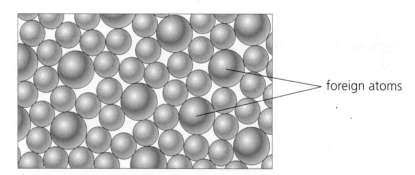

foreign atoms

△ Fig. 3.20 Atoms in an alloy.

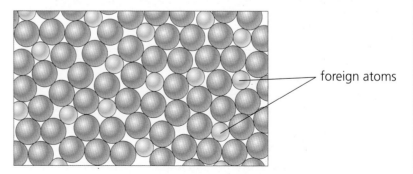

foreign atoms

△ Fig. 3.21 Even smaller atoms make the metal stronger.

Steel that is heated to red heat and then plunged into cold water is made harder by the process of 'jumbling up' the metal atoms. Further heat treatment is used to increase the strength and toughness of the alloy.

QUESTIONS

1. Metals are often *ductile*. What does this mean?

2. Metals are usually *malleable*. What does this mean?

3. What is an alloy?

4. Which alloy is used to make many coins?

5. Explain why an alloy of aluminium is likely to be stronger than pure aluminium.

SCIENCE LINK

BIOLOGY – PLANT NUTRITION

- Metal ions are important for the healthy growth of plants – for example, magnesium ions for making chlorophyll.

PHYSICS – ELECTRIC CIRCUITS

- The metallic bonding structure allows a number of electrons to be 'free' of particular atoms – metals are good conductors.

- Having conduction electrons is the basis of electric circuits, where the property of electric charge allows us to give a large number of electrons a general 'drift' in one direction – leading to an overall energy transfer.

- Metals are also good thermal conductors since the electrons are also able to transfer thermal energy – in addition to the energy transferred by the ions in the structure which can transfer energy by vibration as in insulators.

REACTIVITY SERIES

The Periodic Table is a way of ordering the chemical elements that highlights their similar and their different properties. The reactivity series is another way of classifying elements, this time in order of their reactivity to help explain or predict their reactions. This has many practical applications, such as being able to predict how metals can be extracted from their ores and how the negative effects of the chemical process of rusting can be reduced.

The more reactive metals react with oxygen to form oxides:

calcium   +   oxygen   →   calcium oxide
$2Ca(s)$ + $O_2(g)$ → $2CaO(s)$

Less reactive metals, such as gold, do not react with oxygen.

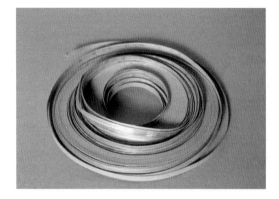

△ Fig. 3.22 Sodium, magnesium, gold – these are all metals, but they have very different reactivities.

Elements can be arranged in order of their reactivity. The more reactive a metal is, the easier it is to form compounds and the harder it is to break those compounds down. We can predict how metals might react by looking at the reactivity series (Fig. 3.23).

The most reactive metals react with water at room temperature. For example, potassium, sodium and lithium in Group I and calcium in Group II react rapidly with water:

sodium   +   water   →   sodium hydroxide   +   hydrogen
$2Na(s)$ + $2H_2O(l)$ → $2NaOH(aq)$ + $H_2(g)$

The less reactive metals such as magnesium and iron react with steam:

magnesium   +   steam   →   magnesium oxide   +   hydrogen
$Mg(s)$ + $H_2O(g)$ → $MgO(s)$ + $H_2(g)$

Some of the mid-reactivity series metals produce hydrogen when they react with dilute acids. So, for example, magnesium, aluminium, zinc and iron all release hydrogen when they react with dilute hydrochloric acid:

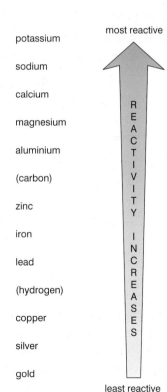

potassium
sodium
calcium
magnesium
aluminium
(carbon)
zinc
iron
lead
(hydrogen)
copper
silver
gold

most reactive

REACTIVITY INCREASES

least reactive

△ Fig. 3.23 The reactivity series shows elements, mainly metals, in order of decreasing reactivity.

zinc   +   hydrochloric acid   →   zinc chloride   +   hydrogen

$Zn(s)$ + $2HCl(aq)$ → $ZnCl_2(aq)$ + $H_2(g)$

The metals below hydrogen in the reactivity series do not react to form hydrogen with water or dilute acids.

Another use of the reactivity series is to predict how metals can be extracted from their ores. The elements below carbon in the reactivity series can be obtained by heating their oxides with carbon:

zinc oxide   +   carbon   →   zinc   +   carbon dioxide

$2ZnO(s)$ + $C(s)$ → $2Zn(s)$ + $CO_2(g)$

copper(II) oxide   +   carbon   →   copper   +   carbon dioxide

$2CuO(s)$ + $C(s)$ → $2Cu(s)$ + $CO_2(g)$

This type of reaction is called a **displacement reaction**. A more reactive element, such as carbon, 'pushes' (or displaces) a less reactive metal, such as copper, out of its compound. In this reaction the copper(II) oxide has lost oxygen and been reduced. The carbon has gained oxygen and been oxidised.

EXTENDED

The position of a metal in the reactivity series depends on how easily it forms ions. More reactive metals will form ions more readily than less reactive metals.

Any element higher up the reactivity series can displace an element lower down the series.

For example, magnesium is higher up the reactivity series than copper. So if magnesium powder is heated with copper(II) oxide, then copper and magnesium oxide are produced:

magnesium   +   copper(II) oxide   →   magnesium oxide   +   copper

$Mg(s)$ + $CuO(s)$ → $MgO(s)$ + $Cu(s)$

This reaction is an example of a redox reaction. The magnesium has been oxidised to magnesium oxide and the copper(II) oxide has been reduced to copper. Because the magnesium is responsible for the reduction of the copper(II) oxide, it is acting as a reducing agent. Similarly, the copper(II) oxide is responsible for the **oxidation** of the magnesium, so it is acting as an oxidising agent. In a redox reaction, the reducing agent is always oxidised and the oxidising agent is always reduced.

INORGANIC CHEMISTRY

What will happen if copper is heated with magnesium oxide? Nothing happens, because copper is lower in the reactivity series than magnesium.

Using displacement reactions to establish a reactivity series

Displacement reactions of metals and their compounds in aqueous solution can be used to work out the order in the reactivity series.

In the same way that a more reactive element can push a less reactive element out of a compound, a more reactive metal ion in aqueous solution can displace a less reactive one.

For example, if you add zinc to copper(II) sulfate solution, the zinc displaces the copper because zinc is more reactive than copper. When the experiment is carried out, the blue colour of the copper(II) ion will fade as copper is produced and zinc ions are made:

zinc　　+　copper(II) sulfate solution　　→　zinc sulfate solution　　+　copper

$Zn(s) + Cu^{2+}(aq) + SO_4^{2-}(aq) \rightarrow Zn^{2+}(aq) + SO_4^{2-}(aq) + Cu(s)$

To build up a whole reactivity series, a set of reactions can be tried to see if metals can displace other metal ions. By following the general rule that a more reactive metal can displace a less reactive metal it is possible to establish the reactivity series.

For example, you may have seen the reaction of copper wire with silver nitrate solution. As the reaction proceeds, a shiny grey precipitate appears (this is silver) and the solution begins to turn blue as Cu(II) ions are produced from the copper.

copper　+　silver nitrate　→　copper(II) nitrate　+　silver

$Cu(s) + 2AgNO_3(aq) \rightarrow Cu(NO_3)_2(aq) + 2Ag(s)$

This shows that silver can be displaced by copper, and so silver is below copper in the reactivity series.

END OF EXTENDED

QUESTIONS

1. Will copper react with dilute hydrochloric acid to produce hydrogen? Explain your answer.

2. **EXTENDED** Write a balanced equation for the reaction of potassium with water.

3. Can carbon displace magnesium from magnesium oxide? Explain your answer.

4. **EXTENDED** Write a balanced equation for the reaction between magnesium and lead(II) oxide.

Developing investigative skills

A student was asked to carry out some possible displacement reactions. She was given samples of four metals A, B, C and D and a solution of each of their metal nitrates. She set up a series of test tube reactions as summarised in the table:

Solution	Metal A	Metal B	Metal C	Metal D
Metal A nitrate, $A(NO_3)_2$ (aq)		Yes	Yes	No
Metal B nitrate, $B(NO_3)_2$ (aq)	No		No	No
Metal C nitrate, $C(NO_3)_2$ (aq)	No	Yes		No
Metal D nitrate, $D(NO_3)_2$ (aq)	10	11	12	

She decided that she would need 12 test tubes. In each test tube she put a 1 cm depth of one of the solutions and then added a small piece of one of the metals. She left the tubes for 10 minutes and then examined the solution and the piece of metal to see if any reaction was evident. She then recorded a 'yes' if a displacement reaction had taken place and a 'no' where no reaction was evident. She didn't have time to record her results for the metal D nitrate solution (tubes 10, 11 and 12).

Using and organising techniques, apparatus and materials

❶ Why didn't the student set up the tubes represented by the white rectangles?

❷ Even though the student didn't record her results for metal D nitrate solution, explain why she would still be able to put the metals in order of reactivity.

Interpreting observations and data

❸ Use the results to put the four metals in order of reactivity. Start with the most reactive metal.

❹ Complete the results you would expect for the three reactions 10, 11 and 12.

❺ Write a balanced equation for the displacement reaction between metal B and metal C nitrate solution. (Use the symbols B and C for the two metals.)

❻ Metal D nitrate solution was blue and metal D was a shiny orange colour. Suggest a name for metal D.

EXTRACTION OF METALS

Metals are found in the form of **ores** containing **minerals** mixed with unwanted rock. In almost all cases, the mineral is a compound of the metal, not the pure metal. One exception is gold, which can exist naturally in a pure state.

Extracting a metal from its ore usually involves two steps:

1. The mineral is physically separated from unwanted rock.

2. The mineral is broken down chemically to obtain the metal.

Extracting iron

Iron is produced on a very large scale by reduction using carbon. The reaction takes place in a huge furnace called a blast furnace.

Three important raw materials are put in the top of the furnace: iron ore (iron(III) oxide), coke (the source of carbon for the reduction) and limestone, to remove the impurities as slag. Iron ore is also known as haematite.

Fig. 3.24 Coke (nearly pure carbon).

Δ Fig. 3.25 Iron ore.

Δ Fig. 3.26 Limestone.

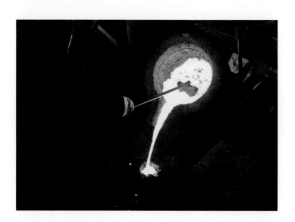

Δ Fig. 3.27 Molten iron.

Δ Fig. 3.28 Slag.

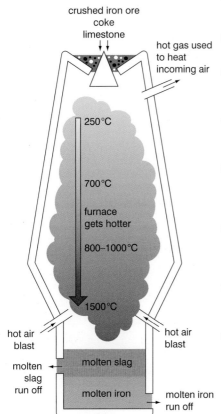

crushed iron ore
coke
limestone

hot gas used
to heat
incoming air

250°C

700°C

furnace
gets hotter

800–1000°C

1500°C

hot air
blast

hot air
blast

molten
slag
run off

molten slag

molten iron

molten iron
run off

1. Crushed iron ore, coke and limestone are fed into the top of the blast furnace.

2. Hot air is blasted up the furnace from the bottom.

3. Oxygen from the air reacts with coke to form carbon dioxide:
$$C(s) + O_2(g) \longrightarrow CO_2(g)$$

4. Carbon dioxide reacts with more coke to form carbon monoxide:
$$CO_2(g) + C(s) \longrightarrow 2CO(g)$$

5. Carbon monoxide is a reducing agent. Iron(III) oxide is reduced to iron:
┌─ reduction = loss of oxygen ─┐
$$Fe_2O_3(s) + 3CO(g) \longrightarrow 2Fe(l) + 3CO_2(g)$$

6. Dense molten iron runs to the bottom of the furnace and is run off. There are many impurities in iron ore. The limestone helps to remove these as shown in processes 7 and 8.

7. Limestone is broken down by heat to calcium oxide:
$$CaCO_3(s) \longrightarrow CaO(s) + CO_2(g)$$

8. Calcium oxide reacts with impurities like sand (silicon dioxide) to form a liquid called 'slag':
$$CaO(s) + SiO_2(s) \longrightarrow CaSiO_3(l)$$
impurity   slag
The liquid slag runs to the bottom of the furnace and is tapped off.

△ Fig. 3.29 How iron is extracted in a blast furnace.

The overall reaction is:

iron(III) oxide	+	carbon	→	iron	+	carbon dioxide
$2Fe_2O_3(s)$	+	$3C(s)$	→	$4Fe(s)$	+	$3CO_2(g)$

The reduction happens in three stages.

Stage 1 – The coke (carbon) reacts with oxygen 'blasted' into the furnace:

carbon	+	oxygen	→	carbon dioxide
$C(s)$	+	$O_2(g)$	→	$CO_2(g)$

Stage 2 – The carbon dioxide is reduced by unreacted coke to form carbon monoxide:

carbon dioxide	+	carbon	→	carbon monoxide
$CO_2(g)$	+	$C(s)$	→	$2CO(g)$

Stage 3 – The iron(III) oxide is reduced by the carbon monoxide to iron:

iron(III) oxide	+	carbon monoxide	→	iron	+	carbon dioxide
$Fe_2O_3(s)$	+	$3CO(g)$	→	$2Fe(s)$	+	$3CO_2(g)$

In a blast furnace the iron(III) oxide is reduced to iron by carbon monoxide, formed when the carbon reacts with the air blasted into the furnace. In the reduction of iron(III) oxide, the carbon monoxide is oxidised to carbon dioxide.

Making steel from iron

Iron from the blast furnace is brittle because it contains a relatively large percentage (usually 4%) of carbon (from the coke). It also rusts very easily. Because of this, most iron is converted into steel, an alloy of iron. Mild steel is used for car bodies and machinery and stainless steel for chemical plant and cutlery.

In steel making, the molten iron straight from the blast furnace is heated and oxygen is passed through it to remove some of the carbon present:

$$C(s) \; + \; O_2(g) \; \rightarrow \; CO_2(g)$$

Limestone ($CaCO_3$) is also added and is changed into calcium oxide:

$$CaCO_3(s) \; \rightarrow \; CaO(s) \; + \; CO_2(g)$$

The calcium oxide reacts with oxide impurities to form a slag, which can be removed from the steel.

$$CaO(s) \; + \; SiO_2(s) \; \rightarrow \; CaSiO_3(s)$$

Steel is iron with 0.1–1.5% carbon content. Steel is more resistant to corrosion and is less brittle than iron. It has a wide range of uses, depending on its carbon content. For example:

- low carbon (<0.3%): car bodies
- medium carbon (0.3–0.9%): railway tracks
- high carbon (0.9–1.5%): knives.

Stainless steels are made by adding a wide range of metals, such as chromium, nickel, vanadium and cobalt, to the steel. Each gives the steel particular properties for specific uses. For example, vanadium steel is used to make high-precision, hard-wearing industrial tools.

QUESTIONS

1. What solid raw materials are used in the blast furnace?

2. The iron ore used in the blast furnace is usually haematite. What is the name of the main compound present in the ore?

3. What gases will escape from the top of the blast furnace?

4. Write a balanced equation to show the reduction of iron(III) oxide by carbon.

5. This question is about steel.

   a) Steel is an *alloy*. What is an 'alloy'?

   b) The iron produced in the blast furnace contains a relatively high proportion of carbon. How is this proportion reduced when iron is converted into steel?

   c) Why is steel often used instead of the iron produced in the blast furnace?

The reactivity series of metals is useful to scientists in determining methods for metal extraction, ways of preventing corrosion and ensuring safe storage for reactive metals. Use the reactivity series to help answer the questions below.

6. The thermite process can be used to extract iron from iron(III) oxide using aluminium metal.

   a) Write a balanced equation for the extraction of iron using this process.

   b) Using the reactivity series, explain why this reaction occurs.

   c) Name two other metals that could be used to extract iron from its oxide indicating whether the reactions would be more or less reactive than when using aluminium.

   d) This reaction could be described as either a displacement or a redox reaction. Explain why.

7. Iron is a metal in common use, but unfortunately it rusts.

   a) Give the conditions needed for iron to rust.

   b) Chromium is used in chromium plating to prevent iron from rusting. Give a reason for this.

   c) Aluminium's position in the reactivity series indicates that it is a highly reactive metal. However, aluminium does not rust. Suggest a reason for this.

END OF EXTENDED

Reactivity of metals

The chemical method chosen to break down a mineral depends on the reactivity of the metal. The more reactive a metal is, the harder it is to break down its compounds. The more reactive metals are obtained from their minerals by the process of electrolysis. For example, aluminium is obtained from its ore, bauxite, by electrolysis. For more detail on this process look at the Electricity and Chemistry topic.

The less reactive metals can be obtained by heating their oxides with carbon. This method will only work for metals below carbon in the reactivity series. It involves the **reduction** of a metal oxide to the metal.

Metal		Extraction method
Potassium	}	The most reactive metals are obtained using electrolysis
Sodium		
Calcium		
Magnesium		
Aluminium		
(Carbon)		
Zinc	}	These metals are below carbon in the reactivity series and so can be obtained by heating their oxides with carbon
Iron		
Tin		
Lead		
Copper		
Silver	}	The least reactive metals are found as pure elements
Gold		

△ Table 3.9 Methods for extracting different metals.

RECYCLING

Extracting metals from their ores is an expensive process and so recycling metal objects can be economically worthwhile as well as environmentally more efficient. Recycling of metals essentially involves melting the metal and then using the molten metal to form a new object. Steel and aluminium are metals which are often recycled. One potential problem is separating the different types of metal. For example, a motor car as well as being made of steel may include some parts made of aluminium (as well as a range of other materials). Separating the two different metals needs to be done before they can be recycled. In some cases recycling could prove more expensive than extracting the metal from its ore. However, the supplies of metal ores are limited and will eventually be used up. Recycling metals such as steel and aluminium will therefore become increasingly essential.

USES OF METALS

Uses of aluminium

The uses of aluminium are based on its properties of having a low density but being quite a strong metal. These properties make it useful in the manufacture of aircraft (because it is light and strong) and food containers (because it does not corrode).

EXTENDED

The unreactivity of aluminium

Aluminium's position in the reactivity series suggests that it should be quite reactive. However, it does not react with acids and is resistant to corrosion. This is because, although it may look shiny, it has a thin coating of aluminium oxide, Al_2O_3, all over its surface. Aluminium oxide is very unreactive and protects the aluminium below its surface.

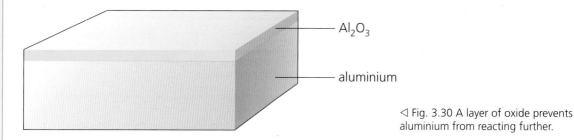

— Al_2O_3

— aluminium

◁ Fig. 3.30 A layer of oxide prevents aluminium from reacting further.

Uses of zinc

Zinc is used to make the alloy brass by mixing it with copper. Covering iron with zinc is called **galvanising**, and the zinc stops the iron from rusting (corroding).

SCIENCE IN CONTEXT

THE EXTRACTION OF METALS

The reactivity of a metal determines how it can be extracted from ores from the Earth's crust. It also explains why some metals have been used for thousands of years while others have only been used much more recently.

The most unreactive metals can be found in their 'native' state, which is as the pure metal and not combined with other elements. Examples of such metals include gold and silver – metals that have been used for thousands of years. It is estimated that gold was first discovered in about 3000 BC.

△ Fig. 3.31 This gold shoulder cape from North Wales is nearly 4000 years old and still in good condition.

Metals below carbon in the reactivity series can be extracted by heating their ores with carbon. Examples include lead and iron. It is possible that lead was discovered by accident when the silvery element was seen in the ashes of a wood fire that had been made above a deposit of lead ore. It is estimated that lead was first discovered in about 2000 BC.

The most reactive metals, all those above carbon in the reactivity series, have to be extracted from their minerals by electrolysis. This process is a much more recent development and explains why these metals were not used until relatively recently. Aluminium was first extracted in 1825.

THE SACRIFICIAL PROTECTION OF IRON AND MILD STEEL

Rusting is a chemical reaction between iron, water and oxygen. Water and oxygen must both be present for rusting to occur. The process is speeded up if there are also electrolytes, such as salt, in the water. This is why rusting takes place much faster in seawater.

The rusting of iron and steel can be prevented in a number of ways. The use of grease, oil or paint prevent water and oxygen from reaching the metal surface. Plastic coating does the same. However, these coatings can be damaged and then rusting will take place.

Iron can be prevented from rusting by using what we know about the reactivity series. Zinc is above iron in the reactivity series; that is, zinc reacts more readily than iron.

Galvanised iron is iron that is coated with a layer of zinc. To begin with, the coating will protect the iron. If the coating is damaged or scratched, the iron is still protected from rusting. This is because zinc is more reactive than iron and so it reacts and corrodes instead of the iron.

If zinc blocks are attached to the hulls of ships, they will corrode instead of the hull. The zinc block is called a **sacrificial anode**.

△ Fig. 3.32 Galvanised iron or steel resists corrosion by air and water.

END OF EXTENDED

QUESTIONS

1. What conditions are necessary for iron to rust?

2. What is the disadvantage of using grease to prevent the rusting of iron?

3. EXTENDED a) What is *galvanising*?

   b) Why is galvanised iron or steel still protected from corrosion when its surface has been scratched?

End of topic checklist

Key terms

alloy, displacement reaction, galvanising, mineral, ore, oxidation, reduction, sacrificial anode

During your study of this topic you should have learned:

○ How to describe the general physical properties of metals.

○ How to describe metallic bonding as a lattice of positive ions in a 'sea of elections'.

○ **EXTENDED** How to describe alloys, such as brass, as mixtures of a metal with other elements.

○ How to explain in terms of their properties why alloys are used instead of pure metals.

○ **EXTENDED** That the properties of iron are changed by the controlled use of additives to form steel alloys.

○ **EXTENDED** How to identify representations of an alloy from a diagram of its structure.

○ About the order of reactivity of metals – potassium, sodium, calcium, magnesium, aluminium, (carbon), zinc, iron, (hydrogen) and copper – by reference to the reactions, if any, of the metals with water or steam, or dilute hydrochloric acid.

○ About which metal oxides can be reduced by carbon.

○ **EXTENDED** How to describe the reactivity series as being related to the tendency of a metal to form its positive ion, illustrated by its reaction, if any, with the aqueous ions or the oxides of the other metals.

○ **EXTENDED** How to account for the apparent unreactivity of aluminium in terms of the oxide layer that forms on the surface of the metal.

○ **EXTENDED** That the method of extraction of a metal from its ore depends on its position in the reactivity series.

○ How to deduce an order of reactivity from a given set of experimental results.

○ **EXTENDED** How to describe the essential reactions in the extraction of iron from haematite.

○ That aluminium is extracted from the ore bauxite by electrolysis.

○ That metal ores are a finite resource and so metals need to be recycled.

○ That aluminium is used in the manufacture of aircraft because of its strength and low density.

○ That aluminium is used in food containers because of its resistance to corrosion.

○ That mild steel is used to make car bodies and machinery and that stainless steel is used to make chemical plant and cutlery.

○ **EXTENDED** That zinc can be used for galvanising and for making brass.

End of topic questions

Note: The marks given for these questions indicate the level of detail required in the answers. In the examination, the number of marks given to questions like these may be different.

1. Arrange the following metals in order of reactivity, starting with the most reactive:

calcium, copper, magnesium, sodium, zinc.   **(2 marks)**

2. This question is about four metals represented by the letters Q, X, Y and Z. A series of displacement reactions was carried out and the results are shown below:

Reaction 1: Q oxide + Y → Y oxide + Q

Reaction 2: X oxide + Z → Z oxide + X

Reaction 3: Q oxide + Z→ no change

a) Arrange the metals in order of reactivity starting with the most reactive. **(2 marks)**

b) In reaction 1:

　i) which substance has been oxidised?   **(1 mark)**

　ii) which substance has been reduced?   **(1 mark)**

　iii) which substance is the oxidising agent?   **(1 mark)**

　iv) which substance is the reducing agent?   **(1 mark)**

3. The least reactive metals such as gold and silver are found in their native state. What do you understand by this?   **(1 mark)**

4. Iron is extracted from iron ore (iron(III) oxide) in a blast furnace by heating with coke (carbon).

a) Write a balanced equation including state symbols for the overall reaction.
                              (2 marks)

b) Is the iron(III) oxide oxidised or reduced in this reaction? Explain your answer.   **(1 mark)**

c) Why is limestone also added to the blast furnace?   **(2 marks)**

End of topic questions continued

5. Explain the following:

   a) Aluminium is used in the manufacture of aircraft. **(2 marks)**

   b) Aluminium is used in the manufacture of food containers. **(1 mark)**

6. **a)** Name one use of mild steel. **(1 mark)**

   b) Name one use of stainless steel. **(1 mark)**

7. **EXTENDED** This question is about the reaction between magnesium and lead(II) oxide.

   a) Write a balanced equation for the reaction. **(2 marks)**

   b) Which is the more reactive metal, magnesium or lead? **(1 mark)**

   c) This is an example of a redox reaction. Explain the term *redox*. **(1 mark)**

8. **EXTENDED** Zinc can be extracted from zinc oxide by heating with carbon.

   a) Write the balanced equation, including state symbols, for this reaction.
   (2 marks)

   b) Zinc could also be extracted by the electrolysis of molten zinc oxide. Suggest why heating with carbon is the preferred method of extraction. **(2 marks)**

9. **EXTENDED** Copper(II) sulfate solution reacts with zinc as shown below:

   $$CuSO_4(aq) + Zn(s) \rightarrow ZnSO_4(aq) + Cu(s)$$

   a) What type of chemical reaction is this? **(1 mark)**

   b) What can be deduced about the relative reactivities of copper and zinc? **(1 mark)**

10. **EXTENDED** Zinc prevents iron ship hulls from rusting (corroding).

    a) What is the name for this way of preventing rusting? **(1 mark)**

    b) How does zinc protect iron from rusting? **(2 marks)**

    c) Name three other methods of preventing iron from rusting. **(3 marks)**

Air and water

△ Fig. 3.33 The smog over the Forbidden City in Beijing is so thick that it obscures the view from Feng Shui Hill.

INTRODUCTION

Clean air is precious. It provides the oxygen that all living things need to survive, and the carbon dioxide that plants need when they photosynthesise. Nitrogen in the air is also very important for healthy plant growth, but not all plants can make use of nitrogen in this form. Unfortunately not all the air we breathe is clean. It may contain a number of pollutants that can be harmful to living things and the environment. It is important to understand how these pollutants are produced and how they can be prevented from contaminating the air. Water vapour is also present in the air. With oxygen, this causes rusting, a process that can be very destructive.

KNOWLEDGE CHECK

✓ Know that oxygen is present in the air and forms oxides when substances burn in it.
✓ Know that oxides of non-metals are acidic.
✓ Know that acids react with carbonates to make salts.
✓ Know that salts can be anhydrous or hydrated.

LEARNING OBJECTIVES

✓ Be able to describe a chemical test for identifying the presence of water using cobalt(II) chloride and copper(II) sulfate.
✓ Be able to describe in outline the treatment of the water supply in terms of filtration and chlorination.
✓ Know that clean air is approximately 78% nitrogen and 21% oxygen with the remainder made up of a mixture of noble gases, water vapour and carbon dioxide.
✓ Know that the common pollutants in the air are carbon monoxide, sulfur dioxide and oxides of nitrogen.
✓ Know the sources of carbon monoxide, sulfur dioxide and the oxides of nitrogen.
✓ Know the adverse effects of the common pollutants on buildings and health.
✓ **EXTENDED** Be able to describe some approaches to reducing emissions of sulfur dioxide, including the use of low-sulfur petrol and flue gas desulfurisation by calcium oxide.
✓ **EXTENDED** Be able to describe how a catalytic converter removes nitrogen monoxide and carbon monoxide from exhaust emission.
✓ Be able to state the conditions required for the rusting of iron.
✓ Be able to describe methods of rust protection including using paint and other coatings to exclude oxygen.
✓ Be able to describe the need for fertilisers containing nitrogen, phosphorus and potassium.

- ✓ Be able to describe the displacement of ammonia from its salts.
- ✓ Know that carbon dioxide and methane are greenhouse gases.
- ✓ **EXTENDED** Know that increased concentrations of greenhouse gases may contribute to climate change.
- ✓ Be able to describe the formation of carbon dioxide from the complete combustion of carbon-containing substances, respiration, the reactions between an acid and a carbonate, and the thermal decomposition of a carbonate.
- ✓ **EXTENDED** Be able to describe sacrificial protection in terms of the reactivity series of metals and galvanising as a method of rust prevention.
- ✓ **EXTENDED** Be able to describe the essential conditions for the manufacture of ammonia by the Haber process, including the sources of nitrogen (air) and hydrogen (reaction of natural gas with steam).

A CHEMICAL TEST FOR WATER

The test for water is to add it to anhydrous copper(II) sulfate solid. If the liquid contains water, the powder will turn from white to blue as hydrated copper(II) sulfate forms.

△ Fig. 3.34 Chemical test for water.

The equation for the reaction is:

anhydrous copper(II) sulfate + water → hydrated copper(II) sulfate

$$CuSO_4(s) + 5H_2O(l) \rightarrow CuSO_4.5H_2O(s)$$

The presence of water can also be detected using anhydrous cobalt(II) chloride. The pink anhydrous cobalt(II) chloride turns to blue hydrated cobalt(II) chloride. A convenient way of performing the test is to use cobalt(II) chloride paper:

anhydrous cobalt(II) chloride	+	water	$\rightarrow$	hydrated cobalt(II) chloride
$CoCl_2(s)$	+	$6H_2O(l)$	$\rightarrow$	$CoCl_2.6H_2O(s)$

Neither of these tests shows the water is pure – only that the liquid has water in it.

SCIENCE IN CONTEXT — THE WATER CYCLE

The recirculation of water that takes place all over the Earth is called the **water cycle**.

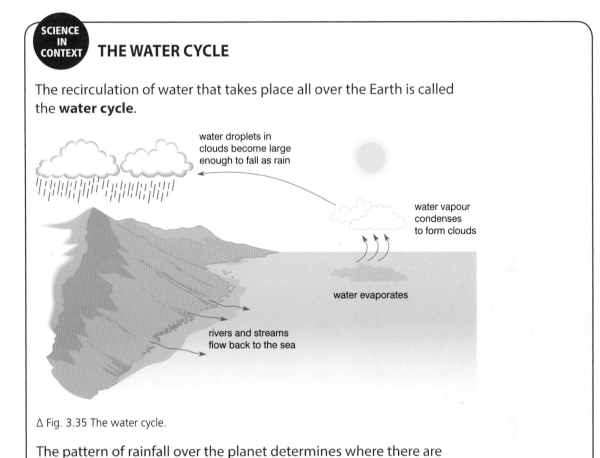

△ Fig. 3.35 The water cycle.

The pattern of rainfall over the planet determines where there are deserts, rainforests and areas of land that can or cannot be used for growing plants.

Water stored in reservoirs must be purified to produce drinkable tap water.

Fig. 3.36 Water pipes discharging in Thailand.

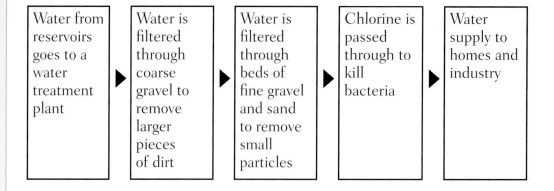

THE COMPOSITION OF CLEAN AIR

Air is a mixture of gases that has remained fairly constant for the last 200 million years. The amount of water vapour varies around the world. For example, air above a desert area has a low proportion of water vapour.

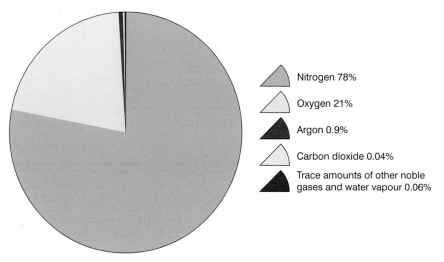

Nitrogen 78%

Oxygen 21%

Argon 0.9%

Carbon dioxide 0.04%

Trace amounts of other noble gases and water vapour 0.06%

Δ Fig. 3.37 Components of air.

The composition of the air is kept fairly constant by the **nitrogen cycle** and the **carbon cycle**.

THE NITROGEN CYCLE

Living things need nitrogen to make proteins. These are required, for example, to make new cells for growth.

The air is 78% nitrogen gas (N_2), but this gas is very unreactive and cannot be used by plants or animals. Instead, plants use nitrogen in the form of nitrates (NO_3^- ions).

The process of getting nitrogen into this useful form is called **nitrogen fixation**.

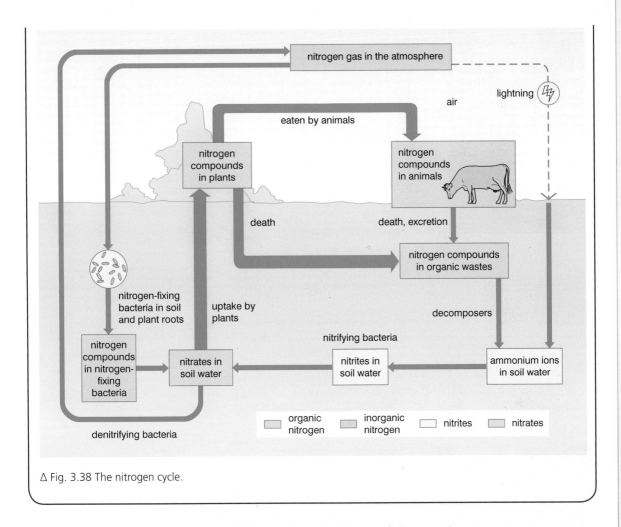

△ Fig. 3.38 The nitrogen cycle.

The nitrogen in the soil can easily be used up by plants, for example when farmers are growing crops. Additional nitrogen can be added to the soil by using artificial fertilisers. Most of the nitrogen-containing artificial fertilisers are either nitrates or ammonium compounds. Other vital nutrients such as phosphorus (in the form of phosphates; it helps root growth) and potassium (in the form of potassium nitrate; it encourages flower and fruit formation) are often included with the nitrogen in what are called NPK fertilisers.

◁ Fig. 3.39 Ammonium nitrate fertiliser being sprayed onto a field. In some parts of the world, liquid ammonia is pumped directly into the ground as a fertiliser. This can be quite dangerous because liquid ammonia can cause chemical burns and irritate the respiratory tract.

◁ Fig. 3.40 Excess phosphate and nitrate nutrients in river water cause accelerated growth of green algae. The algae form a thick surface layer, which causes underwater plants and fish to die. Increased algal growth in the sea near river estuaries is also of concern.

Note: In the soil, ammonium compounds are converted first to ammonia and then to nitrates by bacteria. In the laboratory, ammonium compounds can be converted into ammonia by heating with an alkali such as sodium hydroxide.

EXTENDED

Ammonia is used to make nitrogen-containing fertilisers. It is manufactured in the **Haber process** from nitrogen and hydrogen. This process requires an iron catalyst, a temperature of 450 °C and 200 times atmospheric pressure.

◁ Fig. 3.41 A fertiliser containing nitrogen.

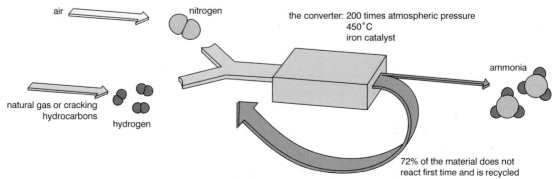

△ Fig. 3.42 The Haber process for making ammonia. Nitrogen is obtained from the air and hydrogen from the reaction of methane/natural gas with steam. The reactants must be recycled to increase the efficiency of the process.

The conditions in the Haber process are chosen carefully to give the highest possible **yield** of ammonia with a suitable rate of reaction.

nitrogen   +   hydrogen   →   ammonia

$N_2(g)$ + $3H_2(g)$ ⇌ $2NH_3(g)$ ΔH =   exothermic

The greatest yield of ammonia would be made using a low temperature (the reaction is exothermic), but it would be slow. The temperature of 450 °C is a compromise: less is made, but it is produced faster. The iron catalyst is also used to increase the rate; it does not increase the yield. High pressure increases the yield.

Fig. 3.43 shows the effect of temperature and pressure on the yield of ammonia.

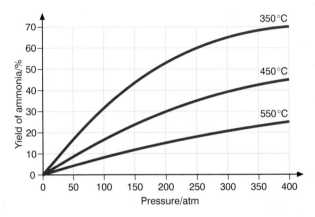

△ Fig. 3.43 Effect of temperature and pressure on yield of ammonia.

The ammonia is liquefied and removed from the reaction vessel and the unused nitrogen and hydrogen are recycled.

Ammonia is commonly used in domestic cleaning agents, in the manufacture of nitric acid and to make NPK fertilisers. 'NPK' means the fertiliser contains nitrogen (N), phosphorus (P) and potassium (K).

END OF EXTENDED

QUESTIONS

1. What does *anhydrous* mean?

2. What colour change would you observe if water was added to anhydrous cobalt(II) chloride?

3. In the purification of water there are two important stages.

   a) In the first stage, the water is filtered twice. What is used as the filter in each case?

   b) In the second stage, bacteria are killed. What chemical is used to kill the bacteria?

4. This question is about the composition of the air.

    a) What is the percentage of nitrogen in clean air?

    b) What is the percentage of carbon dioxide in clean air?

5. <u>EXTENDED</u> What temperature and pressure are used in the Haber process?

POLLUTANTS IN THE AIR

Pollutants in the air come from a variety of sources. Some come from burning waste and some from power stations burning coal or gas. Industry produces pollutants as well.

The most common pollutants in the air are:

- carbon monoxide – from the incomplete combustion of hydrocarbons (petrol/coal/gas/diesel)
- sulfur dioxide – from burning fossil fuels such as petrol and coal which contain sulfur compounds
- oxides of nitrogen – from burning fossil fuels (petrol/diesel/coal).

△ Fig. 3.44 Cycling is encouraged in Amsterdam to reduce air pollution.

EXTENDED

Under normal conditions nitrogen is a very unreactive gas. However, in a petrol engine temperatures of 1000 °C can be reached, and in these conditions nitrogen reacts with oxygen to make oxides of nitrogen. Nitrogen oxides are often represented by NO_x, but they are mainly nitrogen monoxide, NO. A catalytic converter in the car's exhaust system can reduce the nitrogen oxides back to nitrogen:

$2NO(g) \rightarrow N_2(g) + O_2(g)$

A catalytic converter will also reduce the amount of carbon monoxide produced.

$$2CO(g) + O_2(g) \rightarrow 2CO_2(g)$$

$$2NO(g) + 2CO(g) \rightarrow N_2(g) + 2CO_2(g)$$

END OF EXTENDED

HOW IS THE ATMOSPHERE CHANGING, AND WHY?

There are two major impacts caused by the burning of **fossil fuels** – the **greenhouse effect** and **acid rain**.

The greenhouse effect

Carbon dioxide, methane and CFCs (chlorofluorocarbons) are known as **greenhouse gases**. The levels of these gases in the atmosphere are increasing due to the burning of fossil fuels, pollution from farm animals and the use of CFCs in aerosols and refrigerators.

Short-wave radiation from the sun warms the ground, and the warm Earth gives off heat as long-wave radiation. Much of this radiation is stopped from escaping from the Earth by the greenhouse gases. This is known as the greenhouse effect.

EXTENDED

The greenhouse effect is responsible for keeping the Earth warmer than it would otherwise be. This is normal – and important for life on Earth. However, most scientists think that increasing levels of greenhouse gases are stopping even more heat escaping and that the Earth is slowly warming up. This is known as **global warming**. If global warming continues the Earth's climate may change, polar ice may melt and sea levels may rise flooding low-lying areas – some of them highly populated.

The Earth's average temperature is gradually increasing, but nobody knows for certain if the greenhouse effect is responsible. It may be that the recent rise in global temperatures is part of a natural cycle – there have been ice ages and intermediate warm periods all through history. Many people are concerned, however, that it is not part of a natural cycle and they say we should act now to reduce emissions of these greenhouse gases.

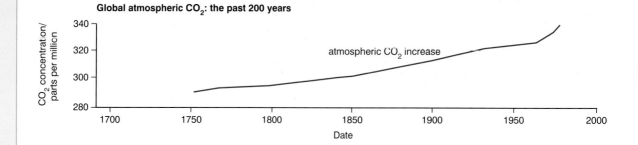

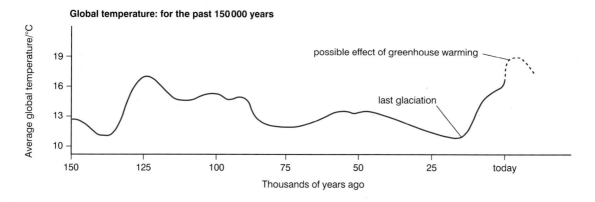

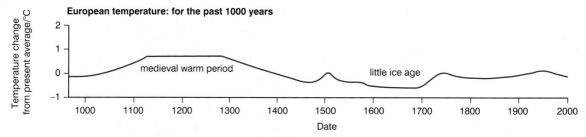

△ Fig. 3.45 How atmospheric carbon dioxide and temperature have varied.

END OF EXTENDED

Acid rain

Burning fossil fuels gives off many gases, including sulfur dioxide and various nitrogen oxides:

sulfur	+	oxygen	$\rightarrow$	sulfur dioxide
$S(s)$	+	$O_2(g)$	$\rightarrow$	$SO_2(g)$

Sulfur dioxide combines with water and oxygen to form sulfuric acid. Nitrogen oxide combines with water to form nitric acid. These substances can make the rain acidic (called acid rain).

sulfur dioxide	+	oxygen	+	water	$\rightarrow$	sulfuric acid
$2SO_2(g)$	+	$O_2(g)$	+	$2H_2O(l)$	$\rightarrow$	$2H_2SO_4(aq)$

SCIENCE IN CONTEXT   **SOME INTERESTING FACTS ABOUT METHANE**

1. Methane makes up about 97% of natural gas.

2. It is formed by the decay of plant matter where there is no oxygen (anaerobic decay).

3. Biogas contains 40–70% methane. Biodigesters convert organic wastes into a nutrient-rich liquid fertiliser and biogas, a **renewable** source of electrical and heat energy. These are widely used in non-industrialised countries, particularly India, Nepal and Vietnam. Biodigesters can help families by providing a cheap source of fuel, reducing environmental pollution from the run-off from animal pens, and reducing diseases caused by the use of untreated manure as fertiliser. However, biodigesters only work efficiently in hot countries; they are not as effective at low temperatures.

△ Fig. 3.46 A commercial biodigester.

4. Methane is one of the greenhouse gases, thought by some scientists to be responsible for global warming. It has almost 25 times the effect of the same volume of carbon dioxide.

5. Ruminant animals such as cows and sheep produce methane. It has been estimated that a cow can produce as much as 200 litres of methane per day. So could cows be one of the causes of global warming?

Buildings are damaged by acid rain, particularly those made of limestone and marble – both are forms of calcium carbonate, $CaCO_3$. Metal structures are also attacked by sulfuric acid.

Acid rain harms plants that take in the acidic water and the animals that live in the affected rivers and lakes. Acid rain also washes ions such as calcium and magnesium out of the soil, depleting the minerals available to plants. It also washes aluminium ions out of the soil and into rivers and lakes, where it poisons fish.

Nitrogen monoxide can be oxidised to a brown gas called nitrogen dioxide, NO_2. Under certain atmospheric conditions this can build up as a brown haze in large cities. Nitrogen dioxide is dangerous because it can cause respiratory diseases such as bronchitis.

Reducing emissions of the gases that cause acid rain is expensive. Part of the problem is that the acid rain usually falls a long way from the places where the gases were released.

EXTENDED

Power stations are now being fitted with flue-gas desulfurisation (FGD) plants to reduce the amount of sulfur dioxide released into the atmosphere. FGD uses calcium oxide (a base) to neutralise the acidic sulfur dioxide.

Catalytic converters are fitted to the exhaust systems of vehicles to reduce the level of pollutants released from burning petrol or diesel. Petrol with a low sulfur content also helps to reduce acid rain.

END OF EXTENDED

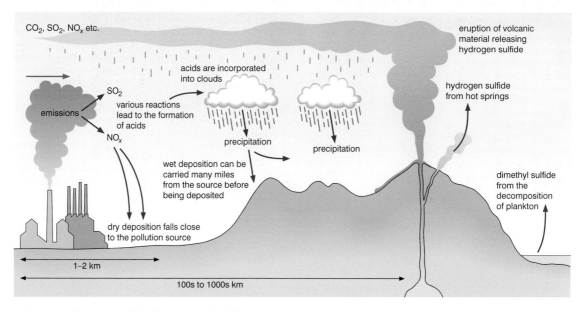

Δ Fig. 3.47 The process of the formation of acid rain.

QUESTIONS

1. Carbon monoxide is a common pollutant in the air. Name a major source of carbon monoxide.

2. a) Name two gases that are responsible for causing acid rain.

   b) For each gas you named in part a) name the acid it forms.

   c) List three problems caused by acid rain in the environment.

3. **EXTENDED** Nitrogen monoxide (NO) is produced in the high temperature of a car engine.

   a) Write a balanced equation to show how the nitrogen monoxide is formed.

   b) What is the nitrogen monoxide converted to in a catalytic converter?

CARBON DIOXIDE

Carbon dioxide is an important gas. It is formed as a product in the complete combustion of carbon-containing substances:

$$C(s) + O_2(g) \rightarrow CO_2(g)$$

Carbon dioxide is also formed in respiration. It can be made in the laboratory by the reaction of dilute hydrochloric acid and calcium carbonate in the form of marble chips.

▷ Fig. 3.48 Charcoal is mainly carbon. When it burns it gives off carbon dioxide.

calcium carbonate + hydrochloric acid → carbon dioxide + water + calcium chloride

$$CaCO_3(s) \qquad + 2HCl(aq) \qquad \rightarrow CO_2(g) \qquad + H_2O(l) + CaCl_2(aq)$$

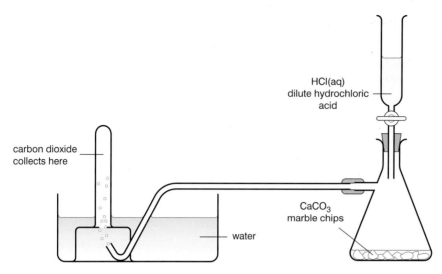

HCl(aq)
dilute hydrochloric
acid

carbon dioxide
collects here

CaCO₃
marble chips

water

△ Fig. 3.49 The laboratory preparation of carbon dioxide gas.

If the gas is bubbled through limewater (calcium hydroxide solution), a white precipitate forms. This is used as a laboratory test for carbon dioxide.

Carbon dioxide can also be prepared by the **thermal decomposition** of certain metal carbonates. Copper(II) carbonate and zinc carbonate are examples:

copper(II) carbonate	$\rightarrow$	copper(II) oxide	+	carbon dioxide
$CuCO_3(s)$	$\rightarrow$	$CuO(s)$	+	$CO_2(g)$
green		black		

zinc carbonate	$\rightarrow$	zinc oxide	+	carbon dioxide
$ZnCO_3(s)$	$\rightarrow$	$ZnO(s)$	+	$CO_2(g)$
white		white (yellow when hot)		

METHODS OF PREVENTING RUSTING

Over time, the oxygen and water in the atmosphere affect metals. If they react together the metal is corroded. The corrosion of iron is called **rusting**.

In the presence of water, the following chemical reaction takes place:

$$4Fe(s) + 3O_2(g) \rightarrow 2Fe_2O_3(s)$$

In fact, rust is hydrated iron(III) oxide, $Fe_2O_3 \cdot xH_2O$. The 'x' can vary depending on the conditions.

Methods of preventing rusting fall into three main categories:

- Stopping oxygen and water reaching the iron – for example oiling/greasing, as with bicycle chains; painting, as with car bodies.
- Alloying iron is mixed with other metals to produce alloys such as stainless steel that do not rust.

- **Sacrificial protection** – the iron is covered by, or put in contact with, another metal that is higher in the reactivity series, that is, more reactive than iron. The more reactive metal corrodes instead of the iron, so it is said to be 'sacrificed' to protect the iron.

Ship hulls made of iron have zinc bars attached to them. The zinc bars corrode, not the hull.

In **galvanising**, iron is covered with a coating of zinc. Even if the zinc surface is scratched exposing the iron, the zinc corrodes, not the iron.

Developing investigative skills

A student set up the apparatus as shown in Fig. 3.50 with the long tube turned upside-down in a trough of water. Previously some iron filings had been sprinkled into the tube, and many of these had stuck to the inside of the tube. With the same levels of water in the tube and the trough, the student recorded the volume of air in the tube (100 cm³).

After a few days he returned to the apparatus, equalised the water levels as before and took a second reading of the volume of air in the tube (85 cm³). He then worked out how much of the air had been replaced by water.

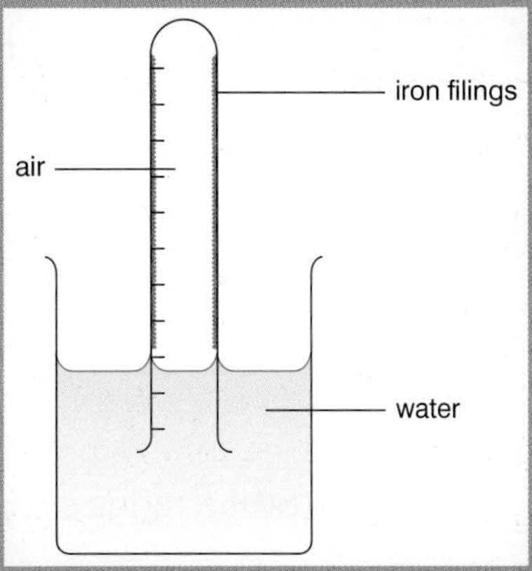

△ Fig. 3.50 Apparatus for experiment.

Observing, measuring and recording

❶ What changes would you have expected to see in the iron filings that were put in the tube at the beginning of the experiment?

Interpreting observations and data

❷ What chemical reaction was taking place in the tube? Write a balanced equation for the reaction.

❸ What do the results indicate about the composition of the air in the tube?

Evaluating methods

❹ The results in this experiment are different from those obtained by other students. Suggest some possible reasons for this.

❺ Why did the student equalise the water levels in the trough and the tube before taking the reading of the volume of gas in the tube?

QUESTIONS

1. Carbon dioxide is formed in the complete combustion of carbon. What product might form if carbon is burned in a limited supply of air?

2. In the laboratory, carbon dioxide can be prepared by the reaction of an acid with a metal carbonate.

   a) Write a word equation for the reaction between copper(II) carbonate and dilute hydrochloric acid.

   b) Write a balanced equation for the reaction in part a).

3. Carbon dioxide can also be prepared by the action of heat on a metal carbonate.

   a) Write a word equation for the action of heat on calcium carbonate.

   b) Write a balanced equation for the reaction in part a).

4. What is the name of the chemical compound present in rust?

5. Name two ways of preventing water and oxygen from getting into contact with the surface of an iron object.

6. EXTENDED What is *galvanising*?

7. EXTENDED Refer to the reactivity series to explain how zinc is able to offer sacrificial protection to iron.

BIOLOGY – HUMAN INFLUENCES ON ECOSYSTEMS

- Pollutant gases, for example from the burning of fossil fuels, affect ecosystems over a range of distances and time scales.

- Water quality can be affected by a number of factors, including some linked to chemical changes.

PHYSICS – ENERGY TRANSFERS, THERMAL PHYSICS

- The range of sources used to supply energy on a large scale have an impact on the air and water, at least on a local scale.

- The management of the energy sources is an issue that involves all aspects of the sciences.

- Large-scale heating of the atmosphere by the sun leads to convection currents which drive weather systems.

End of topic checklist

Key terms

acid rain, carbon cycle, fossil fuel, galvanising, global warming, greenhouse effect, greenhouse gas, Haber process, nitrogen cycle, nitrogen fixation, renewable energy, rusting, sacrificial protection, thermal decomposition, water cycle

During your study of this topic you should have learned:

○ How to describe chemical tests for identifying the presence of water using cobalt(II) chloride and copper(II) sulfate.

○ How to describe in outline the treatment of the water supply in terms of filtration and chlorination.

○ That clean air is approximately 78% nitrogen and 21% oxygen with the remainder made up of a mixture of noble gases, water vapour and carbon dioxide.

○ That the common pollutants in the air are carbon monoxide, sulfur dioxide and oxides of nitrogen.

○ That the source of carbon monoxide is the incomplete combustion of carbon-containing substances.

○ That the source of sulfur dioxide is the combustion of fossil fuels that contain sulfur compounds.

○ That a source of the oxides of nitrogen is car exhausts.

○ About the adverse effects of the common pollutants on buildings and health.

○ **EXTENDED** About some approaches to reducing emissions of sulfur dioxide, including the use of low-sulfur petrol and flue gas desulfurisation by calcium oxide.

○ That oxygen and water are needed for rusting to occur.

○ How to describe methods of rust protection, including using paint and other coatings to exclude oxygen.

○ How to describe the need for fertilisers containing nitrogen, phosphorus and potassium.

○ How to describe the displacement of ammonia from its salts.

○ That carbon dioxide and methane are greenhouse gases and may contribute to climate change.

End of topic checklist continued

○ **EXTENDED** That increased concentrations of greenhouse gases cause an enhanced greenhouse effect, which may contribute to climate change.

○ How to describe the formation of carbon dioxide from:

- the complete combustion of carbon-containing substances
- the process of respiration
- the reactions between an acid and a carbonate
- the thermal decomposition of a carbonate.

○ **EXTENDED** How to describe and explain the presence of oxides of nitrogen in car exhausts and their catalytic removal.

○ **EXTENDED** How to describe sacrificial protection in terms of the reactivity series of metals and galvanising as a method of rust prevention.

○ **EXTENDED** How to describe the essential conditions for the manufacture of ammonia by the Haber process, including the sources of nitrogen (air) and hydrogen (hydrocarbons or steam).

End of topic questions

Note: The marks given for these questions indicate the level of detail required in the answers. In the examination, the number of marks given to questions like these may be different.

1. This question is about the composition of a sample of clean air.

   a) What is the proportion of oxygen? (1 mark)

   b) What is the proportion of carbon dioxide? (1 mark)

2. **a)** What could you use to detect the presence of water? (1 mark)

   b) What would you observe if water was present? (2 marks)

3. The table shows some of the pollutants found in air. For each pollutant identify the source of the pollution and how it gets into the air.

Pollutant	What is the source of the pollutant?	How does the pollutant get into the air?
Carbon monoxide		
Sulfur dioxide		
Oxides of nitrogen		

(6 marks)

4. This question is about the greenhouse effect.

   a) What is the greenhouse effect?   **(2 marks)**

   b) EXTENDED Name two greenhouse gases.   **(2 marks)**

   c) EXTENDED Apart from an increase in greenhouse gases, what else could be causing global warming?   **(1 mark)**

5. Carbon dioxide can be prepared using the reaction between calcium carbonate and dilute hydrochloric acid.

   a) How can the gas be collected in this reaction?   **(1 mark)**

   b) Write a balanced equation for the reaction.   **(2 marks)**

6. Carbon dioxide can be made by the thermal decomposition of copper(II) carbonate.

   a) What does *thermal decomposition* mean?   **(2 marks)**

   b) Write a balanced equation for this reaction.   **(2 marks)**

7. EXTENDED This question is about the manufacture of ammonia.

   a) What are the two reactants used in the reaction?   **(2 marks)**

   b) What is the source of each reactant?   **(2 marks)**

   c) Write a balanced equation for the reaction.   **(2 marks)**

   d) What reaction conditions are needed?   **(3 marks)**

Sulfur

△ Fig. 3.51 About two-thirds of the sulfur found in the atmosphere comes from gases emitted by volcanoes.

INTRODUCTION

Sulfur is a non-metallic element in Group VI of the Periodic Table. It is the tenth most common element in the Universe and is found as the native (pure) element in certain parts of the world. Most often, though, it is found in the form of metal sulfides. Sulfur is often deposited in the craters of volcanoes and the characteristic smell close to active volcanoes is sulfur dioxide. Large quantities of sulfur are used to manufacture sulfuric acid. When converted into sulfur dioxide, it is used as a bleach to manufacture wood pulp, for making paper and as a food preservative because it kills bacteria.

KNOWLEDGE CHECK

✓ Know that non-metals are positioned on the right side of the Periodic Table.
✓ Know that non-metals generally form acidic oxides.
✓ Know that dilute sulfuric acid will react with metals, bases and carbonates to form salts.

LEARNING OBJECTIVES

✓ Be able to name the use of sulfur in the manufacture of sulfuric acid.
✓ **EXTENDED** Be able to describe the manufacture of sulfuric acid by the contact process, including the essential conditions and reactions.

SULFURIC ACID

Sulfuric acid is made in industry from sulfur.

EXTENDED

THE CONTACT PROCESS

Sulfuric acid is a very important starting material in the chemical industry. It is used in the manufacture of many other chemicals including fertilisers, detergents and paints.

Sulfuric acid is manufactured in the **contact process**, in which sulfur dioxide is oxidised to sulfur trioxide.

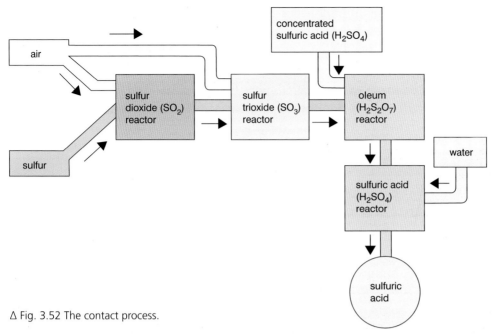

△ Fig. 3.52 The contact process.

The equations for the steps in making sulfuric acid are shown below:

1.

sulfur	+	oxygen	→	sulfur dioxide
S(s)	+	$O_2(g)$	→	$SO_2(g)$

2.

sulfur dioxide	+	oxygen	⇌	sulfur trioxide	
$2SO_2(g)$	+	$O_2(g)$	⇌	$2SO_3(g)$	ΔH = exothermic

3.

sulfur trioxide	+	sulfuric acid	→	'oleum' (concentrated)
$SO_3(g)$	+	$H_2SO_4(l)$	→	$H_2S_2O_7(l)$

4.

'oleum'	+	water	→	sulfuric acid
$H_2S_2O_7(l)$	+	$H_2O(l)$	→	$2H_2SO_4(l)$

Does it seem simpler to you to make sulfuric acid by adding sulfur trioxide straight to water and skipping steps 3 and 4?

$$H_2O(l) + SO_3(g) \rightarrow H_2SO_4(l)$$

This is dangerous because the reaction is very exothermic and an 'acid mist' is made.

Step 2 is the main reaction of the contact process. The highest yield of sulfur trioxide would be made at a low temperature (the reaction is exothermic), but this would be slow. Using a compromise temperature of 450 °C makes less sulfur trioxide, but in a shorter time.

High pressure is not used because the yield is 98 per cent. Unconverted reactants are recycled. Vanadium(V) oxide is used as a catalyst to increase the rate, but it does not increase the yield.

REMEMBER

A low temperature often gives a good conversion of reactant into product but a very slow rate of reaction.

The temperature chosen for an industrial process is often a compromise between one that favours the forward reaction (rather than the backward reaction) and one that gives a suitable rate of reaction.

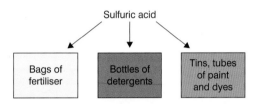

△ Fig. 3.53 Uses of sulfuric acid.

CONCENTRATED SULFURIC ACID

Concentrated sulfuric acid is highly corrosive. It often acts as a dehydrating agent and absorbs hydrogen and oxygen from compounds in the form of water. For example, when added to glucose carbon is formed.

$$C_6H_{12}O_6 \longrightarrow 6C(s) + 6H_2O(g)$$

This reaction is highly exothermic and steam is produced. A honeycomb structure of black carbon is also formed.

QUESTIONS

1. In the contact process, a better yield of sulfur trioxide would be obtained at room temperature than at 450 °C. Why is a higher temperature used?

2. What catalyst is used in the contact process?

3. The yield of sulfur trioxide could be increased if a higher pressure was used. Give a reason for not doing this.

4. Sulfuric acid is used to make ammonium sulfate, $(NH_4)_2SO_4$, fertiliser. What substance reacts with sulfuric acid to make ammonium sulfate? Write a balanced equation for the reaction.

END OF EXTENDED

End of topic checklist

Key term

contact process

During your study of this topic you should have learned:

○ That sulfur is used in the manufacture of sulfuric acid.

○ EXTENDED How to describe the manufacture of sulfuric acid by the contact process and about the essential reactions and conditions:

● a temperature of 450 °C

● a catalyst of vanadium(V) oxide

● atmospheric pressure.

End of topic questions

Note: The marks given for these questions indicate the level of detail required in the answers. In the examination, the number of marks given to questions like these may be different.

1. Name one use of sulfur. (1 mark)

2. EXTENDED This question is about the contact process for making sulfuric acid.

   a) Write a balanced equation, including state symbols, for the reaction between sulfur dioxide and oxygen. (3 marks)

   b) Copy and complete the table, giving the reaction conditions for the contact process. (3 marks)

Reaction factor	Conditions chosen
Temperature	
Pressure	
Catalyst	

   c) Give two uses of sulfuric acid. (2 marks)

△ Fig. 3.54 The chalk cliffs of southern England are composed largely of calcium carbonate.

Carbonates

INTRODUCTION

Carbonates are salts of **carbonic acid**, a weak acid that is made when carbon dioxide dissolves in water. They react with dilute hydrochloric acid and dilute sulfuric acid forming carbon dioxide. Many metals exist in nature as metal carbonates – the most important of these is calcium carbonate or limestone. Limestone is used for building but it has other important uses as well.

HOW IS LIMESTONE USED?

For centuries limestone has been heated in lime kilns to make 'quicklime' (lime) or calcium oxide, CaO:

$CaCO_3(s)$ $\xrightarrow{1200\,°C}$ $CaO(s) + CO_2(g)$

limestone   quicklime

This is an example of **thermal decomposition**, the use of heat ('thermal') to break up a substance.

A modern rotary kiln is shown in Fig. 3.55.

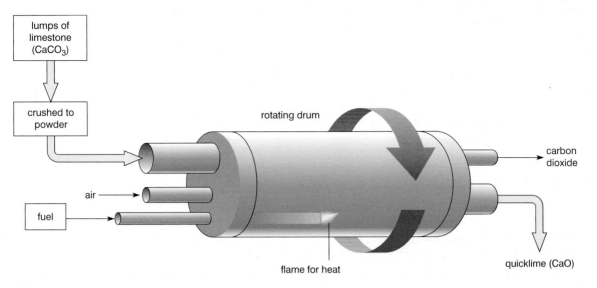

△ Fig. 3.55 A modern rotary kiln.

When water is added to calcium oxide (quicklime), a vigorous exothermic (heat-producing) reaction takes place, and slaked lime – calcium hydroxide, $Ca(OH)_2$ – is formed:

$$CaO(s) \quad + \quad H_2O(l) \quad \rightarrow \quad Ca(OH)_2(s)$$

quicklime   slaked lime

Slaked lime is an alkali, which is the basis of many of its uses.

The major uses of limestone, quicklime and slaked lime are listed below.

Limestone ($CaCO_3$):

• crushed and used as aggregate for road building
• added as a powder to lakes to **neutralise** acidity
• mixed and heated with clay to make cement
• used to extract iron in the blast furnace.

Quicklime (CaO):

• added to soil to neutralise acidity
• used as a drying agent in industry
• used to neutralise acid gases, such as sulfur dioxide, SO_2, produced by power stations (flue-gas desulfurisation).

Slaked lime ($Ca(OH)_2$):

- added to soil to neutralise acidity
- used in mortar for building
- in solution it is called limewater used in testing for carbon dioxide, $CO_2(g)$
- used to neutralise acid gases such as SO_2 produced by power stations (flue-gas desulfurisation).

△ Fig. 3.56 Pouring concrete to form the foundation of a house.

End of topic checklist

Key terms

carbonic acid, neutralisation, thermal decomposition

During your study of this topic you should have learned:

◯ How to describe the manufacture of lime (calcium oxide) from limestone (calcium carbonate).

◯ The uses of lime in treating acidic soil and neutralising acidic industrial waste products.

◯ How to describe the thermal decomposition of calcium carbonate (limestone).

End of topic questions

Note: The marks given for these questions indicate the level of detail required in the answers. In the examination, the number of marks given to questions like these may be different.

1. Name two uses of calcium carbonate. **(2 marks)**

2. Write balanced equations, including state symbols, for the following:

    a) changing limestone into quicklime **(2 marks)**

    b) changing quicklime into slaked lime. **(2 marks)**

3. a) Describe the limewater test for carbon dioxide. **(2 marks)**

    b) Write the word equation and the balanced equation (including state symbols) for the reaction occurring in the limewater test. **(3 marks)**

4. Why is quicklime (CaO) used in power stations? **(3 marks)**

Organic chemistry is distinct from other branches of chemistry, such as inorganic and physical chemistry. It may be described as the chemistry of living processes (often referred to as biochemistry) but extends beyond that. Organic chemistry focuses almost entirely on the chemistry of covalently bonded carbon molecules. As well as life processes, it includes the chemistry of other types of compounds including plastics, petrochemicals, drugs and paint.

Early chemists never imagined that complex chemicals of living processes could ever be manufactured in a laboratory. However, today medical drugs can be made and then their structures modified to achieve improvements in their effectiveness.

An understanding of organic chemistry begins with knowledge of the structure of a carbon atom and how it can combine with other carbon atoms by forming covalent bonds. In this section you will be introduced to a few of the 'families' or series of organic compounds. This knowledge will provide a sound basis for further work in chemistry or biology.

STARTING POINTS

1. Where is carbon in the Periodic Table of elements?

   What can you work out about carbon from its position?

2. What is the atomic structure of carbon? How are its electrons arranged?

3. How does carbon form covalent bonds? Show the bonding in methane (CH_4), the simplest of organic molecules.

4. You will be learning about a series of organic compounds which are hydrocarbons. What do you think a hydrocarbon is?

5. You will be learning about methane. Where can methane be found and what it is used for?

6. You will also be learning about ethanol, which belongs to a particular series of organic compounds. Do you know where you could find ethanol in everyday products?

SECTION CONTENTS

a) Organic chemistry

4
Organic chemistry

△ Oil rigs are used to extract hydrocarbons from the Earth.

Organic chemistry

Most common fuels are organic chemicals and many of them are obtained from crude oil using a process of fractional distillation. The process of cracking is then used to make sure that the larger organic chemicals are converted into more useful smaller ones. Organic chemicals are grouped into homologous series and you will be looking in detail at structures and key properties of three different homologous series, namely the alkanes, alkenes and alcohols. The section finishes by looking at some common polymers, how they are made and their uses.

△ Fig. 4.1 Bottled gas contains organic chemicals called propane or butane

KNOWLEDGE CHECK

✓ Know that the burning of fossil fuels produces carbon dioxide, a greenhouse gas.
✓ Know that burning some fossil fuels can also produce pollutant gases such as sulfur dioxide and nitrogen oxides.
✓ Know that there are alternative energy sources to fossil fuels.
✓ Understand the nature of covalent bonds.
✓ Know the typical physical properties of compounds that exist as simple molecules.
✓ Understand that combustion involves burning in oxygen or air.
✓ Understand the sharing of electrons in a double covalent bond.

LEARNING OBJECTIVES

✓ Know that coal, natural gas and petroleum are fossil fuels that produce carbon dioxide on combustion.
✓ Know that methane is the main constituent of natural gas.
✓ Be able to describe petroleum as a mixture of hydrocarbons and its separation into useful fractions by fractional distillation.
✓ **EXTENDED** Be able to describe the properties of molecules within a fraction.
✓ Know the uses of the fractions obtained from petroleum.
✓ Be able to name and draw the structures of methane and ethane and the products of some of their reactions.
✓ Know that a chemical with a name ending in 'ane' is an alkane.
✓ **EXTENDED** Be able to name and draw the structures of the unbranched alkanes containing up to four carbon atoms per molecule.
✓ **EXTENDED** Be able to describe the homologous series of alkanes and alkenes as families of compounds with the same general formula and similar chemical properties.
✓ Be able to describe alkanes as saturated hydrocarbons whose molecules contain only single covalent bonds.
✓ Be able to describe the properties of alkanes (as shown by methane) as being generally unreactive, except in terms of burning.

- ✓ Be able to describe the complete combustion of hydrocarbons to give carbon dioxide and water.
- ✓ Know that a chemical name ending in 'ene' is an alkene.
- ✓ **EXTENDED** Be able to name and draw the structures of unbranched alkenes containing up to four carbon atoms per molecule.
- ✓ Be able to describe alkenes as unsaturated hydrocarbons whose molecules contain one double bond.
- ✓ Know that cracking is a reaction that produces alkenes.
- ✓ Be able to recognise saturated and unsaturated hydrocarbons from their molecular structures and by their reaction with aqueous bromine.
- ✓ **EXTENDED** Be able to describe the properties of alkenes in terms of addition reactions with bromine, hydrogen and steam.
- ✓ **EXTENDED** Be able to describe the formation of smaller alkanes, alkenes and hydrogen by the cracking of larger alkane molecules and state the conditions required for cracking.
- ✓ Be able to state the uses of ethanol as a solvent and as a fuel.
- ✓ Know that ethanol may be formed by fermentation and by reaction between ethene and steam.
- ✓ Be able to describe the complete combustion of ethanol to give carbon dioxide and water.
- ✓ Know that a chemical name ending in 'ol' is an alcohol.
- ✓ **EXTENDED** Be able to describe the formation of ethanol by fermentation and by the catalytic addition of steam to ethene.
- ✓ Be able to describe polymers as long-chain molecules built up from smaller units (monomers).
- ✓ Be able to describe the formation of poly(ethene) as an example of addition polymerisation of monomer units.
- ✓ **EXTENDED** Be able to deduce the structure of the polymer product from a given alkene and vice versa.
- ✓ **EXTENDED** Be able to describe the formation of nylon as a simple condensation polymer.
- ✓ **EXTENDED** Understand that different polymers have different units and/or different linkages.
- ✓ **EXTENDED** Be able to explain the differences between condensation polymerisation and addition polymerisation.

FUELS

The most common fuels used today either are fossil fuels or are made from fossil fuels. There are problems associated with using fossil fuels – burning them produces a number of polluting gases and releases carbon dioxide, a greenhouse gas. Nevertheless, fossil fuels are a very important source of energy.

What are fossil fuels?

Petroleum (crude oil), natural gas (mainly methane) and coal are **fossil fuels**.

△ Fig. 4.2 Crude oil contains a mixture of hydrocarbons.

Crude oil was formed millions of years ago from the remains of animals and plants that were pressed together under layers of rock. It is usually found deep underground, trapped between layers of rock that it can't seep through (impermeable rock). Natural gas is often trapped in pockets above crude oil.

The supply of fossil fuels is limited – having taken millions of years to form, these fuels will eventually run out. They are called finite or **non-renewable** fuels. This makes them an extremely valuable resource that must be used efficiently.

Fossil fuels contain many useful chemicals (known as **fractions**) and these must be separated so that they are not wasted.

△ Fig. 4.3 Fractional distillation takes place in oil refineries, like this one in the Netherlands..

Fractional distillation

The chemicals in petroleum are separated into useful fractions by a process known as **fractional distillation**.

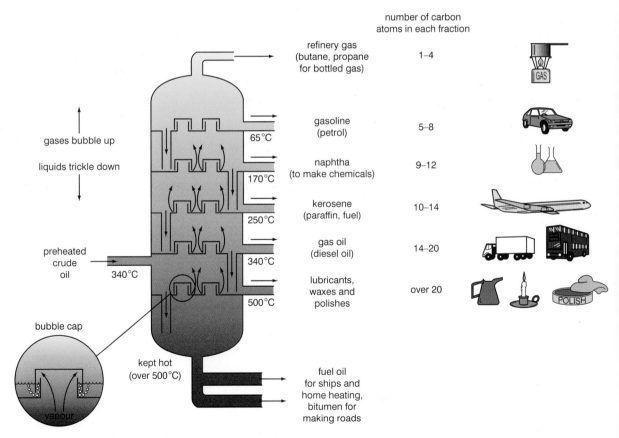

△ Fig. 4.4 A fractionating column converts crude oil into many useful fractions. The fractions you need to name are: refinery gas, gasoline, naphtha, diesel oil/gas oil and bitumen.

The crude oil is heated in a furnace and passed into the bottom of a fractionating column. It gives off a mixture of vapours that rise up the column, and the different fractions condense out at different heights. The fractions that come off near the top are light-coloured, runny

ORGANIC CHEMISTRY

liquids. Those removed near the bottom of the column are dark and sticky. Thick liquids that are not runny, such as those at the bottom of the fractionating column, are described as **viscous**.

The components of petroleum separate because they have different boiling points. A simple particle model explains why their boiling points differ. Petroleum is a mixture of **hydrocarbon** molecules, which contain only carbon and hydrogen. The molecules are chemically bonded in similar ways with strong covalent bonds but contain different numbers of carbon atoms.

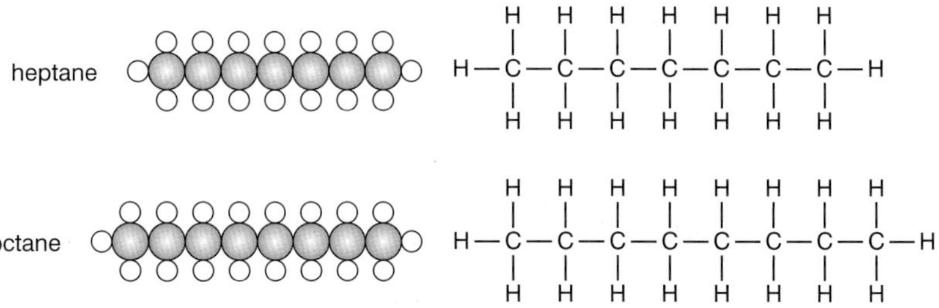

heptane

octane

△ Fig. 4.5 Octane has one more carbon atom and two more hydrogen atoms than heptane. Their formulae differ by CH_2.

The longer the molecule, the stronger the attractive force between the molecules.

The weak attractive forces between the molecules must be broken for the hydrocarbon to boil. The longer a hydrocarbon molecule is, the stronger the intermolecular forces between the molecules. The stronger these forces of attraction, the higher the boiling point because more energy is needed to overcome the forces.

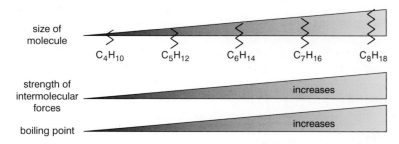

size of molecule

C_4H_{10} C_5H_{12} C_6H_{14} C_7H_{16} C_8H_{18}

strength of intermolecular forces — increases

boiling point — increases

△ Fig. 4.6 How the properties of hydrocarbons change as molecules get longer.

The smaller-molecule hydrocarbons are more **volatile** – they form a vapour easily. For example, we can smell petrol (with molecules containing between 5 and 10 carbon atoms) much more easily than we can smell engine oil (with molecules containing between 14 and 20 carbon atoms) because petrol is more volatile.

Another difference between the fractions is how easily they burn and how smoky their flames are.

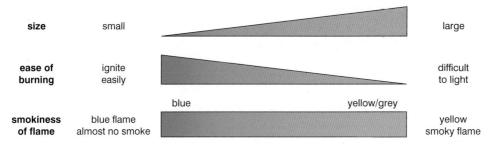

size	small		large
ease of burning	ignite easily		difficult to light
smokiness of flame	blue flame almost no smoke	blue yellow/grey	yellow smoky flame

△ Fig. 4.7 How different hydrocarbons burn.

END OF EXTENDED

QUESTIONS

1. Petroleum is a 'non-renewable' fuel. What does this mean?

2. When drilling for oil, there is often excess gas to be burned off. What is this gas? Where does it come from?

3. **EXTENDED** One of the oil fractions obtained from the fractional distillation of crude oil is light-coloured and runny.

   Is this fraction more likely to have a short chain of carbon atoms or a long chain?

4. **EXTENDED** Another of the oil fractions obtained from the fractional distillation of petroleum burns with a very sooty yellow flame.

   Is this fraction more likely to have a small chain of carbon atoms or a long chain?

5. **EXTENDED** Some fractions obtained from petroleum are very 'volatile'. What does this mean?

CRACKING THE OIL FRACTIONS

The composition of petroleum varies in different parts of the world. Table 4.1 shows the composition of a sample of petroleum from the Middle East after fractional distillation.

Fraction (in order of increasing boiling point)	Typical percentage produced by fractional distillation
Liquefied petroleum gases (LPG)	3
Gasoline	13
Naphtha	9
Kerosene	12
Diesel	14
Heavy oils and bitumen	49

△ Table 4.1 Oil fractions.

Small molecules are much more useful than the larger molecules. Larger molecules can be broken down into smaller ones by **catalytic cracking**. This requires a high temperature of between 600 and 700 °C and a catalyst of silica or alumina.

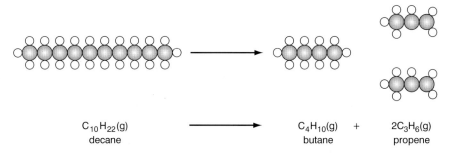

$C_{10}H_{22}(g)$ → $C_4H_{10}(g)$ + $2C_3H_6(g)$

decane   butane   propene

△ Fig. 4.8 The decane molecule ($C_{10}H_{22}$) is converted into the smaller molecules butane (C_4H_{10}) and propene (C_3H_6) in cracking.

The butane and propene formed in this example have different types of structures.

REMEMBER

Propene belongs to a family of hydrocarbons called **alkenes**.

Alkenes are much more reactive (and hence useful) than hydrocarbons like decane (an alkane).

Developing Investigative Skills

A group of students set up an experiment to see if they could 'crack' some liquid paraffin. They soaked some mineral wool in liquid paraffin and assembled the apparatus as shown in Fig. 4.9. They then heated the pottery pieces very strongly, occasionally letting the flame heat the mineral wool. Bubbles of gas started to collect in the test tube. After a few minutes they had collected three test tubes full of gas and so they stopped heating. Almost immediately, water from the trough started to travel back up the delivery tube towards the boiling tube.

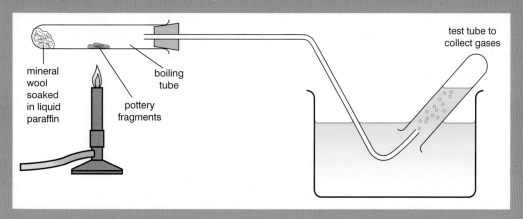

test tube to collect gases

mineral wool soaked in liquid paraffin

boiling tube

pottery fragments

△ Fig. 4.9 Apparatus for experiment.

Evaluating methods

❶ The gas or gases produced in this reaction can be collected by displacement of water. What property of gas(es) does this demonstrate?

❷ Why did the water start to travel back up the delivery tube when heating was stopped?

Using and organising techniques, apparatus and materials

❸ What are the hazards involved in this experiment? What safety precautions would minimise them?

❹ The first test tube of gas collected did not burn, but the second one did. Explain this difference.

❺ The third test tube of gas decolourised bromine water. What does this suggest about the gas present?

Interpreting observations and data

❻ One of the students suggested that one of the two products was ethene (C_2H_4). Assuming that liquid paraffin has the formula $C_{14}H_{30}$, write an equation for the cracking of the liquid paraffin used in this experiment.

QUESTIONS

1. The cracking of hydrocarbons often produces ethene. To which homologous series does ethene belong?

2. Why is cracking needed in addition to the fractional distillation of crude oil?

3. What conditions are needed for the cracking of oil fractions?

SCIENCE IN CONTEXT **THE FOSSIL FUEL DILEMMA**

There is widespread agreement that supplies of the non-renewable fossil fuels – oil, gas and coal – will eventually run out. However, it is not easy to estimate exactly when they will run out. Many different factors need to be considered, including how much of each deposit is left in the Earth, how fast we are using each fossil fuel at the moment, whether or not countries that have supplies will sell to those that don't, and how this is likely to change in the future. If we start switching to alternative fuel sources that are renewable, the reserves that we currently have will last longer.

Current estimates suggest that crude oil (petroleum) will run out between 2025 and 2070. The estimate for natural gas is similar, with 2060 a possible date.

The situation with coal is very different. Most coal deposits have not yet been tapped, and the decline of the coal mining industry in countries such as the UK means that many coal seams are lying undisturbed. If we carry on using coal at the same rate as we do today, there could be enough to last well over a thousand years. However, as other fossil fuels run out, particularly oil, the use of coal may increase, reducing that timespan considerably.

So should we increase our efforts to develop renewable forms of energy such as wind and solar energy; should we put greater emphasis on nuclear power; or should we plan to make much greater use of coal? Perhaps we should do all three? Solving this dilemma is likely to depend as much on political decisions as scientific ones. What would you recommend?

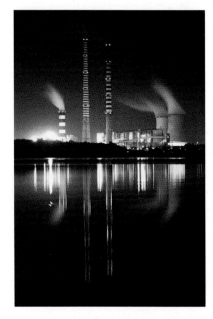

△ Fig. 4.10 A coal-fired power station.

ALKANES

Alkanes are the simplest family or **homologous series** of **organic molecules**. The first alkane, methane, is the major component of natural gas, a common fossil fuel. Other alkanes are obtained from petroleum and are widely used as fuels.

△ Fig. 4.11 Natural gas is being extracted from beneath the ocean floor.

EXTENDED

HOMOLOGOUS SERIES

Alkanes form a **homologous series**. Members of a homologous series have similar chemical properties.

They contain the same **functional group** (the part of the molecule that is responsible for the similar chemical properties) – in this case, the functional group is a C–H single bond.

The general characteristics of a homologous series include:

• They have the same general formula. For alkanes this is C_nH_{2n+2}.

• They have similar chemical properties.

△ Fig. 4.12 Formula 1 cars use specially blended mixtures of alkane hydrocarbons.

- They show a gradual change in physical properties, such as melting point and boiling point.
- They differ from the previous member of the series by $-CH_2-$.

END OF EXTENDED

Alkanes are **hydrocarbons**, which are molecules that contain only carbon and hydrogen atoms. They are made up of carbon atoms linked together by only single covalent bonds and are known as **saturated hydrocarbons**.

Many alkanes are obtained from crude oil by fractional distillation. The smallest alkanes are used extensively as fuels. Apart from burning, however, they are remarkably unreactive.

Alkane	Molecular formula	Displayed formula	Boiling point (°C)	State at room temperature and pressure
Methane	CH_4	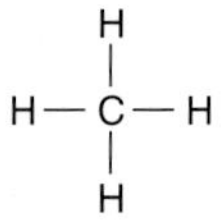 H—C—H with H above and H below	−162	Gas
Ethane	C_2H_6	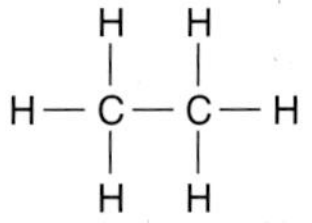 H—C—C—H with H above and below each C	−89	Gas

EXTENDED

Alkane	Molecular formula	Displayed formula	Boiling point (°C)	State at room temperature and pressure
Propane	C_3H_8	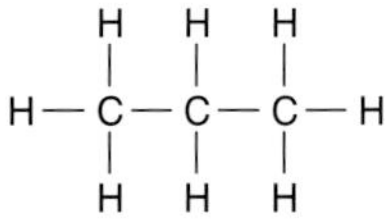 H—C—C—C—H with H above and below each C	−42	Gas
Butane	C_4H_{10}	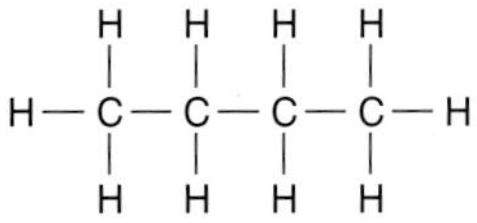 H—C—C—C—C—H with H above and below each C	0	Gas

△ Table 4.2 Alkanes and their molecular structures.

END OF EXTENDED

SCIENCE LINK

BIOLOGY – BIOLOGICAL MOLECULES

- The ability of carbon atoms to form long chains is the basis for many of the compounds that make up living things – leading to the title of 'organic chemistry.'

- Studying hydrocarbons, such as alkanes and alkenes, helps to show the patterns and ideas that will help understand the properties of many biological substances.

- Studying alcohols helps to introduce the idea that adding atoms of other elements into the hydrocarbon chain can create substances with different properties and can lead on to the complexity of the compounds of living organisms.

- The idea of joining smaller units together to create larger molecules (polymerisation) links to the idea of forming starch molecules by joining together glucose molecules.

THE PROPERTIES OF ALKANES

The properties of alkanes are given in Table 4.3.

	Properties of alkanes
General formula	C_nH_{2n+2}
Description	Saturated (no double C=C bond)
Combustion	Burn in oxygen to form CO_2 and H_2O (CO if limited supply of oxygen)
Reactivity	Low
Chemical test	None
Uses	Fuels

△ Table 4.3 Properties of alkanes.

△ Fig. 4.13 Methane is burning in the oxygen in the air to form carbon dioxide and water.

1. Alkanes are saturated hydrocarbons.

  a) What is meant by the word *saturated*?

  b) What is meant by the word *hydrocarbon*?

2. a) What is the chemical formula for the alkane with 15 carbon atoms?

  b) What products would you expect to be formed if this alkane were burned in a plentiful supply of oxygen?

Combustion of alkanes

In a plentiful supply of air, alkanes burn to form carbon dioxide and water. A blue flame, as produced by a Bunsen burner, indicates complete combustion:

methane	+	oxygen	→	carbon dioxide	+	water
$CH_4(g)$	+	$2O_2(g)$	→	$CO_2(g)$	+	$2H_2O(l)$

When the oxygen supply is limited, as when a Bunsen burner burns with a yellow flame, incomplete combustion occurs:

methane	+	oxygen	→	carbon	+	water
$CH_4(g)$	+	$O_2(g)$	→	$C(s)$	+	$2H_2O(l)$

The incomplete combustion of hydrocarbons such as methane can be very dangerous. It can produce carbon monoxide, which is extremely poisonous.

methane	+	oxygen	→	carbon monoxide	+	water
$2CH_4(g)$	+	$3O_2(g)$	→	$2CO(g)$	+	$4H_2O(l)$

Carbon monoxide is difficult to detect without special equipment, because it has no colour or smell. Gas and oil heaters or boilers must be serviced regularly. This is to ensure that jets do not become blocked and limit the air supply, or that exhaust flues don't become blocked and allow small quantities of carbon monoxide to enter the room. The flame in such a boiler or heater should always be blue in colour.

△ Fig. 4.14 The gas in this cooker is burning completely.

1. How can you tell if a fuel is burning without enough oxygen?
2. Name two products that can form when methane burns in an insufficient supply of oxygen.
3. How does carbon monoxide act as a poison?
4. Suggest some alternative ways of generating electricity that do not involve burning fossil fuels.

ALKENES

Alkenes are another homologous series, so they have similar chemical properties and physical properties that change gradually from one member to the next.

Alkenes are often formed by the catalytic cracking of larger hydrocarbons. Hydrogen is also formed in this process. Alkenes contain one or more carbon-to-carbon double bonds. Hydrocarbons with at least one double bond are known as **unsaturated** hydrocarbons. Alkenes burn well and are reactive in other ways also. Their reactivity is due to the carbon-to-carbon double bond.

△ Fig. 4.15 The plastic objects above are made from alkenes.

Alkene	Molecular formula	Structural formula	Boiling point (°C)	State at room temperature and pressure
Ethene	C_2H_4	ethene $\begin{array}{c}H\quad\quad H\\ \diagdown\;\;\diagup\\ C=C\\ \diagup\;\;\diagdown\\ H\quad\quad H\end{array}$	−104	Gas

EXTENDED

Alkene	Molecular formula	Structural formula	Boiling point (°C)	State at room temperature and pressure
Propene	C_3H_6	propene $\begin{array}{c}H\;\;H\\ H-C\quad H\\ \diagdown\;\diagup\\ C=C\\ \diagup\;\;\diagdown\\ H\quad H\end{array}$ or $\begin{array}{c}H\quad\quad H\\ \mid\quad\quad\;\diagup\\ H-C-C=C\\ \mid\quad\;\mid\quad\diagdown\\ H\quad H\quad H\end{array}$	−48	Gas
Butene	C_4H_8	butene $\begin{array}{c}H\;\;H\quad\quad H\\ \mid\;\;\mid\quad\quad\diagup\\ H-C-C-C=C\\ \mid\;\;\mid\quad\;\mid\quad\diagdown\\ H\;\;H\quad H\quad H\end{array}$	−6	Gas

△ Table 4.4 Structure and state of alkenes.

A simple test to distinguish alkenes from alkanes, or an unsaturated hydrocarbon from a saturated one, is to add bromine water to the hydrocarbon. Alkanes do not react with bromine water, so the colour does not change. An alkene does react with the bromine, and the bromine water loses its colour.

EXTENDED

. The type of reaction is known as an **addition reaction**:

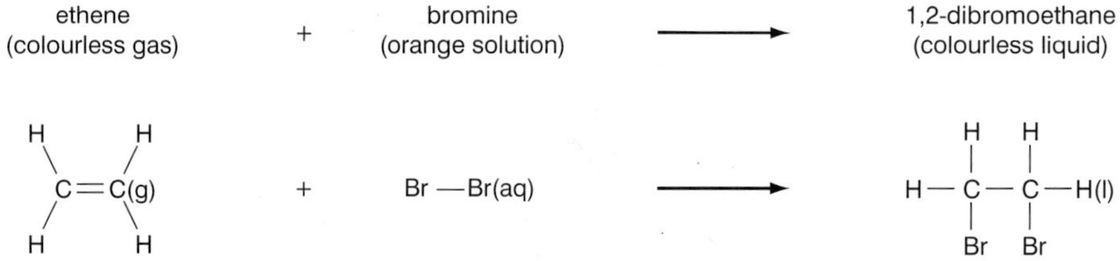

ethene   +   bromine   ⟶   1,2-dibromoethane
(colourless gas)   (orange solution)   (colourless liquid)

$\triangle$ Fig. 4.16 The reaction of ethene and bromine water.

The bromine molecule (Br_2) splits and the two bromine atoms add on to the carbon atoms on either side of the double bond.

END OF EXTENDED

Ethene can also form poly(ethene) or polythene in an addition reaction, a process known as addition **polymerisation**. Ethene is the monomer and reacts with other ethene monomers to form an addition **polymer**, poly(ethene). Further information about this reaction is included on page 267.

EXTENDED

Ethene undergoes other addition reactions. It reacts with bromine in a similar way to its reaction with bromine water, forming 1,2-dibromoethane. It also reacts with hydrogen to form ethane:

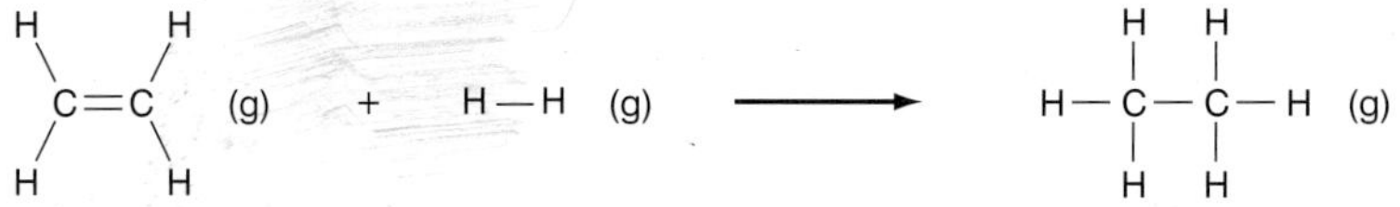

$\triangle$ Fig. 4.17 Ethene reacts with hydrogen to form ethane.

$C_2H_4(g) + H_2(g) \rightarrow C_2H_6(g)$

Ethene also reacts with steam to form ethanol, a reaction that is used in the manufacture of ethanol.

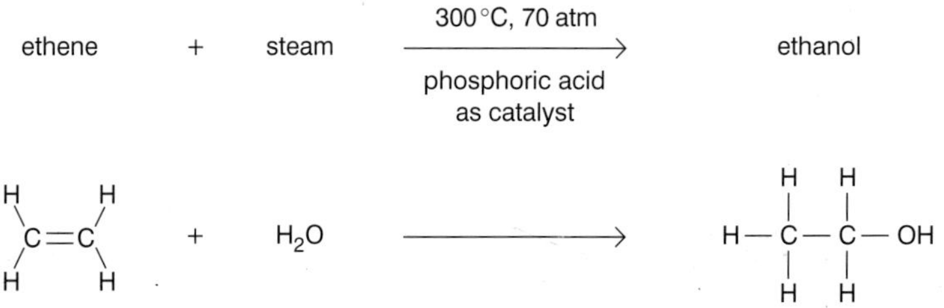

ethene   +   steam $\xrightarrow[\text{phosphoric acid as catalyst}]{300\,^\circ C,\ 70\ atm}$ ethanol

$\triangle$ Fig. 4.18 Ethene reacts with steam to form ethanol.

	Properties of alkenes
General formula	C_nH_{2n}
Description	Unsaturated (contain a double C=C bond)
Combustion	Burn in oxygen to form CO_2 and H_2O (CO if limited supply of oxygen)
Reactivity	High (because of the double C=C bonds); undergo addition reactions
Chemical test	Turn bromine water from orange to colourless (an addition reaction)
Uses	Making polymers (addition reactions) such as polythene

△ Table 4.5 Properties of alkenes.

Alkenes can also form **isomers**.

For example, the isomers of butene (C_4H_8) are:

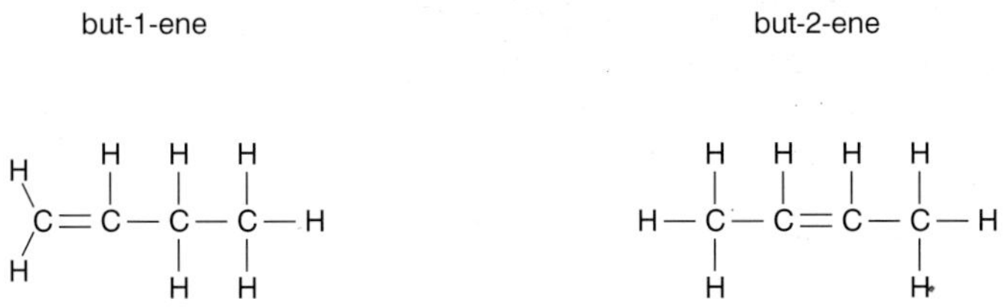

but-1-ene   but-2-ene

△ Fig. 4.19 But-1-ene and but-2-ene.

QUESTIONS

1. Ethene is an unsaturated hydrocarbon. What does *unsaturated* mean?

2. Name a large-scale use of ethene.

SATURATED AND UNSATURATED FATS

We all need some **fat** in our diet because it helps the body to absorb certain nutrients. Fat is also a source of energy and provides essential fatty acids. However, it is best to keep the amount of fat we eat at sensible levels and to eat unsaturated fats rather than saturated fats whenever possible. A diet high in saturated fat can cause the level of cholesterol in the blood to build up over time. Raised cholesterol levels increase the risk of heart disease.

Foods high in saturated fat include:

- fatty cuts of meat
- meat products and pies
- butter
- cheese, especially hard cheese
- cream and ice cream
- biscuits and cakes.

△ Fig. 4.20 Margarine is made from olive oil, whose unsaturated molecules have been saturated with hydrogen.

Unsaturated fat is found in:

- oily fish such as salmon, tuna and mackerel
- avocados
- nuts and seeds
- sunflower and olive oils.

So having a carbon-to-carbon double bond does make a difference.

EXTENDED

Most of the compounds discovered in the world today are organic. There are many of these due to the ability of carbon to form different types of bonds. Alkanes and alkenes are just two examples of homologous series of compounds from the vast number of organic compounds known to date. Use your knowledge of basic organic chemistry to answer the following questions.

QUESTIONS

1. Alkanes have a general formula C_nH_{2n+2} and alkenes C_nH_{2n}. When $n = 5$ the alkane formed is pentane and the alkene is pentene.

   a) Alkanes and alkenes are both hydrocarbons. State why alkanes are called *saturated* hydrocarbons whereas alkenes are *unsaturated*.

b) Give the formula for the alkane and the alkene where $n = 6$ (hexane and hexene). Draw displayed formulae for hexane and hexene and label the different types of bonds.

2. These questions are based on combustion reactions.

    a) Alkanes are useful as fuels. What is the reason for this?

    b) Explain why incomplete combustion can be dangerous if the products of this type of combustion are inhaled.

    c) Describe how the products of combustion of a short-chain hydrocarbon differ from those of a long-chain hydrocarbon.

END OF EXTENDED

ALCOHOLS

Alcohols are molecules that contain the OH **functional group**, which is responsible for their properties and reactions.

Alcohols have the general formula $C_nH_{2n+1}OH$ and belong to the same homologous series, part of which is shown in Table 4.6.

△ Fig. 4.21 The ethanol being made here could be used in alcoholic drinks or as a fuel in cars.

Alcohol	Formula	Structural formula	Boiling point (°C)
Methanol	CH_3OH	H | H—C—OH | H	65
Alcohol	**Formula**	**Structural formula**	**Boiling point (°C)**
Ethanol	C_2H_5OH	H H | | H—C—C—OH | | H H	78

△ Table 4.6 The first two alcohols.

Ethanol burns readily in air to form carbon dioxide and water:

Ethanol	+	oxygen	→	carbon dioxide	+	water
$C_2H_5OH(l)$	+	$3O_2(g)$	→	$2CO_2(g)$	+	$3H_2O(l)$

Ethanol – the most common alcohol

Ethanol, commonly just called 'alcohol', is the most widely used of the alcohol family. Its major uses are given in Table 4.7.

Use of ethanol	Reason
Solvent – such as in disinfectants and perfumes	The OH group allows it to dissolve in water, and it dissolves other organic compounds.
Fuel – such as for cars	It only releases CO_2 and H_2O into the environment, not other pollutant gases as from petrol. It is a renewable resource because it comes from plants, for example sugar beet and sugar cane.
Alcoholic drinks – such as wine, beer, spirits	In ancient times, fermented drinks were sometimes considered safer than polluted water supplies. However, alcohol affects the brain. It is a depressant, so it slows reactions. It is poisonous and can damage the liver and other organs.

△ Table 4.7 Uses of ethanol.

△ Fig. 4.22 Brazilians use *alcool* as vehicle fuel. It is made from the fermented and distilled juice of sugar cane.

1. What would be the formula of the alcohol butanol, which has four carbon atoms?

2. What are the advantages of using ethanol as a fuel in cars?

3. Ethanol is commonly used as a *solvent*. What is a solvent?

Manufacturing ethanol by fermentation

Ethanol is made by **fermentation**. This involves mixing a sugar solution with yeast and maintaining the temperature between 25 and 30 °C. The yeast contains **enzymes**, which catalyse (speed up) the breaking down of the sugar. Enzymes are not effective if the temperature is too low, and they are destroyed (denatured) if the temperature is too high.

EXTENDED

Fermentation of ethanol takes place in large vats. However, even with the yeast as a catalyst, the process is slow and it takes several days to be completed. As the concentration of the ethanol increases, the activity of the yeast decreases, so eventually fermentation stops.

The balanced equation for fermentation is:

sugar $\xrightarrow{\text{yeast}}$ ethanol $+$ carbon dioxide

$C_6H_{12}O_6(aq) \xrightarrow{\text{yeast}} 2C_2H_5OH(l) + 2CO_2(g)$

The source of the sugar determines the type of alcoholic drink produced – for example, grapes for wine, barley for beer.

Fermentation takes time because it is an enzymic reaction (yeast) and a batch process. After fermentation, a more concentrated solution of alcohol is extracted by fractional distillation. The mixture is boiled and the alcohol vapour reaches the top of the fractionating column, where it condenses back to a liquid.

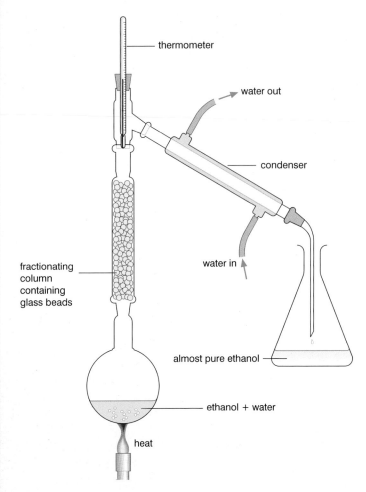

thermometer

water out

condenser

fractionating
column
containing
glass beads

water in

almost pure ethanol

ethanol + water

heat

Δ Fig. 4.23 Laboratory apparatus for fractional distillation of alcohol. In large-scale manufacture, different equipment would be used but the principles of separation are the same.

END OF EXTENDED

QUESTIONS

1. What does *fermentation* mean?

2. EXTENDED What is the optimum temperature for fermentation?

3. EXTENDED Why is yeast needed in the fermentation process?

4. EXTENDED After fermentation is complete, why is fractional distillation used to obtain pure ethanol?

Developing Investigative Skills:

A group of chemists needed to carry out the fermentation of sugar in the laboratory to make some ethanol for fuel. They set up the apparatus shown in Fig. 4.24. To prevent the oxidation of ethanol to vinegar, the apparatus was set up so that air could not enter the flask. At first there seemed to be nothing happening, but by the next morning the reaction had started. When the reaction had finished, the chemists used fractional distillation to obtain some pure alcohol.

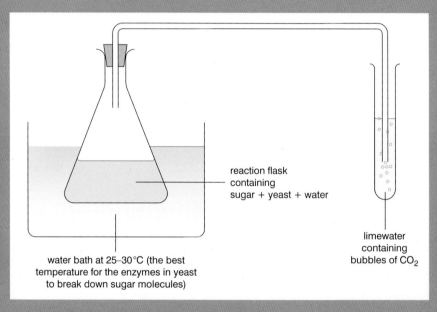

reaction flask
containing
sugar + yeast + water

limewater
containing
bubbles of CO_2

water bath at 25–30°C (the best
temperature for the enzymes in yeast
to break down sugar molecules)

△ Fig. 4.24 Fermentation apparatus for making ethanol in the laboratory.

Evaluating methods

❶ How could the chemists have tried to maintain the temperature of the water bath while the reaction was proceeding?

❷ What was the purpose of the limewater?

❸ What would the chemists have observed to indicate that a reaction had started?

❹ How would the chemists know when the reaction was complete?

❺ In the fractional distillation process, which liquid would be collected first – ethanol or water? Explain your answer.

EXTENDED

Manufacturing ethanol from ethene

On an industrial scale, ethanol is also made from ethene, which is obtained from crude oil. This is an example of an addition reaction. The reaction is:

ethene   +   steam $\xrightarrow[\substack{\text{phosphoric acid} \\ \text{as catalyst}}]{300\,°C,\ 70\,atm}$ ethanol

$$\underset{H}{\overset{H}{>}}C=C\underset{H}{\overset{H}{<}}\text{(g)} \quad + \quad H_2O\text{(g)} \quad \xrightarrow{} \quad H-\underset{\underset{H}{|}}{\overset{\overset{H}{|}}{C}}-\underset{\underset{H}{|}}{\overset{\overset{H}{|}}{C}}-OH\text{(g)}$$

△ Fig. 4.25 Reaction of ethane and steam to make ethanol.

These are quite extreme conditions in terms of energy (300 °C) and specialist plant equipment is required to withstand a pressure of 70 atmospheres, so the process is expensive.

Unlike fermentation, this process is continuous and produces ethanol at a fast rate.

END OF EXTENDED

SCIENCE IN CONTEXT — ETHANOL AS A FUEL

The development of ethanol as a fuel for cars has a long history. In the USA, until 1908, cars made by Ford (especially the Model T) used ethanol as a fuel. Now most cars in the USA can run on blends of petrol/ethanol containing up to 10 percent ethanol.

△ Fig. 4.26 In the USA, the ethanol in gasohol is made from corn (maize).

Brazil and the USA are the world's top producers of ethanol. In Brazil about one-fifth of all cars can use 100% ethanol fuel, known as E100; many other cars use petrol/ethanol blends. Brazil makes its ethanol mostly from fermented sugar obtained from sugar cane; in the USA, corn (maize) is used as the source of the sugar. Starting from sugar cane is much more efficient, and so ethanol is much cheaper to produce in Brazil than in the USA.

One problem with using ethanol as a fuel is that it readily absorbs water from the atmosphere. This causes some problems when transporting the fuel and makes it more expensive than petrol to transport.

A key question is, should food be used to make a fuel? Is it better to use fuel made from crude oil? Some people argue that food is needed for people to eat and should not be used to run cars. They say that using so much land for growing sugar cane and corn to make ethanol means that less land is available for growing food. This leads to food shortages and increases in the price of food. What do you think?

POLYMERS

Polymers are long-chain molecules formed from small units, which are called monomers. There are some important naturally occurring polymers such as **proteins** and **carbohydrates**. This section is only concerned with manufactured polymers, which are called synthetic polymers. Common synthetic polymers include **plastics** such as polythene as well as fabrics which are often used in clothing and have common names such as 'polyester' or 'polyamide'. Some polymers contain just one monomer (for example, polythene), other polymers contain two monomers which link together alternately (for example, nylon).

SYNTHETIC POLYMERS

There are two types of synthetic polymers, **addition polymers** and **condensation polymers**.

Addition polymers

Alkenes can be used to make polymers, which are very large molecules made up of many identical smaller molecules called **monomers**. Alkenes are able to react with themselves. They join together into long chains, like adding beads to a necklace. When the monomers add together like this, the material produced is called an addition polymer. Poly(ethene) or polythene is made this way.

By changing the atoms or groups of atoms attached to the carbon-to-carbon double bond, a range of different polymers can be made.

The double bond within the alkene molecule breaks to form a single covalent bond to a carbon atom in an adjacent molecule. This process is repeated rapidly as the molecules link together.

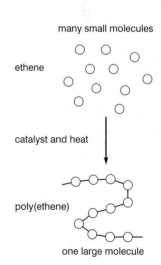

many small molecules

ethene

catalyst and heat

poly(ethene)

one large molecule

△ Fig. 4.27 Ethene molecules link together to produce a long polymer chain of poly(ethene).

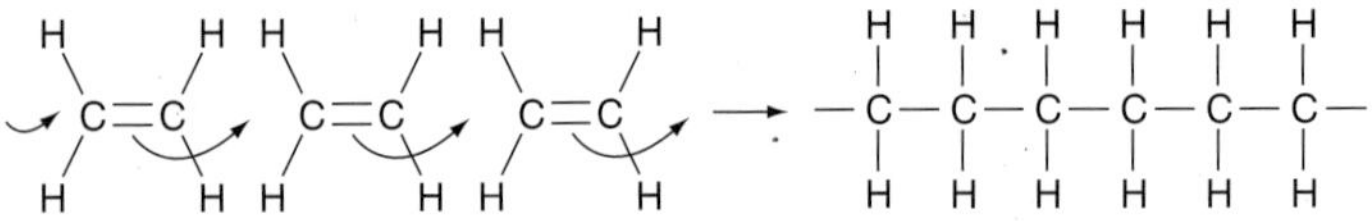

△ Fig. 4.28 Poly(ethene) from ethene.

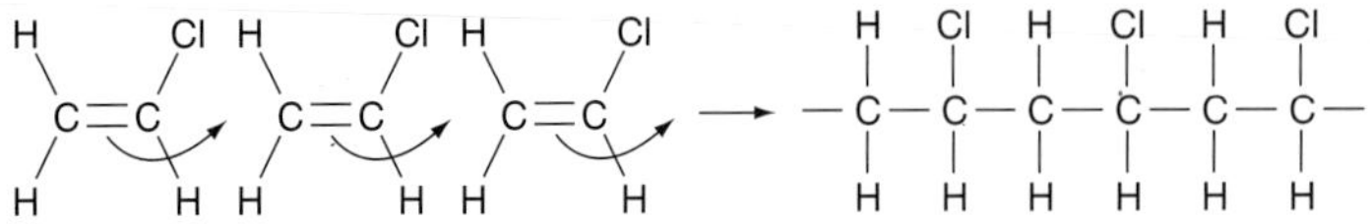

△ Fig. 4.29 Poly(chloroethene) from chloroethene.

REMEMBER

In some cases the polymer is made from just one monomer, in other polymers there are two or more different monomers.

EXTENDED

Name of monomer	Displayed formula of monomer	Name of polymer	Displayed formula of polymer	Uses of polymer
Ethene	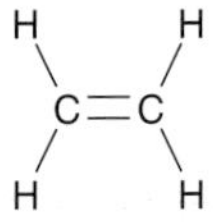	Poly(ethene)	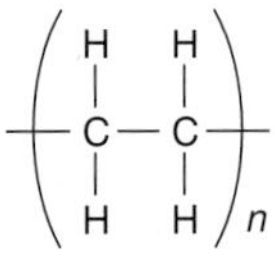	Buckets, bowls, plastic bags
Propene	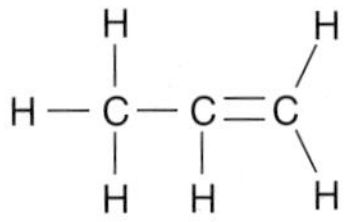	Poly(propene)	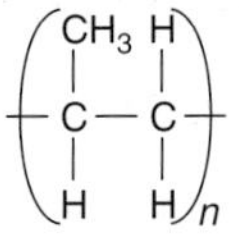	Packaging, ropes, carpets
Chloroethene (vinyl chloride)	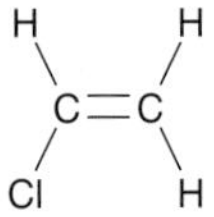	Poly (chloroethene) (polyvinylchloride)	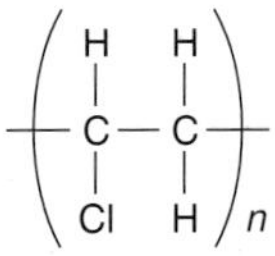	Plastic sheets, artificial leather
Phenylethene (styrene)	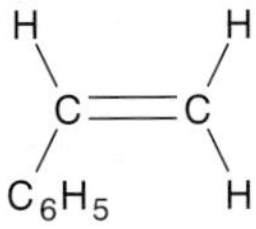	Poly (phenylethene) (polystyrene)	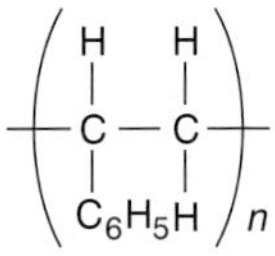	Yoghurt cartons, packaging
Tetrafluoroethene	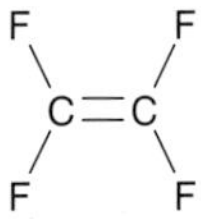	Poly (tetrafluroethene) or PTFE	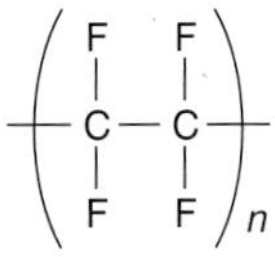	Non-stick coating in frying pans

△ Table 4.8 Monomers and their polymers.

◁ Fig. 4.30 This pan is coated with PTFE non-stick plastic. How is PTFE made?

QUESTIONS

1. In what way is a polymer like a string of beads?

2. Name the polymer used extensively to make plastic bags.

3. EXTENDED The diagram shows the structural formula of chloroethene.

$$\begin{array}{ccc} H & & Cl \\ \diagdown & & \diagup \\ & C = C & \\ \diagup & & \diagdown \\ H & & H \end{array}$$

   a) Show how two molecules of chloroethene join together to form part of the polymer poly(chloroethene).

   b) Draw the structure of the repeat unit of the polymer.

4. EXTENDED What type of polymer is poly(chloroethene)?

Condensation polymers

Polymers can also be made by joining together two different monomers so that they react together. When they react, they expel a small molecule. Because the molecule is usually water, the process is called condensation polymerisation and the products are condensation polymers.

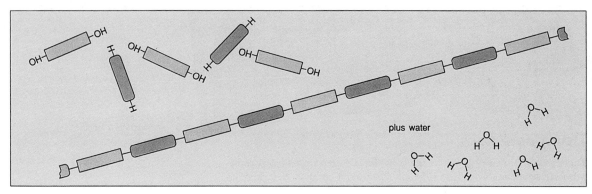

plus water

△ Fig. 4.31 Condensation polymerisation.

ORGANIC CHEMISTRY

269

Nylon is a common synthetic condensation polymer.

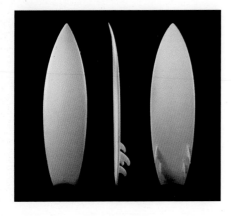

◁ Fig. 4.32 Surfboards are made from a condensation polymer called polyurethane.

Nylon is made from a molecule with a carboxylic acid group (COOH) and another molecule with an **amine** group (NH$_2$).

They react to form an **amide** link:

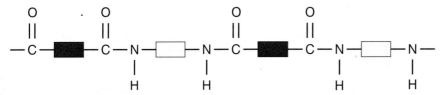

△ Fig. 4.33 Nylon is a polyamide.

By changing the atoms or groups of atoms attached to the carbon–carbon double bond, a whole range of different polymers can be made.

QUESTIONS

1. Nylon is an example of a condensation polymer. How is this type of polymer different from an addition polymer?

2. Why is it important that the monomers that join together to make nylon have reactive groups at each end of the molecule?

END OF EXTENDED

End of topic checklist

Key terms

addition polymer, addition reaction, alcohol, alkane, alkene, amide, amine, carbohydrate, condensation polymer, enzyme, fermentation, fossil fuel, fraction, fractional distillation, functional group, homologous series, hydrocarbon, isomer, monomer, non-renewable, organic molecules, plastic, polymer, polymerisation, protein, saturated hydrocarbons, unsaturated, viscous, volatile

During your study of this topic you should have learned:

○ About the fuels coal, natural gas and petroleum (crude oil) as fossil fuels that produce carbon dioxide on combustion.

○ That methane is the main constituent of natural gas.

○ That petroleum is a mixture of hydrocarbons and it can be separated into useful fractions by fractional distillation.

○ **EXTENDED** How to describe the properties of molecules within a fraction.

○ About the uses of the following fractions obtained from petroleum:

- refinery gas for bottled gas for heating and cooking
- gasoline fraction for fuel (petrol) in cars
- naphtha fraction for making chemicals
- diesel/gas oil for fuel in diesel engines
- bitumen for road surfaces.

○ The names and structures of methane, ethane, ethene and ethanol.

○ How to state the type of compound present from a chemical name ending in –ane, –ene and –ol, or a molecular structure.

○ **EXTENDED** How to name and draw the structures of the unbranched alkanes and alkenes containing up to four carbon atoms per molecule.

○ **EXTENDED** How to describe the homologous series of alkanes and alkenes as families of compounds with the same general formula and similar chemical properties.

○ How to describe the complete combustion of hydrocarbons to give carbon dioxide and water.

○ How to describe the properties of alkanes (as shown by methane) as being generally unreactive, except in terms of burning.

End of topic checklist continued

○ How to describe alkanes as saturated hydrocarbons whose molecules contain only single covalent bonds.

○ That cracking is a reaction that produces alkenes.

○ **EXTENDED** How to describe the formation of smaller alkanes, alkenes and hydrogen by the cracking of larger alkane molecules.

○ How to describe alkenes as unsaturated hydrocarbons whose molecules contain one double bond.

○ How to recognise saturated and unsaturated hydrocarbons:

- from their molecular structures
- by reaction with aqueous bromine.

○ **EXTENDED** How to describe the properties of alkenes in terms of addition reactions with:

- bromine
- hydrogen
- steam.

○ About the uses of ethanol as a solvent and as a fuel.

○ That ethanol may be formed by fermentation and by reaction between ethene and steam.

○ How to describe the complete combustion of ethanol to give carbon dioxide and water.

○ **EXTENDED** How to describe the formation of ethanol by fermentation and the catalytic addition of steam to ethene.

○ That polymers are long-chain molecules built up from smaller units (monomers).

○ How to describe the formation of poly(ethene) as an example of addition polymerisation of monomer units.

○ **EXTENDED** How to deduce the structure of the polymer product from a given alkene and vice versa.

○ **EXTENDED** That different polymers have different units and/or different linkages.

○ **EXTENDED** How to explain the differences between condensation polymerisation and addition polymerisation.

○ **EXTENDED** How to describe the formation of a simple condensation polymer such as nylon.

End of topic questions

Note: The marks given for these questions indicate the level of detail required in the answers. In the examination, the number of marks given to questions like these may be different.

1. a) How was crude oil (petroleum) formed? **(2 marks)**

  b) Why is crude oil called a 'non-renewable' fuel? **(1 mark)**

2. The diagram shows a column used to separate the components present in petroleum.

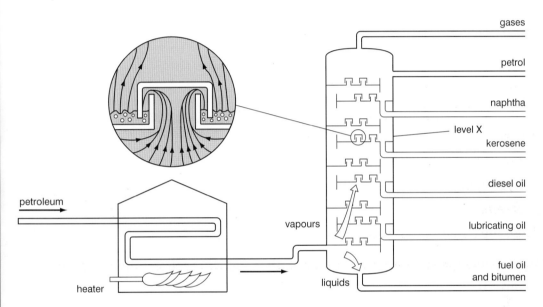

  a) Name the process used to separate petroleum into fractions. **(1 mark)**

  b) What happens to the boiling point of the mixture as it goes up the column? **(1 mark)**

  c) The mixture of vapours arrives at level X. What now happens to the various parts of the mixture? **(2 marks)**

3. <u>**EXTENDED**</u> The cracking of decane molecules is shown by the equation $C_{10}H_{22} \rightarrow Y + C_2H_4$.

  a) Decane is a *hydrocarbon*. What is a hydrocarbon? **(1 mark)**

  b) What reaction conditions are needed for cracking? **(2 marks)**

  c) Write down the molecular formula for hydrocarbon Y. **(1 mark)**

  d) What 'family' does hydrocarbon Y belong to? **(1 mark)**

  e) Why is the cracking of petroleum fractions so important? **(2 marks)**

End of topic questions continued

4. <u>EXTENDED</u> Petrol is a hydrocarbon with a formula of C_8H_{18}.

   a) What are the products formed when petrol burns in a plentiful supply of air? **(2 marks)**

   b) Write a balanced equation, including state symbols, for the reaction when petrol burns in a plentiful supply of air. **(2 marks)**

   c) When petrol is burned in a car engine, carbon monoxide may be formed. Explain why carbon monoxide is dangerous. **(2 marks)**

5. <u>EXTENDED</u> What is a *homologous series*? **(1 mark)**

6. <u>EXTENDED</u> What is the molecular formula for an alkane with 10 carbon atoms? **(1 mark)**

7. Is the compound with the formula $C_{15}H_{30}$ a member of the alkane series? Explain your answer. **(1 mark)**

8. Ethane burns in oxygen.

   a) What is the molecular formula of ethane? **(1 mark)**

   b) Name the products formed when ethane burns in excess oxygen. **(2 marks)**

   c) What colour flame would indicate that the ethane was burning in excess oxygen? **(1 mark)**

   d) Write a balanced equation for the reaction. **(2 marks)**

   e) Name two additional products that could be formed if the oxygen supply was limited. **(2 marks)**

   f) What colour flame would indicate that the ethane was burning in a limited supply of oxygen? **(1 mark)**

9. <u>EXTENDED</u> **a)** Draw a structural formula for octane, an alkane with 8 carbon atoms. **(1 mark)**

   b) What will be the physical state of octane at room temperature and pressure? **(1 mark)**

   c) Is octane a saturated or an unsaturated hydrocarbon? Explain your answer. **(1 mark)**

10. <u>EXTENDED</u> Ethene burns in oxygen.

    a) Name the products formed when there is a plentiful supply of oxygen. **(2 marks)**

    b) i) Write a balanced equation for the burning of ethene in a plentiful supply of oxygen. **(2 marks)**

    ii) What colour would the flame be? **(1 mark)**

c) When ethene is burned in a limited supply of air, carbon and water are formed.

   i) Write a balanced equation for this reaction.   **(2 marks)**

   ii) What colour would the flame be?   **(1 mark)**

11. EXTENDED **a)** Draw structural formulae for butane and butene.   **(2 marks)**

   b) Which hydrocarbon is unsaturated?   **(1 mark)**

   c) Which substance could you use to distinguish between butane and butene?   **(1 mark)**

12. EXTENDED Propene gas is bubbled through some bromine water.

   a) Describe the colour change that would occur.   **(2 marks)**

   b) Write a balanced equation for this reaction.   **(2 marks)**

   c) What type of chemical reaction is this an example of?   **(1 mark)**

13. EXTENDED A hydrocarbon has the formula C_7H_{14}.

   a) Is the hydrocarbon saturated or unsaturated? Explain your answer.   **(1 mark)**

   b) What is the name of the hydrocarbon?   **(1 mark)**

14. EXTENDED Octene is an alkene.

   a) Write down the molecular formula of octene.   **(1 mark)**

   b) What state of matter will octene exist in at room temperature and pressure? Explain your answer.   **(1 mark)**

15. What are the two main sources of sugar used in the manufacture of ethanol by fermentation?   **(2 marks)**

16. EXTENDED In the laboratory fermentation experiment to make ethanol from sugar using yeast, explain the importance of the following:

   a) The reaction temperature is kept between the range 25–30 °C.   **(2 marks)**

   b) Oxygen from the air cannot enter the reaction flask.   **(2 marks)**

17. EXTENDED In the industrial manufacture of ethanol from ethene:

   a) what is the source of the ethene?   **(1 mark)**

   b) what is the function of the phosphoric acid?   **(1 mark)**

   c) what conditions of temperature and pressure are used?   **(2 marks)**

   d) Write a balanced equation for the reaction.   **(1 mark)**

18. EXTENDED Pentanol is an alcohol with five carbon atoms.

    a) What is the molecular formula of pentanol?   **(1 mark)**

    b) Draw the structural formula of pentanol.   **(1 mark)**

19. Explain what is meant by the following:

    a) *monomer*   **(1 mark)**

    b) *polymer*.   **(1 mark)**

20. EXTENDED This question is about addition polymers.

    a) What is an *addition polymer*?   **(1 mark)**

    b) What structural feature do all monomers that form addition polymers have in common?   **(1 mark)**

    c) Use structural formulae to show how propene molecules react to form poly(propene).   **(2 marks)**

    d) Explain why a polymer called poly(propane) does not exist.   **(2 marks)**

21. EXTENDED This question is about condensation polymers.

    a) In what ways is a condensation polymer different from an addition polymer?   **(2 marks)**

    b) Name an example of a condensation polymer.   **(1 mark)**

Doing well in examinations

INTRODUCTION

Examinations will test how good your understanding of scientific ideas is, how well you can apply your understanding to new situations and how well you can analyse and interpret information you have been given. The assessments are opportunities to show how well you can do these.

To be successful in exams you need to:

✓ have a good knowledge and understanding of science

✓ be able to apply this knowledge and understanding to familiar and new situations

✓ be able to interpret and evaluate evidence that you have just been given.

You need to be able to do these things under exam conditions.

OVERVIEW

Ensure you are familiar with the structure of the examinations you are taking. Consult the relevant syllabus for the year you are entering your examinations for details of the different papers and the weighting of each, including the papers to test practical skills. Your teacher will advise you of which papers you will be taking.

You will be required to perform calculations, draw graphs and describe, explain and interpret chemical ideas and information. In some of the questions the content may be unfamiliar to you; these questions are designed to assess data-handling skills and the ability to apply chemical principles and ideas in unfamiliar situations.

ASSESSMENT OBJECTIVES AND WEIGHTINGS

For the Cambridge IGCSE Co-ordinated Sciences examination, the assessment objectives and weightings are as follows:

✓ AO1: Knowledge with understanding (50%)

✓ AO2: Handling information and problem solving (30%)

✓ AO3: Experimental skills and investigations (20%).

The types of questions in your assessment fit the three assessment objectives shown in the table.

Assessment objective	Your answer should show that you can...
AO1 Knowledge with understanding	Recall, select and communicate your knowledge and understanding of science.
AO2 Handling information and problem solving	Apply skills, including evaluation and analysis, knowledge and understanding of scientific contexts.
AO3 Experimental skills and investigations	Use the skills of planning, observation, analysis and evaluation in practical situations.

EXAMINATION TECHNIQUES

To help you to work to your best abilities in exams, there are a few simple steps to follow.

Check your understanding of the question

✓ **Read the introduction to each question carefully before moving on to the questions themselves**.

✓ Look in detail at any **diagrams**, **graphs** or **tables**.

✓ Underline or circle the **key words** in the question.

✓ **Make sure you answer the question that is being asked** rather than the one you wish had been asked!

✓ Make sure that you understand the meaning of the '**command words**' in the questions.

REMEMBER

Remember that any information you are given is there to help you to answer the question.

EXAMPLE 1

✓ '**Give**', '**state**', '**name**' are used when recall of knowledge is required – for example you could be asked to give a definition, write a list of examples or provide the best answers from a list of options.

✓ '**Describe**' is used when you have to give the main feature(s) of, for example, a chemical process or structure.

✓ '**Explain**' is used when you have to give reasons, for example for some experimental results or a chemical fact or observation. You will often be asked to 'explain your answer', that is give reasons for it.

✓ '**Suggest**' is used when you have to come up with an idea to explain the information you're given – there may be more than one possible answer, no definitive answer from the information given, or it may be that you will not have learned the answer but have to use the knowledge you do have to come up with a sensible one.

✓ **'Calculate'** means that you have to work out an answer in figures.

✓ **'Plot'**, **'Draw a graph'** are used when you have to use the data provided to produce graphs and charts.

Check the number of marks for each question

✓ Look at the **number of marks** allocated to each question.

✓ Look at the **space provided** to guide you as to the length of your answer.

✓ Make sure you include at least as many points in your answer as there are marks.

✓ Write neatly and keep within the space provided.

REMEMBER

Beware of continually writing too much because it probably means you are not really answering the questions. Do not repeat the question in your answer.

Use your time effectively

✓ Don't spend so long on some questions that you don't have time to finish the paper.

✓ If you are really stuck on a question, leave it, finish the rest of the paper and come back to it at the end.

✓ Even if you eventually have to guess at an answer, you stand a better chance of gaining some marks than if you leave it blank.

ANSWERING QUESTIONS

Multiple choice questions

✓ Select your choice in pencil on a separate answer sheet.

Short-answer and structured questions

✓ In short-answer questions, **don't write more than you are asked for**.

✓ You may not gain any marks, even if the first part of your answer is correct, if you've written down something incorrect later on or which contradicts what you've said earlier. This may give the impression that you haven't really understood the question or are guessing.

✓ You should aim to use **good English** and **scientific language** to make your answer as clear as possible.

- ✓ Present the information in a logical sequence.
- ✓ Don't be afraid to also use **labelled diagrams** or **flow charts** if it helps you to show your answer more clearly.

Questions with calculations

- ✓ **In calculations always show your working**.
- ✓ Even if your final answer is incorrect you may still gain some marks if part of your attempt is correct.
- ✓ If you just write down the final answer and it is incorrect, you will get no marks at all.
- ✓ Write down your answers to as many **significant figures** as are used in the numbers in the question (and no more). If the question doesn't state how many significant figures then a good rule of thumb is to quote 3 significant figures.
- ✓ Don't round off too early in calculations with many steps.
- ✓ You may also lose marks if you don't use the correct **units**. In some questions the units will be mentioned, for example calculate the mass in grams; or the units may also be given on the answer line. If numbers you are working with are very large, you may need to make a conversion, for example convert joules into kilojoules, or kilograms into tonnes.

Finishing your exam

- ✓ When you've finished your exam, **check through** your paper to make sure you've answered all the questions.
- ✓ Check that you haven't missed any questions at the end of the paper or turned over two pages at once and missed questions.
- ✓ Cover over your answers and read through the questions again and check that your answers are as good as you can make them.

REMEMBER

You will be asked questions on investigative work. It is important that you understand the methods used by scientists when carrying out investigative work.

More information on carrying out practical work and developing your investigative skills are given in the next section.

TEACHER'S COMMENTS

a) It is important to identify the states of matter:

A = gas, B = liquid, C = solid.

i) Correct – evaporation process.

ii) Correct – solidifying.

iii) Incorrect – should be 'AC' order because ethene is a gas, poly(ethene) a solid.

Exam-style questions
Sample student answer

Note: The questions, sample answers and marks in this section have been written by the authors as a guide only. The marks given for these questions indicate the level of detail required in the answers. In the examination, the number of marks given to questions like these may be different.

Question 1

a) The diagrams show the arrangement of particles in the three states of matter.

Each circle represents a particle.

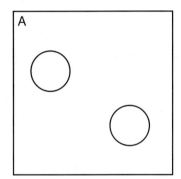 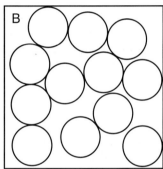 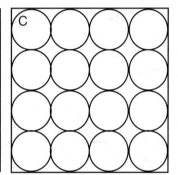

Use the letters A, B and C to give the starting and finishing states of matter for each of the changes in the table. For the mark, both the starting state and the finishing state need to be correct.

Change	Starting state	Finishing state	
i) The formation of water vapour from a puddle of water on a hot day	B	A	✓ ①
ii) The formation of solid iron from molten iron	B	C	✓ ①
iii) The manufacture of poly(ethene) from ethene	B	A	✗

(3)

Exam-style questions continued

b) Which state of matter is the *least* common for the elements of the Periodic Table at room temperature?

gases ✗ .... (1)

c) The manufacture of sulfuric acid can be summarised by the equation:

$$2S(s) + 3O_2(g) + 2H_2O(l) \rightarrow 2H_2SO_4(l)$$

Tick one box in each line to show whether the formulae in the table represent a compound, an element or a mixture.

	Compound	Element	Mixture	
i) $2S(s)$		✓		✓ ①
ii) $2S(s) + 3O_2(g)$		✓		✗
iii) $3O_2(g) + 2H_2O(l)$			✓	✓ ①
iv) $2H_2SO_4(l)$	✓			✓ ①

(4)

b) Answer is 'liquid'. In the Periodic Table, at room temperature the majority of elements are solids, a few are gases but only two are liquids – mercury and bromine.

c) **i)** Correct – sulfur.

ii) Incorrect – this is a 'mixture' of two elements.

iii) Correct – a mixture of an element (O_2) and a compound (H_2O).

iv) Correct – sulfuric acid.

The answers rely on using the state symbols for the equation and a thorough knowledge of the terms elements, mixtures and compounds.

(Total 8 marks)

 $\frac{5}{8}$

Question 2

This question is about atoms.

a) **i)** Choose words from the box to label the diagram of an atom. (3)

proton	neutron	electron	ion

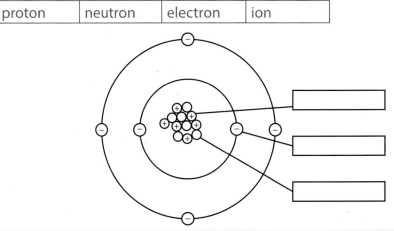

ii) What is the proton number of this atom? (1)

iii) What is the nucleon number of this atom? (1)

b) Carbon has three isotopes. State one way in which the atoms of the three isotopes are:

i) the same (1)

ii) different. (1)

(Total 7 marks)

Question 3

a) Some elements combine together to form ionic compounds. Use words from the box to complete the sentences.

Each word may be used once, more than once or not at all.

gained	high	lost	low
medium	metals	non-metals	shared

Ionic compounds are formed between _____ and _____ .

Electrons are _____ by atoms of one element and _____ by atoms of the other element.

The ionic compound formed has a _____ melting point and a _____ boiling point. (6)

b) Two elements react to form an ionic compound with the formula $MgCl_2$.
(proton number of Mg = 12; proton number of Cl = 17)

i) Give the electronic configurations of the two elements in this compound *before* the reaction. (2)

ii) Give the electronic configurations of the two elements in this compound *after* the reaction. (2)

(Total 10 marks)

Question 4

9.12 g of iron(II) sulfate was heated. It decomposes to sulfur dioxide ($SO_2(g)$) and sulfur trioxide ($SO_3(g)$) and iron(III) oxide. Calculate the mass of iron(III) oxide formed and the volume of sulfur trioxide produced (measured at room temperature and pressure).

$2FeSO_4(s) \rightarrow Fe_2O_3(s) + SO_2(g) + SO_3(g)$

(A_r: O = 16; S = 32; Fe = 56; 1 mole of gas at room temperature and pressure occupies 24 000 cm³)

(Total 6 marks)

Question 5

The following equation shows the reaction between potassium hydroxide solution and dilute sulfuric acid:

$$2KOH \text{ (aq)} + H_2SO_4 \text{ (aq)} \rightarrow K_2SO_4 \text{ (aq)} + 2H_2O \text{ (l)}$$

A 25.0 cm^3 sample of 0.15 mol/dm^3 potassium hydroxide solution was titrated with dilute sulfuric acid. It was found that 15.0 cm^3 of dilute sulfuric acid was needed to neutralise the potassium hydroxide solution.

a) Describe how you would carry out the titration experiment. You should include details of the apparatus you would use and how you would know when the potassium hydroxide had been neutralised. (4)

b) Use the equation and the experimental results to calculate the concentration of the sulfuric acid. (4)

(Total 8 marks)

Question 6

The structures of some substances are shown here:

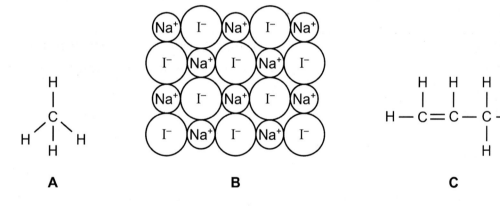

| A | B | C |

H — Br

D

E

a) Answer these questions using the letters **A**, **B**, **C**, **D** or **E**.

   i) Which structure is methane?   **(1)**

  ii) Which two structures are giant structures?   **(1)**

 iii) Which two structures are hydrocarbons?   **(1)**

  iv) Which structure contains ions?   **(1)**

  v) Which two structures have very high melting points?   **(1)**

b) Structure **E** is a form of carbon.

   i) What is the name of this structure? Put a ring around the correct answer.

     carbide   graphite   lead   poly(hexene)   **(1)**

  ii) Name another form of carbon.   **(1)**

c) Write the simplest formula for substance **B**.   **(1)**

d) Is substance **D** an element or a compound? Explain your answer.   **(3)**

                                                (Total 11 marks)

Question 7

Strontium and sulfur chlorides both have a formula of the type XCl_2 but they have different properties.

Property	Strontium chloride	Sulfur chloride
Appearance	White crystalline solid	Red liquid
Melting point /°C	873	−80
Particles present	Ions	Molecules
Electrical conductivity of solid	Poor	Poor
Electrical conductivity of liquid	Good	Poor

a) The formulae of the chlorides are similar because both elements have a valency of 2.
   Explain why Group II and Group VI elements both have a valency of 2.   **(2)**

b) Draw a dot and cross diagram of one covalent molecule of sulfur chloride. Use x to represent an electron from a sulfur atom. Use o to represent an electron from a chlorine atom.   **(3)**

c) Explain the difference in electrical conductivity between the following:

   i) solid and liquid strontium chloride   **(1)**

  ii) liquid strontium chloride and liquid sulfur chloride.   **(1)**

                                                  (Total 7 marks)

Exam-style questions
Sample student answer

The questions, sample answers and marks in this section have been written by the authors as a guide only. The marks given for these questions indicate the level of detail required in the answers. In the examination, the number of marks given to questions like these may be different.

Question 1

Solutions of silver nitrate and sodium chloride react together to make the insoluble substance silver chloride.

The equation for the reaction is

$AgNO_3(aq) + NaCl(aq) \rightarrow NaNO_3(aq) + AgCl(s)$

An investigation was carried out to find out how much precipitate formed with different volumes of silver nitrate solution.

A student measured out 15 cm³ of sodium chloride solution using a measuring cylinder.

He poured this solution into a clean boiling tube.

Using a clean measuring cylinder, he measured out 2 cm³ of silver nitrate solution (of the same concentration as the sodium chloride solution). He added this to the sodium chloride solution.

A cloudy white mixture formed and the precipitate was left to settle.

TEACHER'S COMMENTS

a) i) Correct point marked.

ii) Correct explanation. Also correct would be tube not being vertical when being set up so precipitate not level.

iii) Correct response.

b) Correct response – also correct is 'silver nitrate in excess'.

c) i) Correct reading of ruler.

ii) Answer is 3.9 cm³ – the student has misread the horizontal axis scale.

d) i) Correct response.

ii) Correct – this is the purpose of the experiment.

e) 2 marks have been lost here because the filtered-off precipitate needs to be washed (1) and 'dried' (1) before being weighed.

The student then measured the height (in cm) of the precipitate using a ruler.

The student repeated the experiment using different volumes of silver nitrate. The graph shows the results obtained.

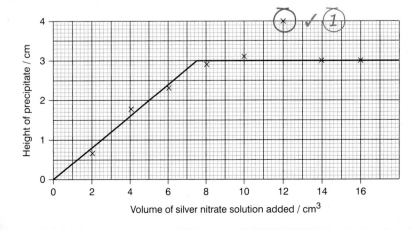

a) **i)** On the graph, circle the point that seems to be anomalous. (1)

ii) Explain two things that the student may have done in the experiment to give this anomalous result.

Precipitate not settled ✓ ①   *Because not left long enough* ✓ ①   (2)

iii) Why must the graph line go through (0, 0)?

Cannot have a precipitate if no silver nitrate added yet. ✓ ① (1)

b) Suggest a reason why the height of the precipitate stops increasing.

No more sodium chloride left to react. ✓ ① (1)

c) **i)** How much precipitate has been made in the tube drawn on the right?

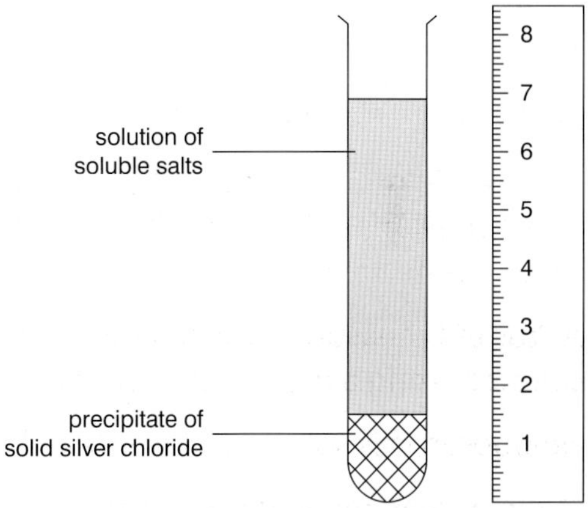

1.5 cm ✓ ① (1)

ii) Use the graph to find the volume of silver nitrate solution needed to make this amount of precipitate.

solution of soluble salts

2.9 cm ✗ (1)

d) After he had plotted the graph, the student decided he should obtain some more results.

precipitate of solid silver chloride

i) Suggest what volumes of silver nitrate solution he should use.

Between 6 cm³ and 10 cm³ ✓ ① (1)

ii) Explain why he should use these volumes.

Need to know exactly where the graph levels off ✓ ① (1)

e) Suggest a different method for measuring the amount of precipitate formed.

Filter ✓ ①   *off each precipitate and weigh it* ✓ ① (4)

(Total 13 marks)

⑩⁄₁₃

Question 2

Dilute nitric acid reacts with marble chips to produce carbon dioxide. The equation is given below:

$$2HNO_3(aq) + CaCO_3(s) \rightarrow Ca(NO_3)_2(aq) + H_2O(l) + CO_2(g)$$

Some students investigated the effect of changing the temperature of the nitric acid on the rate of the reaction. The method is:

● Use a measuring cylinder to pour 50 cm³ of dilute nitric acid into a conical flask.
● Heat the acid to the required temperature.
● Put the flask on the balance.
● Add 15 g (an excess) of marble chips to the flask.
● Time how long it takes for the mass to decrease by 1.00 g.
● Repeat the experiment at different temperatures.

The students' results are shown in the table.

Temperature of acid (°C)	Time to lose 1.00 g (s)
20	93
33	68
44	66
55	40
67	30
76	25

a) **i)** Draw a graph of the results. (3)

    ii) One of the points is inaccurate. Circle this point on your graph. (1)

    iii) Suggest a possible cause for this inaccurate result. (1)

b) Use the graph to find the times taken to lose 1.00 g at 40 °C and 60 °C. (2)

c) The rate of the reaction can be found using the equation:

$$\text{rate of reaction} = \frac{\text{mass lost}}{\text{time taken to lose mass}}$$

    i) Use this equation and your results from **b)** to calculate the rates of reaction at 40 °C and 60 °C. (2)

    ii) What will be the unit for these rates? (1)

iii) State how the rate of reaction changes when the temperature increases. (1)

iv) Explain in terms of particles and collisions why the rate changes when the temperature increases. (1)

d) Describe how the method could be changed to obtain a result at 5 °C. (1)

(Total 13 marks)

Question 3

Sulfuric acid is manufactured in the contact process. Part of the process involves a reaction that produces sulfur trioxide. The equation for this reaction is shown below.

$$2SO_2(g) + O_2(g) \rightleftharpoons 2SO_2(g) \ \Delta H = \text{negative}$$

a) What type of reaction is represented by the sign $\rightleftharpoons$? (1)

b) What information about the reaction can you work out from the information that ΔH is negative? (1)

c) A temperature of 450 °C is used in this reaction. Explain why this temperature has been chosen. (3)

d) i) A catalyst is used to increase the rate of the reaction. How does a catalyst do this? (2)

ii) Name the catalyst used in this reaction. (1)

(Total 8 marks)

Question 4

The diagram shows the apparatus used to electrolyse lead(II) bromide.

a) The wires connected to the electrodes are made of copper.

Explain why copper conducts electricity. (1)

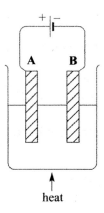

heat

b) Explain why electrolysis does not occur unless the lead(II) bromide is molten. **(2)**

c) The reactions occurring at the electrodes can be represented by the equations shown in the table.

Copy and complete the table to show the electrode (A or B) at which each reaction occurs, and the type of reaction occurring (oxidation or reduction). **(2)**

Electrode reaction	Electrode	Type of reaction
$Pb^{2+} + 2e^- \rightarrow Pb$		
$2Br^- \rightarrow Br_2 + 2e^-$		

(Total 5 marks)

Question 5

Read the following instructions for the preparation of hydrated copper(II) sulfate ($CuSO_4.5H_2O$), then answer the questions that follow.

1. Put 25 cm^3 of dilute sulfuric acid in a beaker.

2. Heat the sulfuric acid until it is just boiling and then add a small amount of copper(II) carbonate.

3. When the copper carbonate has dissolved, stop heating, then add a little more copper carbonate. Continue in this way until copper carbonate is in excess.

4. Filter the hot mixture into a clean beaker.

5. Make the hydrated copper(II) sulfate crystals from the copper(II) sulfate solution.

The equation for the reaction is

$$CuCO_3(s) + H_2SO_4(aq) \rightarrow CuSO_4(aq) + CO_2(g) + H_2O(l)$$

a) What piece of apparatus would you use to measure out 25 cm^3 of sulfuric acid? **(1)**

b) Why is the copper(II) carbonate added in excess? **(1)**

c) When copper(II) carbonate is added to sulfuric acid, there is fizzing. Explain why. **(1)**

d) Draw a diagram to describe step 4. You must label your diagram. **(3)**

e) After filtration, which one of the following describes the copper(II) sulfate in the beaker?

Select the correct answer.

crystals   filtrate   precipitate   water   (1)

f) Explain how you would obtain pure dry crystals of hydrated copper(II) sulfate from the solution of copper(II) sulfate.   (2)

(Total 9 marks)

Question 6

Electroplating iron with chromium involves four stages.

1. Iron object is cleaned with sulfuric acid, then washed with water.

2. The iron is plated with copper.

3. It is then plated with nickel to prevent corrosion.

4. It is then plated with chromium.

a) The equation for Stage 1 is:

$$Fe + H_2SO_4 \rightarrow FeSO_4 + H_2$$

  i) Write a word equation for this reaction.   (2)

  ii) Describe a test for the gas given off in this reaction.   (2)

b) The diagram shows how iron is electroplated with copper.

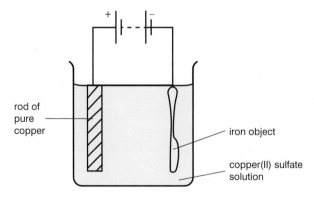

rod of pure copper

iron object

copper(II) sulfate solution

  i) Choose a word from the list below that describes the iron object. Draw a ring around the correct answer.

anion   anode   cathode   cation   (1)

    ii) What is the purpose of the copper(II) sulfate solution?   (1)

    iii) Describe what happens during the electroplating to:

        the iron object   (2)

        the rod of pure copper.   (2)

    iv) Describe a test for copper(II) ions.   (2)

c) Suggest why chromium is used to electroplate articles.   (1)

d) The information below shows the reactivity of chromium, copper and iron with warm hydrochloric acid.

chromium – a few bubbles of gas produced every second

copper – no bubbles of gas produced

iron – many bubbles of gas produced every second

Put these three metals in order of their reactivity with hydrochloric acid, most reactive first.   (1)

(Total 14 marks)

TEACHER'S COMMENTS

a) The mark would have been given for stating that all the elements have the same number of electrons in their outer shell. The student has gone further and correctly stated that they all have one electron in the outer shell.

b) i) The correct answer has been given.

ii) This answer lacks precision. The mark would be given for either explaining that the reaction produced heat or that the reaction was exothermic.

iii) The student has not scored both marks. Apart from stating that the reaction would be more rapid than that with lithium, observations have not been given. The products have been correctly named but these are not what you would *observe*. Marks would be given for: fizzing/effervescence/bubbles (of gas), the sodium floats/moves around on the water, forms a ball/disappears.

iv) The correct answer and explanation have been given.

Exam-style questions
Sample student answer

The questions, sample answers and marks in this section have been written by the authors as a guide only. The marks given for these questions indicate the level of detail required in the answers. In the examination, the number of marks given to questions like these may be different.

Question 1

Lithium (Li), sodium (Na) and potassium (K) are in Group I of the Periodic Table.

a) These elements have similar chemical properties.

Explain why, using ideas about electronic structures.

All the elements have one electron in their outer shell. ✔ ① **(1)**

b) Lithium reacts with water to form a solution of lithium hydroxide and a colourless gas. During this reaction the temperature of the water increases.

i) What is the name of the colourless gas produced?

hydrogen ✔ ① **(1)**

ii) Why does the temperature of the water increase?

The reaction between lithium and water is rapid. ✘ **(1)**

iii) Describe what you would observe if a small piece of sodium is added to water.

The sodium forms sodium hydroxide and hydrogen gas is given off. ✘

The reaction would be more rapid than the lithium reaction. ✔ ① **(2)**

Exam-style questions continued

iv) Caesium (Cs) is another Group I metal.

Is caesium more or less reactive than lithium? Give a reason for your answer.

More reactive, because reactivity in Group I increases down the group.

 (1)

(Total 6 marks)

Question 2

Use the Periodic Table to help you answer this question.

a) State the symbol of the element with proton number 14. (1)

b) State the symbol of the element that has a relative atomic mass of 32. (1)

c) State the number of the group that contains the alkali metals. (1)

d) Which group contains elements whose atoms form ions with a 2+ charge? (1)

e) Which group contains elements whose atoms form ions with a 1– charge? (1)

(Total 5 marks)

Question 3

Three of the elements in Group VII of the Periodic Table are chlorine, bromine and iodine.

a) Chlorine has a proton number of 17. What is the electron configuration of chlorine? (1)

b) How many electrons will be in the outer shell of a bromine atom? (1)

c) Bromine reacts with hydrogen to form hydrogen bromide. The equation for the reaction is:

$Br_2(g) + H_2(g) \rightarrow 2HBr(g)$

What is the colour change during the reaction? (1)

d) Hydrogen iodide and hydrogen chloride have similar properties.

   i) A sample of hydrogen iodide is dissolved in water. A piece of universal indicator paper is dipped into the solution. State, with a reason, the final colour of the universal indicator paper. (2)

   ii) A sample of hydrogen iodide is dissolved in methylbenzene. A piece of universal indicator paper is dipped into the solution. State, with a reason, the final colour of the universal indicator paper. (2)

(Total 7 marks)

Question 4

The reactivity of metals can be compared by comparing their reactions with dilute sulfuric acid. Pieces of zinc, iron and magnesium of identical size are added to separate test tubes containing this acid.

a) What order of reactivity would you expect? Put the most reactive metal first. (1)

b) Write a word equation for the reaction between magnesium and dilute sulfuric acid. (1)

c) Write a balanced equation for the reaction in b). (1)

d) Name a metal that does not react with dilute sulfuric acid. (1)

e) What other reaction could be used to compare the reactivity of metals? (1)

(Total 5 marks)

Question 5

Iron is extracted from iron ore in a blast furnace. Label the diagram of the blast furnace using only the words given below. Each word may be used once, more than once or not at all.

bauxite	sodium hydroxide	cryolite
molten iron	sand	slag

a)

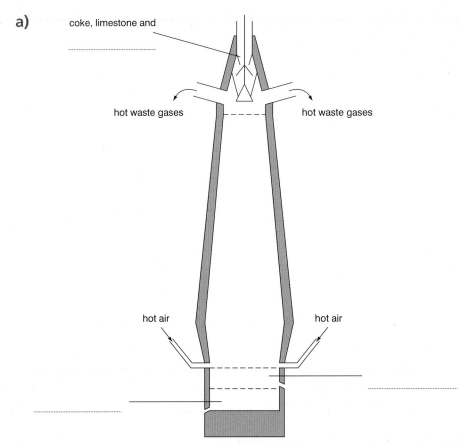

coke, limestone and
....

hot waste gases   hot waste gases

hot air   hot air

....

....

(3)

b) Coke (carbon) burns in the oxygen in the furnace.

i) Write a balanced equation for carbon burning in a plentiful supply of oxygen.   (1)

ii) The product formed in reaction i) above then reacts with more carbon to form a gas. Write a balanced equation for this reaction.   (1)

c) Why is limestone added to the furnace?   (2)

d) Iron is produced in the furnace by the reduction of iron(III) oxide. An equation for the reaction is:

$Fe_2O_3(s) + 3CO(g) \rightarrow 2Fe(s) + 3CO_2(g)$

Explain how you know that the iron(III) oxide has been reduced.   (1)

e) Aluminium is another important metal.

i) Unlike iron, aluminium cannot be obtained from aluminium ore by heating it with carbon. Explain why.   (2)

ii) State one large-scale use of aluminium and a property of aluminium that makes it suitable for this use.   (2)

(Total 12 marks)

Question 6

The table shows the composition of the mixture of gases in typical car exhaust fumes.

Gas	% of the gas in the exhaust fumes
Carbon dioxide	9
Carbon monoxide	5
Oxygen	4
Hydrogen	2
Hydrocarbons	0.2
Nitrogen oxides	0.2
Sulfur dioxide	less than 0.003
Gas X	79.6

a) State the name of the gas X. (1)

b) The carbon dioxide comes from the burning of hydrocarbons, such as octane, in the petrol.

   i) Copy and complete the word equation for the complete combustion of octane.

     octane + _____ → carbon dioxide + _____ (2)

   ii) Which two elements are present in hydrocarbons? (1)

   iii) To which homologous series of hydrocarbons does octane belong? (1)

c) Suggest a reason for the presence of carbon monoxide in exhaust fumes. (1)

d) Nitrogen oxides are present in small quantities in exhaust fumes.

   i) Copy and complete the following equation for the formation of nitrogen dioxide.

     $N_2(g)$ + _____ $O_2(g)$ → _____ $NO_2(g)$ (1)

   ii) State one harmful effect of nitrogen dioxide on organisms. (1)

e) Sulfur dioxide is an atmospheric pollutant and is found in only small amounts in car exhaust fumes.

   i) What is the main source of sulfur dioxide pollution of the atmosphere? (1)

   ii) Sulfur dioxide is oxidised in the air to sulfur trioxide. The sulfur trioxide may dissolve in rainwater to form a dilute solution of sulfuric acid, H_2SO_4. State the meaning of the term *oxidation*. (1)

Exam-style questions continued

iii) Sulfuric acid reacts with metals such as iron. Copy and complete the following word equation for the reaction of sulfuric acid with iron.

sulfuric acid + iron → _____ + _____ (2)

iv) What effect does acid rain have on buildings made of stone containing calcium carbonate? (1)

(Total 13 marks)

Question 7

Look at the list of five elements below:

argon, bromine, chlorine, iodine, potassium

a) Put these five elements in order of increasing proton number. (1)

b) Put these five elements in order of increasing relative atomic mass. (1)

c) The orders of proton number and relative atomic mass for these five elements are different. Which one of the following is the most likely explanation for this?

A The proton number of a particular element may vary.

B The presence of neutrons.

C The atoms easily gain or lose electrons.

D The number of protons must always equal the number of neutrons. (1)

d) Which of the five elements in the list are in the same group of the Periodic Table? (1)

e) i) From the list, choose one element that has one electron in its outer shell. (1)

ii) From the list, choose one element that has a full outer shell of electrons. (1)

f) Which two of the following statements about argon are correct?

A Argon is a noble gas.

B Argon reacts readily with potassium.

C Argon is used to fill weather balloons.

D Argon is used in lightbulbs. (2)

(Total 8 marks)

Question 8

The table gives some information about the elements in Group I of the Periodic Table.

Element	Boiling point (°C)	Density (g/cm³)	Radius of atom in the metal (nm)	Reactivity with water
Lithium	1342	0.53	0.157	
Sodium	883	0.97	0.191	Rapid
Potassium	760	0.86	0.235	Very rapid
Rubidium		1.53	0.250	Extremely rapid
Caesium	669	1.88		Explosive

a) How does the density of the Group I elements change going down the group? (2)

b) Suggest a value for the boiling point of rubidium. (1)

c) Suggest a value for the radius of a caesium atom. (1)

d) Use the information in the table to suggest how fast lithium reacts with water compared with the other Group I metals. (1)

e) State three properties shown by all metals. (3)

f) When sodium reacts with water, hydrogen is given off:

$$2Na(s) + 2H_2O(l) \rightarrow 2NaOH(aq) + H_2(g)$$

i) State the name of the other product formed in this reaction. (1)

ii) Describe a test for hydrogen. (2)

g) The diagrams show three types of hydrogen atom.

i) State the name of the positively charged particle in the nucleus. (1)

ii) What is the name given to atoms with the same number of positive charges in the nucleus but different numbers of neutrons? (1)

iii) State the number of nucleons in a single atom of tritium. (1)

iv) Tritium is a radioactive form of hydrogen. State one medical use of radioactivity. (1)

(Total 15 marks)

Exam-style questions
Sample student answer

The questions, sample answers and marks in this section have been written by the authors as a guide only. The marks given for these questions indicate the level of detail required in the answers. In the examination, the number of marks given to questions like these may be different.

Question 1

This question is about the following organic compounds:

A C_4H_{10} **B** C_2H_5OH **C** C_4H_8

a) Which compound belongs to the alkene group?

   C ✓ ①   (1)

b) Which compound is a saturated hydrocarbon?

   C ✗   (1)

c) Which compound can be made by fermentation?

   B ✓ ①   (1)

d) Which compound will decolourise bromine water?

   C ✓ ①   (1)

e) Name the two products that are formed when compound A burns in a plentiful supply of air.

    carbon dioxide ✓ ① and water ✓ ① (2)

f) Name two other substances that can be produced when compound A burns in a limited supply of air.

   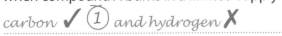 carbon ✓ ① and hydrogen ✗   (2)

   Total 6/8

TEACHER'S COMMENTS

a) Correct answer, alkenes are hydrocarbons with the general formula C_nH_{2n}.

b) The correct answer is A. Compound C is an alkene and is unsaturated, it contains a carbon-to-carbon double bond.

c) Correct answer, ethanol is made by fermentation.

d) Correct answer. The decolourising of bromine water is a test for an alkene.

e) Correct answers. All hydrocarbons burn in a plentiful supply of oxygen forming carbon dioxide and water.

f) Carbon is correct and is responsible for the yellow flame characteristic of incomplete combustion. The missing substance is carbon monoxide, which is extremely poisonous.

Exam-style questions continued

Question 2

The alkanes are a homologous series of saturated hydrocarbons.

a) Say whether each of the following statements about the members of the alkane homologous series is TRUE or FALSE.

   i) They have similar chemical properties. (1)

   ii) They have the same displayed formula. (1)

   iii) They have the same general formula. (1)

   iv) They have the same physical properties. (1)

   v) They have the same relative formula mass. (1)

b) Define the following terms:

   i) hydrocarbon (1)

   ii) saturated. (1)

c) The third member of the alkane homologous series is propane.

   i) What is the molecular formula of propane? (1)

   ii) Draw the displayed formula of propane. (2)

(Total 10 marks)

Question 3

Many useful substances are produced by the fractional distillation of crude oil.

a) Bitumen, fuel oil and gasoline are three fractions obtained from crude oil.

Name the fractions that have the following properties:

   i) the highest boiling point (1)

   ii) molecules with the fewest carbon atoms (1)

   iii) the darkest colour. (1)

b) Some long-chain hydrocarbons can be broken down into more useful products.
What is the name of this process and how is it carried out? (3)

c) Methane is used as a fuel. When methane is burned in a limited supply of air, carbon monoxide is formed.

   i) Write a balanced equation for this reaction. (2)

   ii) Explain why carbon monoxide is dangerous to health. (2)

(Total 10 marks)

Question 4

Propene can be converted into a polymer called poly(propene).

propene

a) Which homologous series does propene belong to? (1)

b) What is the general name given to an individual molecule that combines with other molecules to make a polymer? (1)

c) Use the displayed formula of propene to show how three molecules link together to form part of the poly(propene) molecule. (2)

d) Draw the repeat unit in poly(propene). (2)

e) What type of polymer is poly(propene)? (1)

f) Nylon is a different type of polymer from poly(propene).

   i) What type of polymer is nylon? (1)

   ii) In terms of how it is made, how is nylon different from poly(propene)? (1)

(Total 9 marks)

Question 5

Poly(ethene) is a plastic that is made by polymerising ethene, C_2H_4.

a) Which one of the following best describes the ethene molecules in this reaction? Draw a ring around the correct answer.

alcohols, alkanes, monomers, polymers, products (1)

b) The structure of ethane is shown below.

Explain, by referring to its bonding, why ethane cannot be polymerised. (1)

c) Draw the structure of ethene, showing all its atoms and bonds. (1)

d) Ethene is obtained by cracking alkanes.

   i) Explain the meaning of the term *cracking*. (1)

   ii) What condition is needed to crack alkanes? (1)

   iii) Copy and complete the equation for cracking decane, $C_{10}H_{22}$.

     $C_{10}H_{22} \rightarrow C_2H_4 +$ _____ (1)

e) Some oil companies crack the ethane produced when petroleum is distilled.

  i) Copy and complete the equation for this reaction.

$C_2H_6 \rightarrow C_2H_4 +$ _____ (1)

  ii) Describe the process of fractional distillation, which is used to separate the different fractions in petroleum. (2)

  iii) State a use for the following petroleum fractions:

gasoline fraction (1)
lubricating fraction. (1)

(Total 11 marks)

Developing experimental skills

INTRODUCTION

As part of your IGCSE Co-ordinated Sciences Chemistry course, you will develop practical skills and have to carry out investigative work in science.

This section provides guidance on carrying out an investigation.

The experimental and investigative skills are divided as follows:

1. Using and organising techniques, apparatus and materials

2. Planning experiments and investigations

3. Observing, measuring and recording

4. Interpreting observations and data

5. Evaluating methods

1. USING AND ORGANISING TECHNIQUES, APPARATUS AND MATERIALS

Learning objective: to demonstrate and describe appropriate experimental and investigative methods, including safe and skilful practical techniques.

Questions to ask:

How shall I use the equipment and chemicals safely to minimise the risks – what are my safety precautions?

✓ When writing a Risk Assessment, investigators need to be careful to check that they've matched the hazard with the concentration of a chemical used. Many acids, for instance, are corrosive in higher concentrations but are likely to be irritants or of low hazard in the concentration used when working in chemistry experiments.

✓ Don't forget to consider the hazards associated with all the chemicals, even if these are very low.

✓ In the exam, you may be asked to justify the precautions taken when carrying out an investigation.

How much detail should I give in my description?

✓ You need to give enough detail so that someone else who has not done the experiment would be able to carry it out to reproduce your results.

How should I use the equipment to give me the precision I need?

✓ You should know how to read the scales on the measuring equipment you are using.

✓ You need to show that you are aware of the precision needed.

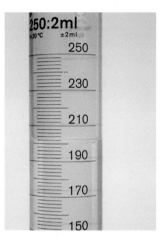

△ Fig. 5.1 The volume of liquid in a burette must be read to the bottom of the meniscus. The volume in this measuring cylinder is 202 cm³ (ml), not 204 cm³.

EXAMPLE 2

This is an extract from a student's notebook. It describes how she carried out a titration experiment using sulfuric acid and potassium hydroxide solutions, with methyl orange as an indicator.

$$2KOH(aq) + H_2SO_4(aq) \rightarrow K_2SO_4(aq) + 2H_2O(l)$$

What are my safety precautions?

Equipment

I will be using a pipette, burette and conical flask all made from glass so I will need to handle them carefully and, in particular, clamp the burette carefully and make sure the pipette does not roll off the bench when I am not using it. I will also be careful when attaching the pipette to the pipette filler so that the pipette does not break.

Chemicals

I have looked up the hazards

Sulfuric acid 0.1M: LOW HAZARD

Potassium hydroxide (0.1M approx.): IRRITANT

COMMENT

The student has used a data source to look up the chemical hazards.
There is no risk assessment for methyl orange.

*I will need to handle the chemicals carefully, have a damp
cloth ready to wipe up any spills and wear eye protection.*

COMMENT

The student has suggested some sensible precautions.

The student's method is given below:

*A pipette and a burette were carefully washed, making sure
they were drained after washing.*

*25.00 cm³ of the potassium hydroxide solution was measured
in a pipette and transferred to a clean conical flask. 3 drops
of methyl orange indicator were then added.*

*The burette was filled with the sulfuric acid solution, making
sure that there were no air bubbles in the jet of the burette.
The first reading of the volume of acid in the burette was
taken.*

*The acid was added to the alkali in the conical flask,
swirling the flask all the time. When the indicator colour was
close to changing, the acid was added drop by drop until the
colour changed. The second reading on the burette was
taken.*

*The whole procedure was repeated twice, making sure that
between each experiment the conical flask was washed
carefully. The results are shown in the table.*

COMMENT

The method is well written and detailed. Point 1 could have been
improved if she had said that the burette and pipette had been washed
with distilled water first and then the chemical to be used (burette –
acid; pipette – alkali).

Precision and accuracy. Some examples from the notebook are:

'25.00 cm³ of the potassium hydroxide solution'

The student has appreciated the accuracy a titration can achieve.

'making sure that there were no air bubbles in the jet of the burette'

An air bubble could easily lead to an inaccurate measurement.

'the acid was added drop by drop until the colour changed'

Again the student tried to get accuracy to within one drop (± 0.05 cm³).

2. PLANNING EXPERIMENTS AND METHODS

Learning objective: to devise and plan investigations, drawing on chemical knowledge and understanding in selecting appropriate techniques.

Questions to ask:

What do I already know about the area of chemistry I am investigating and how can I use this knowledge and understanding to help me with my plan?

✓ Think about what you have already learned and any investigations you have already done that are relevant to this investigation.

✓ List the factors that might affect the process you are investigating.

What is the best method or technique to use?

✓ Think about whether you can use or adapt a method that you have already used.

✓ A method, and the measuring instruments, must be able to produce **valid** measurements. A measurement is valid if it measures what it is supposed to be measuring.

You will make a decision as to which technique to use based on:

✓ The accuracy and precision of the results required.

REMEMBER

Investigators might require results that are as accurate and precise as possible but if you are doing a quick comparison, or a preliminary test to check a range over which results should be collected, a high level of accuracy and precision may not be required.

✓ The simplicity or difficulty of the techniques available, or the equipment required – is this expensive, for instance?

✓ The scale – for example use standard laboratory equipment or a microscale, which may give results in a shorter time period.

✓ The time available to do the investigation.

✓ Health and safety considerations.

What am I going to measure?

✓ The factor you are investigating that is changing is called the **independent variable**. A **dependent variable** is affected or changed by the independent variable that you select.

✓ You need to choose a range of measurements that will be wide enough to allow you to plot a graph of your results and so find out the pattern in your results.

✓ You might be asked to explain why you have chosen your range rather than a lower or higher range.

How am I going to control the other variables?

✓ These are **control variables**. Some of these may be difficult to control.

✓ You must decide how you are going to control any other variables in the investigation and so ensure that you are carrying out a fair test and that any conclusions you draw are valid.

✓ You may also need to decide on the concentration or combination of reactants.

What equipment is suitable and will give me the accuracy and precision I need?

✓ The **accuracy** of a measurement is how close it is to its true value.

✓ **Precision** is related to the smallest scale division on the measuring instrument that you are using – for example when measuring a distance, a rule marked in millimetres will give greater precision than one divided into centimetres only.

✓ A set of precise measurements also refers to measurements that have very little spread about the mean value.

✓ You need to be sensible about selecting your devices and make a judgement about the degree of precision. Think about what is the least precise variable you are measuring and choose suitable measuring devices. There is no point having instruments that are much more precise than the precision you can measure the variable to.

What are the potential hazards of the equipment, chemicals and technique I will be using and how can I reduce the risks associated with these hazards?

✓ In the exam, be prepared to suggest safety precautions when presented with details of a chemistry investigation.

EXAMPLE 3

You have been asked to design and plan an investigation to find out the effect of temperature on the rate of reaction between sodium thiosulfate and hydrochloric acid. In a previous investigation you have used this reaction so you are familiar with what happens and how the rate of the reaction can be measured.

What do I already know?

Previously you looked at the reaction between sodium thiosulfate and hydrochloric acid to investigate the effect of changing the concentration of sodium thiosulfate on the rate of the reaction. So you know that as the reaction takes place a precipitate of sulfur forms in the solution and makes the solution change from colourless (and clear) to pale yellow (and opaque). The time it takes for a certain amount of sulfur to form can be used as a measure of the rate of the reaction.

What is the best method or technique to use?

The technique you used in your previous investigation can be adapted. Previously you added 5 cm³ of hydrochloric acid to 50 cm³ of sodium thiosulfate solution in a conical flask, and then looked down the conical flask and measured the time that was taken until a mark on a piece of paper under the flask was no longer visible.

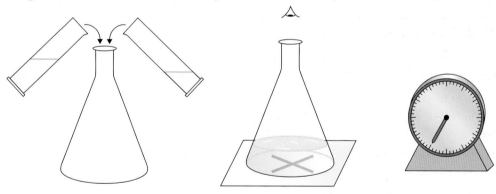

△ Fig. 5.2

What am I going to measure?

You are investigating the effect of temperature on the rate of the reaction. The independent variable is temperature. The time it takes for the mark to become obscured by the sulfur forming in the flask is a dependent variable as it depends on the temperature you select.

Other independent variables you could measure are the temperature of the sodium thiosulfate or the mixture once the acid has been added.

You will need to be able to measure a **range** of temperatures (for example 20 °C to 60 °C). Ideally you will need to repeat the experiment at about five different temperatures (for example 20, 30, 40, 50 and 60 °C).

How am I going to control the other variables?

It is important that you decide on the quantities of sodium thiosulfate and hydrochloric acid (the volumes) you are going to use and then keep these unchanged throughout. As you are familiar with the reaction, you can look back at your previous results and decide which concentrations or combination of reactants would be the most appropriate.

What equipment is suitable and will give me the accuracy and precision I need?

You now know what you will need to measure and so can decide on your measuring devices.

Measurement	Quantity	Device
Volume (sodium thiosulfate)	about 50 cm^3	100 cm^3 measuring cylinder
Volume (hydrochloric acid)	about 5 cm^3	10 cm^3 measuring cylinder
Temperature	20–60 °C	Thermometer (1 °C precision) or a thermostatically controlled water bath
Time	up to 120 s	Stopwatch or stopclock (1 s precision)

△ Table 5.1 Suitable equipment for experiment.

Choosing a burette accurate to 0.1 cm^3, a thermometer accurate to 0.1 °C or a stopclock accurate to 0.01 s would be inappropriate when the technique itself does not have a very precise way of judging when the mark has been obscured.

What are the potential hazards and how can I reduce the risks?

The hazards are as follows:

✓ Concentrated sodium thiosulfate solution: LOW HAZARD

✓ Dilute hydrochloric acid: LOW HAZARD

These indicate that there are no specific hazards you need to be aware of. However, you will be using an acid so it would be sensible to wear eye protection.

In terms of the equipment and technique, the major hazard will be handling the hot solution. You can limit this hazard by choosing a range of temperatures that do not include very high values (for example between room temperature and about 60 °C).

3. OBSERVING, MEASURING AND RECORDING

Learning objective: to make observations and measurements with appropriate precision, record these methodically and present them in a suitable form.

Questions to ask:

How many different measurements or observations do I need to take?

✓ Sufficient readings have been taken to ensure that the data are consistent.

✓ It is usual to repeat an experiment to get more than one measurement. If an investigator takes just one measurement, this may not be typical of what would normally happen when the experiment was carried out.

✓ When repeat readings are consistent they are said to be **repeatable**.

Do I need to repeat any measurements or observations that are anomalous?

✓ An **anomalous result** or **outlier** is a result that is not consistent with other results.

✓ You want to be sure a single result is accurate (as in Example 4). So you will need to repeat the experiment until you get close agreement in the results you obtain.

✓ If an investigator has made repeat measurements, they would normally use these to calculate the arithmetical mean (or just mean or average) of these data to give a more accurate result. You calculate the mean by adding together all the measurements, and dividing by the number of measurements. Be careful though – anomalous results should not be included when taking averages.

✓ Anomalous results might be the consequence of an error made in measurement. But sometimes outliers are genuine results. If you think an outlier has been introduced by careless practical work, you should omit it when calculating the mean. But you should examine possible reasons carefully before just leaving it out.

✓ You are taking a number of readings in order to see a changing pattern. For example, measuring the volume of gas produced in a reaction every 10 seconds for 2 minutes (so 12 different readings).

✓ It is likely that you will plot your results onto a graph and then draw a **line of best fit**.

✓ You can often pick an anomalous reading out from a results table (or a graph if all the data points have been plotted, as well as the mean, to show the range of data). It may be a good idea to repeat this part of the practical again, but it's not necessary if the results show good consistency.

✓ If you are confident that you can draw a line of best fit through most of the points, it is not necessary to repeat any measurements that are obviously inaccurate. If, however, the pattern is not clear enough to draw a line of best fit then readings will need to be repeated.

How should I record my measurements or observations – is a table the best way? What headings and units should I use?

✓ A table is often the best way to record results.

✓ Headings should be clear.

✓ If a table contains numerical data, do not forget to include units; data are meaningless without them.

✓ The units should be the same as those that are on the measuring equipment you are using.

✓ Sometimes you are recording observations that are not quantities, as shown in Example 6. Putting observations in a table with headings is a good way of presenting this information.

EXAMPLE 4

The student from Example 2 has recorded the results in a table as shown in Table 5.2. In this case she needs to get two results within 0.1 cm^3 of each other and so has had to do the titration three times to get that level of agreement.

Volume of potassium hydroxide solution = 25.00 cm^3

Burette reading	1st experiment	2nd experiment	3rd experiment
2nd reading (cm^3)	17.50	19.50	20.50
1st reading (cm^3)	0.00	2.50	3.50
Difference (cm^3)	17.50	17.00	17.00

△ Table 5.2 Readings from titration.

EXAMPLE 5

In an experiment to measure the volume of a gas produced in a reaction the student has sensibly recorded her results in Table 5.3. Notice each column has a heading *and* units.

Time (s)	Volume of gas (cm^3)
0	25
10	45
20	60
30	70
40	74
50	76
60	76

△ Table 5.3 Results of experiment.

EXAMPLE 6

In another experiment, the student has recorded his results obtained in an experiment involving heating magnesium in a crucible to form magnesium oxide.

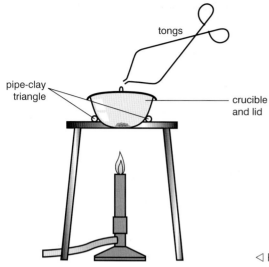

tongs

pipe-clay
triangle

crucible
and lid

◁ Fig. 5.3 Apparatus for the experiment.

Mass of crucible + lid (1)	= 23.00 g
Mass of crucible + lid + magnesium (2)	= 24.13 g
Mass of crucible + lid + magnesium oxide (3)	= 24.20 g
Mass of magnesium (2 − 1)	= 0.13 g
Mass of oxygen (3 − 2)	= 0.07 g

△ Table 5.4 Results of experiment.

COMMENT

In Table 5.4:

The description of each measurement is clear.

The units are given in each case.

EXAMPLE 7

In this example, a student has recorded his observations on mixing various metals with dilute hydrochloric acid in Table 5.5.

Metal	Observations on adding dilute hydrochloric acid
Copper	No reaction.
Iron	Slow effervescence and a colourless gas is produced, a pale green solution forms.
Lead	A few bubbles of gas form on the surface of the metal.
Magnesium	Rapid effervescence and a colourless gas is produced, a colourless solution forms. The magnesium disappears.
Zinc	Quite rapid effervescence and a colourless gas is produced. A colourless solution is formed.

△ Table 5.5 Presenting results in a table.

Terms such as 'effervescence' and 'solution' have been used correctly and chemical names have not been included. For example, although the colourless gas referred to is hydrogen you would not actually observe hydrogen – what you see is effervescence. When interpreting or explaining the observations you may identify this gas as hydrogen.

4. INTERPRETING OBSERVATIONS AND DATA

Learning objectives: to analyse and interpret data to draw conclusions from experimental activities which are consistent with the evidence, using chemical knowledge and understanding, and to communicate these findings using appropriate specialist vocabulary, relevant calculations and graphs.

Questions to ask:

What is the best way to show the pattern in my results? Should I use a bar chart, line graph or scatter graph?

✓ Graphs are usually the best way of demonstrating trends in data.

✓ A bar chart or bar graph is used when one of the variables is a **categoric variable**, for example when the melting points of the oxides of the Group II elements are shown for each oxide, the names are categoric and not continuous variables.

✓ A line graph is used when both variables are continuous, for example time and temperature, time and volume.

✓ Scattergraphs can be used to show the intensity of a relationship, or degree of **correlation**, between two variables.

✓ Sometimes a line of best fit is added to a scatter graph, but usually the points are left without a line.

When drawing bar charts or line graphs:

✓ Choose scales that take up most of the graph paper.

✓ Make sure the axes are linear and allow points to be plotted accurately. Each square on an axis should represent the same quantity. For example, one big square = 5 or 10 units; not 3 units.

✓ Label the axes with the variables (ideally with the independent variable on the x-axis).

✓ Make sure the axes have units.

✓ If more than one set of data is plotted use a key to distinguish the different data sets.

If I use a line graph should I join the points with a straight line or a smooth curve?

✓ When you draw a line, do not just join the dots!

✓ Remember there may be some points that don't fall on the curve – these may be incorrect or anomalous results.

✓ A graph will often make it obvious which results are anomalous and so it would not be necessary to repeat the experiment (see Example 8).

Do I have to calculate anything from my results?

✓ It is usual to calculate means from the data.

✓ Sometimes it is helpful to make other calculations before plotting a graph – for example you might calculate 1/time for a rate of reaction experiment.

✓ Sometimes you will have to do some calculations before you can draw any conclusions.

Can I draw a conclusion from my analysis of the results, and what chemical knowledge and understanding can be used to explain the conclusion?

✓ You need to use your chemical knowledge and understanding to explain your conclusion.

✓ It is important to be able to add some explanation which refers to relevant scientific ideas in order to justify your conclusion.

EXAMPLE 8

A student carried out an experiment to find out how the rate of a reaction changes during the reaction. She added some hydrochloric acid to marble chips and measured the volume of carbon dioxide produced in a gas syringe. She took a reading of the volume of gas in the syringe every 10 seconds for 1.5 minutes.

The apparatus she used and the results obtained are shown in Figs 5.4 and 5.5:

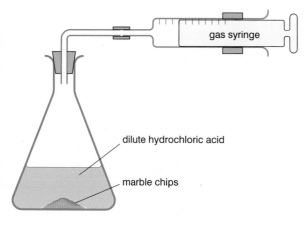

△ Fig. 5.4

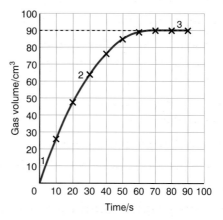

△ Fig. 5.5 Graph of experimental results.

What is the best way to show the pattern in my results?

In this experiment both the volume of gas and time are **continuous variables** and so a line graph is needed.

Straight line or a smooth curve?

With the results obtained in this experiment it is clear that a smooth curve is needed. Drawing a straight line of best fit would not be sensible.

Do I have to calculate anything from my results?

In this experiment the student had to find out how the rate of the reaction changed as the reaction proceeded. She could do this by looking at the change in steepness/gradient of the curve as the reaction proceeded and so she didn't need to do any separate calculations.

Can I draw a conclusion from my analysis of the results?

As the line is steeper at the beginning of the experiment than nearer the end the rate of the reaction decreases as the reaction proceeds.

COMMENT

This is a very clear statement. In addition, the student might have referred to 'the gradient of the line' at points 1, 2 and 3 to make her conclusion even more precise.

What chemical knowledge and understanding can be used to explain the conclusion?

As the reaction proceeds the reacting particles are converted into products. This means that there will be fewer reacting particles as time goes on, there will be fewer effective collisions and so the rate of the reaction will decrease.

COMMENT

This is a good conclusion because it makes direct links to scientific knowledge in relation to collision theory. Reference to 'effective collisions' also indicates a good level of precision. The student might also have mentioned that as the particles react, the concentration of the reactants decreases and with it the rate of the reaction.

5. EVALUATING METHODS

Learning objective: to evaluate data and methods.

Questions to ask:

Do any of my results stand out as being inaccurate or anomalous?

✓ You need to look for any anomalous results or outliers that do not fit the pattern.

✓ You can often pick this out from a results table (or a graph if all the data points have been plotted, as well as the mean, to show the range of data).

What reasons can I give for any inaccurate results?

✓ When answering questions like this it is important to be specific. Answers such as 'experimental error' will not score any marks.

✓ It is often possible to look at the practical technique and suggest explanations for anomalous results.

✓ When you carry out the experiment you will have a better idea of which possible sources of error are more likely.

✓ Try to give a specific source of error and avoid statements such as 'the measurements must have been wrong'.

Your conclusion will be based on your findings, but must take into consideration any uncertainty in these introduced by any possible sources of error. You should discuss where these have come from in your evaluation.

Error is a difference between a measurement you make and its true value.

The two types of errors are:

✓ random error

✓ systematic error.

With **random error**, measurements vary in an unpredictable way. This can occur when the instrument you're using lacks sufficient precision to indicate differences in readings. It can also occur when it's difficult to make a measurement.

With **systematic error**, readings vary in a controlled way. They're either consistently too high or too low. One reason could be down to the way you are making a reading – for example taking a burette reading at the wrong point on the meniscus, or not being directly in front of an instrument when reading from it.

What an investigator *should not* discuss in an evaluation are problems introduced by using faulty equipment, or by using the equipment inappropriately. These errors can be, or could have been, eliminated, by:

✓ checking equipment

✓ practising techniques before the investigation, and taking care and patience when carrying out the practical.

Overall was the method or technique I used precise enough?

✓ If your results were good enough to provide a confident answer to the problem you were investigating then the method was probably good enough.

✓ If you realise your results are not precise when you compare your conclusion with the actual answer it may be you have a **systematic error** (an error that has been made in obtaining all the results). A systematic error would indicate an overall problem with the experimental method.

✓ If your results do not show a convincing pattern then it is fair to assume that your method or technique was not precise enough and there may have been **random errors** (that is, measurements varying in an unpredictable way).

If I were to do the investigation again what would I change or improve upon?

✓ Having identified possible errors it is important to say how these could be overcome. Again you should try to be absolutely precise.

✓ When suggesting improvements, do not just say 'do it more accurately next time' or 'measure the volumes more accurately next time'.

✓ For example, if you were measuring small volumes, you could improve the method by using a burette to measure the volumes rather than a measuring cylinder.

EXAMPLE 9

A student was measuring the height of a precipitate produced in a test tube when different volumes of lead(II) nitrate solution were added to separate 15 cm³ samples of potassium iodide solution:

$$Pb(NO_3)_2(aq) + 2KI(aq) \rightarrow PbI_2(s) + 2KNO_3(aq)$$

Do any of my results stand out as being inaccurate or anomalous?

The student plotted her results on a graph. The inaccurate result stands out from the rest. Given the pattern obtained with the other results there is no real need to repeat the result – you could be very confident that the height should have been 3.0 cm. A result like this is referred to as an anomalous result. It was an error but not a systematic error.

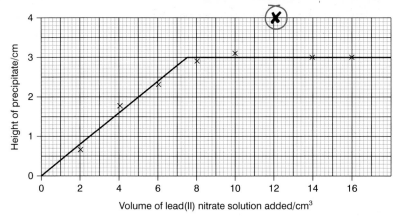

△ Fig. 5.6 Student's graph of experimental results.

What reasons can I give for any inaccurate results?

There are two main possible sources of error – either one of the volumes was measured incorrectly or the height of the precipitate was measured incorrectly.

Perhaps there was some air trapped in the precipitate and it didn't settle like the precipitates in the other tubes.

Was the method or technique I used precise enough?

You can be reasonably confident that 7.5 cm^3 of lead(II) nitrate solution reacted exactly with 15 cm^3 of potassium iodide solution (the point at which the height of precipitate reached its maximum value of 3.0 cm).

How can I improve the investigation?

For example, you could say, 'stir each precipitate to get rid of air bubbles and then let the precipitate settle'.

Periodic Table of elements

Group

Key

atomic number
atomic symbol
name
relative atomic mass

I	II												III	IV	V	VI	VII	VIII(0)
						1 **H** hydrogen 1												2 **He** helium 4
3 **Li** lithium 7	4 **Be** beryllium 9												5 **B** boron 11	6 **C** carbon 12	7 **N** nitrogen 14	8 **O** oxygen 16	9 **F** fluorine 19	10 **Ne** neon 20
11 **Na** sodium 23	12 **Mg** magnesium 24												13 **A** aluminium 27	14 **Si** silicon 28	15 **P** phosphorus 31	16 **S** sulfur 32	17 **C** chlorine 35.5	18 **Ar** argon 40
19 **K** potassium 39	20 **Ca** calcium 40	21 **Sc** scandium 45	22 **Ti** titanium 48	23 **V** vanadium 51	24 **Cr** chromium 52	25 **Mn** manganese 55	26 **Fe** iron 56	27 **Co** cobalt 59	28 **Ni** nickel 59	29 **Cu** copper 64	30 **Zn** zinc 65		31 **Ga** gallium 70	32 **Ge** germanium 73	33 **As** arsenic 75	34 **Se** selenium 79	35 **Br** bromine 80	36 **Kr** krypton 84
37 **Rb** rubidium 85	38 **Sr** strontium 88	39 **Y** yttrium 89	40 **Zr** zirconium 91	41 **Nb** niobium 93	42 **Mo** molybdenum 96	43 **Tc** technetium –	44 **Ru** ruthenium 101	45 **Rh** rhodium 103	46 **Pd** palladium 106	47 **Ag** silver 108	48 **Cd** cadmium 112		49 **Cd** indium 115	50 **Sn** tin 119	51 **Sb** antimony 122	52 **Te** tellurium 128	53 **I** iodine 127	54 **Xe** xenon 131
55 **Cs** caesium 133	56 **Ba** barium 137	57–71 lanthanides	72 **Hf** hafnium 178	73 **Ta** tantalum 181	74 **W** tungsten 184	75 **Re** rhenium 186	76 **Os** osmium 190	77 **Ir** iridium 192	78 **Pt** platinum 195	79 **Au** gold 197	80 **Hg** mercury 201		81 **Tl** thallium 204	82 **Pb** lead 207	83 **Bi** bismuth 209	84 **Po** polonium –	85 **At** astatine –	86 **Rn** radon –
87 **Fr** francium –	88 **Ra** radium –	89–103 actinides	104 **Rf** rutherfordium	105 **Db** dubnium	106 **Sg** seaborgium	107 **Bh** bohrium	108 **Hs** hassium	109 **Mt** meitnerium	110 **Ds** darmstadtium	111 **Rg** roentgenium	112 **Cn** copernicium			114 **Fl** flerovium –		116 **Lv** livermorium		

lanthanoids

57 **La** lanthanum 139	58 **Ce** cerium 140	59 **Pr** praseodymium 141	60 **Nd** neodymium 144	61 **Pm** promethium –	62 **Sm** samarium 150	63 **Eu** europium 152	64 **Gd** gadolinium 157	65 **Tb** terbium 159	66 **Dy** dysprosium 163	67 **Ho** holmium 165	68 **Er** erbium 167	69 **Tm** thulium 169	70 **Yb** ytterbium 173	71 **Lu** lutetium 175

actinoids

89 **Ac** actinium	90 **Th** thorium 232	91 **Pa** protactinium 231	92 **U** uranium 238	93 **Np** neptunium –	94 **Pu** plutonium –	95 **Am** americium –	96 **Cm** curium –	97 **Bk** berkelium –	98 **Cf** californium –	99 **Es** einsteinium –	100 **Fm** fermium –	101 **Md** mendelevium –	102 **No** nobelium –	103 **Lr** lawrencium –

The volume of one mole of any gas is 24 dm³ at room temperature and pressure (r.t.p.)

Glossary

A

acid A substance that contains replaceable hydrogen atoms which form H^+ ions when the acid is dissolved in water. It has a pH less than 7.

acid rain Rain water that contains dissolved acids, typically sulfuric acid and nitric acid.

acidic oxide The oxide of a non-metal.

activation energy The minimum energy that must be provided before a reaction can take place.

addition polymer A polymer that is made when molecules of a single monomer join together in large numbers.

addition reaction The reaction of an alkene and another element or compound to form a single compound.

alcohol A molecule with an OH group attached to a chain of carbon atoms.

alkali A base that is soluble in water, is a proton acceptor and produces OH^- ions. It has a pH greater than 7.

alkali metal A Group I element.

alkane A hydrocarbon in which the carbon atoms are bonded together by single bonds only.

alkene A hydrocarbon that contains a carbon-carbon double bond.

allotropes The different physical forms in which a pure element can exist.

alloy A mixture of a metal and one or more other elements.

amide The functional group in the polymer nylon (nylon is a polyamide).

amine An amine contains the functional group —NH_2 and this is the functional group present in one of the monomers that polymerises in the formation of nylon.

amphoteric oxide An oxide that reacts with both acids and alkalis to form salts.

anhydrous Literally means 'without water' – a compound, usually a salt, with no water of crystallisation.

anion A negatively charged ion, which moves to the anode during electrolysis.

anode A positively charged electrode in electrolysis.

atom The smallest particle of an element. Atoms are made of protons, electrons and neutrons.

atomic number see proton number.

Avogadro constant (or number) The number of particles in one mole of a substance. It is approximately 6.0×10^{23}.

Avogadro's law Equal volumes of all gases at the same temperature and pressure must contain the same number of molecules.

B

base Substance that neutralises an acid to produce a salt and water.

basic oxide The oxide of a metal.

boiling The change of state from liquid to gas.

boiling point The temperature of a boiling liquid – the highest temperature that the liquid can reach and the lowest temperature that the gas can reach.

C

calorimetry A method for determining energy changes in reactions or when substances are mixed together.

carbohydrates Organic compounds containing only carbon, hydrogen and oxygen atoms, usually with a hydrogen: oxygen ratio the same as in water (2:1).

carbon cycle The processes which add carbon dioxide to the atmosphere and the processes which remove carbon dioxide from the atmosphere.

carbonate A salt formed by the reaction of carbon dioxide with alkalis in solution.

carbonic acid An acid formed by the reaction of carbon dioxide with water.

catalyst A chemical that is added to speed up a reaction, but remains unchanged at the end.

cathode A negatively charged electrode in electrolysis.

cation A positive ion, which moves to the cathode during electrolysis.

cell A device for turning chemical energy into electrical energy.

chemical change A change that is not easily reversed because new substances are made.

chemical formula The combination of element symbols that represents a compound or molecule.

chemical reaction A chemical change that produces new substances and which is not usually easily reversed.

chemical symbol A unique symbol that represents a particular chemical element.

chromatogram A visible record (usually a coloured chart or graph) showing the separation of a mixture using chromatography.

chromatography The process for separating dissolved solids using a solvent and filter paper (in the school laboratory).

collision theory A theory used to explain differences in the rates of reactions as a result of the frequency and energy associated with the collisions between the reacting particles.

combustion The reaction that occurs when a substance (usually a fuel) burns in oxygen.

compound A pure substance formed when elements react together.

concentration Amount of chemical dissolved in 1 dm³ of solvent.

condensation The change of state from gas to liquid.

condensation polymer A polymer formed when two monomers react together and eliminate a small molecule such as water or hydrogen chloride.

conductor A material that will allow heat or electrical energy to pass through it.

contact process The process in which sulfuric acid is manufactured from sulfur dioxide and oxygen.

control variable Something that is fixed and is unchanged in an investigation.

covalent bond A bond that forms when electrons are shared between the atoms of two non-metals.

cracking Forming shorter alkanes and alkenes from longer alkanes using high temperatures and a catalyst.

D

decomposition Chemical change that breaks down one substance into two or more substances.

delocalised Electrons that are not attached to a particular atom (as in graphite or a metallic structure).

dependent variable A variable that changes as a result of changes made to the value of the independent variable.

desalination The separation of salt from seawater by evaporation of the water.

diatomic Two atoms combined together (for example in a molecule).

diffusion The random mixing and moving of particles in liquids and gases.

displacement reaction A reaction in which one element takes the place of another in a compound, removing (displacing) it from the compound.

dissociation The splitting of a molecule to form smaller molecules or, in the presence of water, ions.

distillation The process for separating a liquid from a solid (usually when the solid is dissolved in the liquid) or a liquid from a mixture of liquids.

ductile Describing a substance (such as a metal) that can be drawn or pulled into a wire.

E

effective collision A collision between particles with enough energy to cause a chemical reaction.

electrode The carbon or metal material that delivers electric charge in electrolysis reactions.

electrolysis The breaking down of a compound by passing an electric current through it.

electrolyte A substance that allows electric current to pass through it when it is molten or dissolved in water.

electron Negatively charged particle with a negligible mass that forms the outer part of all atoms.

electronic configuration The arrangement of electrons in an atom, molecule or ion.

element A substance that cannot be broken down into other substances by any chemical change.

endothermic A type of reaction in which energy is taken in from the surroundings.

enthalpy change (ΔH) The heat energy change when the reactants shown in a chemical equation react together.

enzyme A chemical that speeds up certain reactions in biological systems, such as digestive enzymes that speed up the chemical digestion of food.

evaporation When liquid changes to gas at a temperature lower than its boiling point.

exothermic A type of reaction in which energy is transferred out to the surroundings.

F

fats Organic compounds that contain an ester functional group.

fermentation The process by which ethanol is made from a solution of sugar and yeast.

filtrate The clear solution produced by filtering a mixture.

fossil fuel Fuel made from the remains of decayed animal and plant matter compressed over millions of years.

fraction A collection of hydrocarbons that have similar molecular masses and boil at similar temperatures.

fractional distillation A process for separating liquids with different boiling points.

freezing Changing a liquid to a solid.

freezing point The temperature at which a liquid changes to a solid.

functional group A part of an organic molecule which is responsible for the characteristic reactions of the molecule.

G

galvanising The process of coating a metal (usually iron) with zinc.

gas The state of matter in which the substance has no volume or shape.

global warming The rise in the average temperature of the Earth's atmosphere and oceans.

greenhouse effect The trapping of long-wave radiation emitted from the Earth's surface by gases in the atmosphere.

greenhouse gas A gas that can trap long-wave radiation emitted from the Earth's surface.

group A vertical column of elements in the Periodic Table.

H

Haber process The process in which ammonia is manufactured from nitrogen and hydrogen.

halogens The Group VII elements (F, Cl, Br, I, At).

homologous series A group of organic compounds with the same general formula, similar chemical properties and physical properties that change gradually from one member of the series to the next.

hydrated Literally means 'containing water' – hydrated salts contain water of crystallisation.

hydrocarbon A compound containing only hydrogen atoms and carbon atoms.

hydrolysis Breaking down a compound using its reaction with water or steam.

I

independent variable A variable that is deliberately changed in an investigation and, as a result, causes changes to the dependent variable.

indicator A substance that changes colour in either an acid or an alkali and so can be used to identify acids or alkalis.

inert electrode An inert electrode is an electrode that will not react when placed in an electrolyte.

insoluble Does not dissolve in water.

intermolecular force The force of attraction or repulsion between molecules.

intramolecular bond A bond within a molecule.

ion A charged atom or molecule.

ionic bond A bond that involves the transfer of electrons to produce electrically charged ions.

ionic compound A compound formed by the reaction between a metal and one or more non-metals.

ionic equation A chemical equation showing how the ions involved react together.

isomers Compounds that have the same molecular formula but different structures.

isotope Atoms of the same element that contain different numbers of neutrons. Isotopes have the same atomic number but different mass numbers.

L

liquid The state of matter in which a substance has a fixed volume but no definite shape.

litmus An indicator that has different colours in acids (red) and alkalis (blue).

M

malleability The measure of how easily a substance can be beaten into sheets.

mass number The number of protons and neutrons in an atom (also known as the nucleon number).

melting Changing a solid into a liquid at its melting point.

melting point The temperature at which a solid changes to a liquid.

metal An element with particular properties (usually hard, shiny and a good conductor of heat and electricity).

metalloid An element that has properties characteristic of both metals and non-metals.

mineral A solid inorganic substance that occurs naturally.

mixture Two or more substances combined without a chemical reaction – they can be separated easily.

mole The amount of a substance containing approximately 6×10^{23} particles (atoms, molecules, ions).

molecule A group of two or more atoms covalently bonded together.

monatomic An element composed of separate atoms.

monomer Small molecules that can be joined in a chain to make a polymer.

N

neutralisation A reaction in which an acid reacts with a base or alkali to form a salt and water.

neutron Particle in the nucleus of atoms that has mass but no charge.

nitrogen cycle The processes by which nitrogen is converted between its various chemical forms – the element, nitrogen oxides, nitrates and ammonium compounds.

nitrogen fixation The process by which nitrogen in the atmosphere is converted into ammonia and ammonium compounds.

noble gas Group 0 elements (He, Ne, Ar, Kr, Xe, Rn). They have full outer electron shells.

non-metal An element with particular properties (usually a gas or soft solid and a poor conductor of heat and electricity).

non-renewable A fuel that cannot be made again in a short time span.

nucleus, atomic The tiny centre of an atom, typically made up of protons and neutrons.

nucleon number (mass number) The total number of protons and neutrons in an atom.

O

ore A mineral from which a metal may be extracted.

organic chemistry The study of covalent compounds of carbon.

organic molecules Carbon-based molecules.

oxidation state The degree of oxidation of an element.

oxidation The addition of oxygen in a chemical reaction. Electrons are lost.

oxide A product of the reaction of oxygen with another element. For example, oxygen reacts with copper to produce copper oxide.

oxidising agent A substance that will oxidise another substance.

P

particle theory The theory describing the movement of particles in solids, liquids and gases.

period A row in the Periodic Table, from an alkali metal to a noble gas.

Periodic Table The modern arrangement of the chemical elements in groups and periods.

periodicity The gradual change in properties of the elements across each row (period) of the Periodic Table.

pH scale A scale measuring the acidity (lower than 7) or alkalinity (higher than 7) of a solution. It is a measure of the concentration of hydrogen ions in a solution.

photosynthesis A reaction that plants carry out to make food.

physical change A change in a substance that is easily reversed and does not involve the making of new chemical bonds.

plastic A synthetic material made from a wide range of organic polymers.

polymer A large molecule made up of linked smaller molecules (monomers). Polythene is a polymer made from ethene.

polymerisation Making polymers from monomers.

precipitation A reaction in which an insoluble salt is formed by mixing two solutions.

products The substances that are produced in a reaction.

proteins Organic compounds (polymers) made from amino acids (monomers).

proton Positively charged particles in the nucleus of atoms.

proton number (atomic number) The number of protons in an atom.

R

radical An element, molecule or ion that is highly reactive.

radioactive A substance that emits radiation (alpha or beta particles or gamma rays).

rate of reaction How fast a reaction goes in a given interval of time.

reactants The substances taking part in a chemical reaction. They change into the products.

reactivity series A list of elements showing their relative reactivities. More reactive elements will displace less reactive ones from their compounds.

redox A reaction involving both oxidation and reduction.

reducing agent A substance that will reduce another substance.

reduction When a substance loses oxygen – electrons are gained.

relative atomic mass (A_r) A number comparing the mass of one mole of atoms of a particular element with the mass of one mole of atoms of other elements. C has the value 12.

relative formula mass (M_r) The sum of the relative atomic masses of each of the atoms or ions in one formula unit of a substance.

relative molecular mass (M_r) The sum of the relative atomic masses of the atoms in a molecule.

renewable energy Energy from a source that will not run out, such as wind, water or solar energy.

retention factor (R_f) The distance travelled by a substance in a chromatography experiment (through the stationary phase) compared to the distance travelled by the solvent in the same time (expressed as a number between 0 and 1).

reversible reaction A reaction in which reactants form products and products form reactants.

rusting The chemical reaction in which iron is oxidised to iron(III) oxide in the presence of air (oxygen) and water.

S

sacrificial protection Covering a metal, or ensuring contact, with another metal so that the more reactive metal corrodes instead of the less reactive metal.

salt A compound formed when the replaceable hydrogen atom(s) of an acid is (are) replaced by a metal.

saturated Describes an organic compound that contains only single bonds (C–C).

shell A grouping of electrons around a nucleus. The first shell in an atom can hold up to 2 electrons, the next can hold up to 8.

soap A cleaning agent made from fats or oils using sodium hydroxide.

solid The state of matter in which a substance has a fixed volume and a definite shape.

soluble A substance that dissolves in a solvent to form a solution.

solute A substance that dissolves in a solvent producing a solution.

solution This is formed when a substance dissolves in a liquid. Aqueous solutions are formed when the solvent used is water.

solvent The liquid in which solutes are dissolved.

spectator ions Ions that play no part and are unchanged in a chemical reaction.

state symbols These denote whether a substance is a solid (s), liquid (l), gas (g) or is dissolved in aqueous solution (aq).

surface area The total area of the outside of an object.

T

thermal decomposition The breaking down of a compound by heat.

titration An accurate method for calculating the concentration of an acid or alkali solution in a neutralisation reaction.

transition metal Elements found between Groups II and III in the Periodic Table. Often used as catalysts and often make compounds that have coloured solutions.

U

universal indicator Indicating solution that turns a specific colour at each pH value.

unsaturated Describes carbon compounds that contain carbon-to-carbon double bonds.

V

valency electrons The outermost electrons of an atom that are involved when the atom reacts with other atoms or compounds.

vapour Another term for gas.

variable A factor that either can be changed in an investigation or changes as a result of other factors changing.

viscous The description of a liquid which does not flow very easily (for example, does not flow as readily as water).

volatile Easily turns to a gas.

W

water cycle The processes that cause the movement of water between the Earth's surface and the atmosphere.

water of crystallisation Water that occurs in crystals.

Y

yield The amount of substance produced in a chemical reaction.

Answers

The answers given in this section have been written by the author and are not taken from examination mark schemes.

SECTION 1 PRINCIPLES OF CHEMISTRY

The particulate nature of matter

Page 13

1. (l)
2. Only the solid state has a fixed shape.
3. Fine sand will pour or flow like a liquid; it takes the shape of the container it is poured into (although under a microscope you would see gaps at the surface of the container).

Page 17

1. The particles in a solid vibrate about a fixed point.
2. The particles are held together the most strongly in solid water (ice).
3. Evaporation is the process that occurs when faster moving particles in a liquid escape from the liquid surface.
4. Melting point is the name of the temperature at which a solid changes into a liquid.

Page 20

1. Diffusion is the mixing and moving of particles in liquids and gases.
2. The particles in the potassium manganate(VII) dissolve in the water and diffuse throughout the solution.
3. The particles of perfume vapour/gas diffuse in the air and spread throughout the whole room.
4. All elements contain atoms.

Experimental techniques

Page 26–27

1. A baseline drawn in pencil will not dissolve in the solvent.
2. If the solvent were above the baseline the substances would just dissolve and form a solution in the beaker.
3. The dye may be insoluble in the solvent.
4. The boiling point will be higher than that of pure water/above 100 $^\circ$C at normal pressure.
5. $R_f = 1.7/10 = 0.17$

Page 29

1. A solvent is a liquid that will dissolve a substance (solute).
2. If a substance is soluble in a solvent it dissolves in that solvent.
3. Distillation.
4. Boiling points.

Atoms, elements and compounds

Page 35

1. In a physical change no new substances are made. In a chemical change at least one new substance is made.
2. In a compound the elements are chemically combined together. In a mixture the elements or components are not chemically combined together.
3. A malleable substance can be beaten or hammered into shape.
4. a) An alloy is a mixture of a metal and one or more other elements.

   b) Brass is made up of copper and zinc.

Page 38

1. The electron has the smallest relative mass.

2. Atoms are neutral. The number of positive charges (protons) must equal the number of negative charges (electrons).

3. a) The nucleon number is 27.

  b) 14 neutrons.

Page 39

1. Isotopes are atoms of the same element with different numbers of neutrons.

Page 43

1. a) Magnesium has two electrons in its outer electron shell.

  b) It is in Group II.

2. a) Aluminium

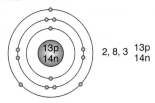

$2, 8, 3$ $\begin{smallmatrix}13p\\14n\end{smallmatrix}$

  b) Calcium

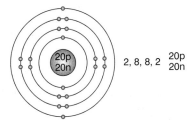

$2, 8, 8, 2$ $\begin{smallmatrix}20p\\20n\end{smallmatrix}$

3. The noble gases have full outer electron shells or have eight electrons in their outer electron shells and so do not easily lose or gain electrons.

Page 45

1.

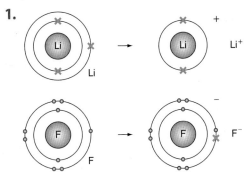

2.

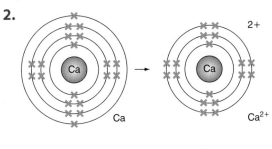

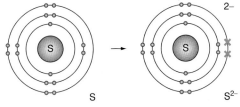

3. Both phosphorus and oxygen are non-metals. (A metal is needed to form an ionic bond.)

Page 48

1. The ions are held together strongly in a giant lattice structure. The ions can vibrate but cannot move around.

2. Sodium chloride is made up of singly charged ions, Na^+ and Cl^-, whereas the magnesium ion in magnesium oxide has a double charge, Mg^{2+}. The higher the charge on the positive ion, the stronger the attractive forces between the positive ion and the negative ion.

Page 51

1.

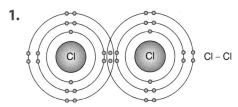

2.

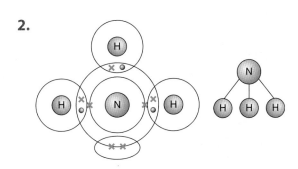

ANSWERS

328

3.

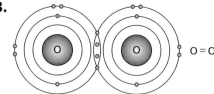

O = O

4.

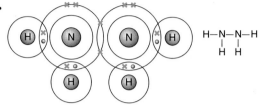

H—N—N—H
   | |
   H H

Page 53

1. The intermolecular forces of attraction between the molecules are weak.

2. No. There are no ions or delocalised electrons present.

Page 56

1. Each carbon atom is strongly covalently bonded to four other atoms forming a very strong giant lattice structure. A very high temperature is needed to break down the structure.

2. In graphite each carbon atom is strongly covalently bonded to three other carbon atoms. The remaining outer shell carbon electron is delocalised and so can move along between the layers formed by the covalently bonded carbon atoms.

Stoichiometry

Page 66

1. **a)** KBr

  b) CaO

  c) $AlCl_3$

  d) CH_4

2. **a)** $Cu(NO_3)_2$

  b) $Al(OH)_3$

  c) $(NH_4)_2SO_4$

  d) $Fe_2(CO_3)_3$

3. **a)** $ZnCl_2$

  b) Cr_2O_3

  c) $Fe(OH)_2$

Page 70

1. **a)** $2Ca(s) + O_2(g) \rightarrow 2CaO(s)$

  b) $2H_2S(g) + 3O_2(g) \rightarrow 2SO_2(g) + 2H_2O(l)$

  c) $2Pb(NO_3)_2(s) \rightarrow 2PbO(s) + 4NO_2(g) + O_2(g)$

2. **a)** $S(s) + O_2(g) \rightarrow SO_2(g)$

  b) $2Mg(s) + O_2(g) \rightarrow 2MgO(s)$

  c) $CuO(s) + H_2(g) \rightarrow Cu(s) + H_2O(l)$

Page 71

1. **a)** $2C_5H_{10}(g) + 15O_2(g) \rightarrow 10CO_2(g) + 10H_2O(l)$

  b) $Fe_2O_3(s) + 3CO(g) \rightarrow 2Fe(s) + 3CO_2(g)$

  c) $2KMnO_4(s) + 16HCl(aq) \rightarrow 2KCl(s) + 2MnCl_2(s) + 8H_2O(l) + 5Cl_2(g)$

Page 74

1. 16

2. 46

3. 48

Page 78

1. **a)** To allow oxygen from the air into the crucible.

  b) To limit the loss of magnesium oxide.

  c) White.

Page 79

1. Fe_2O_3

2. ZnO

Page 85

1. 28 g

2. **a)** 2 moles

  b) 0.01 mole

  c) 0.25 mole

Page 86

1. **a)** 2 moles
   b) 0.5 mole
   c) 0.1 mole
2. **a)** 0.5 mole
   b) 0.1 mole
   c) 2 moles

SECTION 2 PHYSICAL CHEMISTRY

Electricity and chemistry

Page 96

1. The breaking down (decomposition) of an ionic compound by the use of electricity.
2. The positive electrode is the anode.
3. The substance must contain ions and they must be free to move (in molten/liquid state or dissolved in water).

Page 103

1. **a)** An inert electrode is an unreactive electrode; it will not be changed during electrolysis.
   b) Carbon is commonly used as an inert electrode (platinum is another inert electrode).
2. **a)** Lead and chlorine.
   b) Magnesium and oxygen.
   c) Aluminium and oxygen.
3. **a)** Hydrogen (sodium is above hydrogen in the reactivity series).
   b) Hydrogen (zinc is above hydrogen in the reactivity series).
   c) Silver (silver is below hydrogen in the reactivity series).
4. **a)** $2O^{2-} \rightarrow O_2 + 4e^-$
   b) The change takes place at the anode.

Page 105

1. **a)** Diagram as in Fig. 2.11.
   b) At the cathode: $Cu^{2+}(aq) + 2e^- \rightarrow Cu(s)$
   At the anode: $Cu(s) \rightarrow Cu^{2+}(aq) + 2e^-$

Page 107

1. **a)** Cryolite is added to lower the melting point of the electrolyte and so reduce energy costs.
   b) Aluminium forms at the cathode.
   c) $Al^{3+}(l) + 3e^- \rightarrow Al(s)$
   d) The aluminium ions are reduced because they gain electrons.
   e) The oxygen oxidises the carbon anodes forming carbon dioxide.
2. High strength-to-weight ratio, low density and resistance to corrosion are all reasons for choosing aluminium for the construction of an aeroplane.

Page 110

1. **a)** Na^+, Cl^-, H^+, OH^- are ions present in sodium chloride solution.
   b) Na^+ and H^+ ions will be attracted to the cathode. The reactivity of the metal compared to hydrogen will determine which ion is discharged. As hydrogen is less reactive than sodium, hydrogen will be discharged.
   c) $2H^+(aq) + 2e^- \rightarrow H_2(g)$
2. Sodium hydroxide is used in the manufacture of soap, bleach and paper.

Energy changes in chemical reactions

Page 115

1. A reaction that releases heat energy to the surroundings.
2. A reaction that absorbs energy from the surrounding heat energy.
3. Polystyrene is a very good insulator and so very little energy is transferred to the surroundings.

Page 116

1. The reaction is endothermic.
2. The activation energy.
3. a)

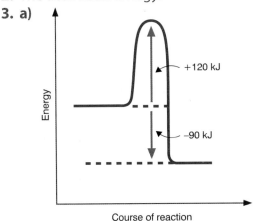

Reaction A

b)

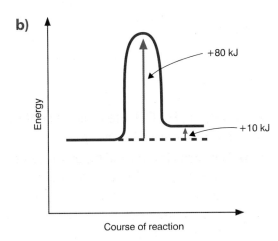

Reaction B

Page 120

1. The sign indicates whether the reaction is exothermic (negative sign) or endothermic (positive sign).
2. Energy is needed to break bonds.
3. In an endothermic reaction more energy is needed to break bonds than is recovered on forming bonds.

Chemical reactions

Page 125

1. The particles must collide; there must be sufficient energy in the collision (to break bonds).
2. An effective collision is one which results in a chemical reaction between the colliding particles.
3. Student's diagram like Fig 2.28. It is an energy barrier. Only collisions that have enough energy to overcome this barrier will lead to a reaction.

Page 128

1. A gas syringe will measure the volume of gas produced accurately.
2. No gas is being produced – the reaction hasn't started or it is finished.
3. The quicker reaction will have the steeper gradient.

Page 132

1. The units of concentration for solutions are mol/dm^3.
2. The particles are closer together and there are more of them, so there will be more (effective) collisions per second.
3. Increasing the temperature means the particles have more (kinetic) energy. So more of the collisions will have energy greater than or equal to the activation energy and there will be more effective/successful collisions per second.

Page 135

1. A catalyst is a substance that changes the rate of a chemical reaction.
2. A biological catalyst is called an enzyme.

Page 140

1. Reduction is the loss of oxygen or the gain of electrons.
2. a) +2
   b) +3
   c) +7
3. Reduced, as it has gained an electron.
4. Oxidised, as it has lost electrons.

Acids, bases and salts

Page 149

1. Both solutions are alkalis. Solution A is weakly alkaline whereas solution B is strongly alkaline.
2. The solution is acidic.
3. Calcium is a metal. The oxides (and hydroxides) of metals are bases.

Page 152

1. Potassium oxide is a basic oxide. Potassium is a metal and most metal oxides are basic.
2. A basic oxide reacts with acids and not alkalis. An amphoteric oxide reacts with both acids and alkalis (to form salts).

Page 156

1. A salt is formed when a replaceable hydrogen of an acid is replaced by a metal.
2. Sulfuric acid.
3. Potassium chloride will be soluble in water (as are all potassium salts).
4. Calcium nitrate.
5. Neutralisation is the reaction between an acid and an alkali or base to form a salt and water.
6. $H^+(aq)$
7. $OH^-(aq)$

Page 157

1. Precipitation is the formation of an insoluble salt as a result of a chemical reaction taking place in aqueous solution.
2. Filtration.
3. Washing with cold water will remove traces of any remaining soluble salts.

Page 162

1. a) A white precipitate, which does not dissolve in excess sodium hydroxide solution.
   b) A white precipitate, which does dissolve in excess sodium hydroxide solution, would be observed.
2. Add sodium hydroxide solution. Fe^{2+} produces a green precipitate; Fe^{3+} produces a reddish-brown precipitate.

Page 165–166

1. Add dilute sodium hydroxide and heat. An alkaline gas (turns red litmus paper blue) indicates the presence of an ammonium compound.
2. a) Carbon dioxide.
   b) Bubble the gas through limewater. A white precipitate forms.
3. The Fe^{3+} ion is present in solution X.
4. The Cl^- ion is present in solution Y.
5. a)

Name of cation	Colour of precipitate
Zinc/lead	white
Magnesium/ calcium	white
Copper(II)	blue
Iron(II)	green/turns brown slowly
Iron(III)	rust brown/orange

b) $Ag^+(aq) + X^-(aq) \rightarrow AgX(s)$ where X^- is Cl^-, Br^-, I^-.

c) HCl is added to remove any carbonate ions that may be present.

6. Plan needs to check for testing of both anion and cation for each sample and should include practical instructions.

Blue compound

- Test for copper(II) – sodium hydroxide: result blue precipitate
  $Cu^{2+}(aq) + 2OH^-(aq) \rightarrow Cu(OH)_2(s)$

- Test for sulfate – hydrochloric acid/ barium chloride: result white precipitate
  $Ba^{2+}(aq) + SO_4^{2-}(aq) \rightarrow BaSO_4(s)$

White compound

- Flame test for Na^+ – yellow

- Test for carbonate – add dilute acid – effervescence/carbon dioxide evolved – turns limewater milky
  $CO_3^{2-}(s) + 2H^+(aq) \rightarrow H_2O(l) + CO_2(g)$

Page 167

1. Ammonia
2. Oxygen
3. Chlorine

SECTION 3 INORGANIC CHEMISTRY

The Periodic Table

Page 176–177

1. a) 20

   b) The proton number is the number of protons (which equals the number of electrons) in an atom of the element. Calcium atoms have 20 protons and 20 electrons.

   c) Group II.

   d) Period 4.

   e) Calcium is a metal.

2. The halogens.

3. The halogens are non-metals.

Page 178

1. Aluminium has three electrons in the outer shell.

2. Oxygen will form an O^{2-} ion (the oxide ion) with a 2– charge.

3. Fluorine (F)

4. Barium (Ba)

Page 180

1. They react with water to form alkaline solutions.

2. They have one electron in the outer shell.

3. They are soft to cut (also have very low melting points).

4. Rubidium will have a lower melting point.

5. The potassium atom is larger than the lithium atom so the outer electron is further from the attraction of the nucleus and can be more easily removed.

Page 182

1. Sodium oxide is white.

2. Hydrogen. The solution formed is potassium hydroxide.

3. The compounds are soluble.

4. a) A group is a vertical column of elements having similar chemical properties because of their outer shell electronic structure.

   b) Lithium, sodium, potassium

   c) All the elements in Group I have one electron in the outer shell.

   d) The reactivity of these elements depends on the ease with which the outer electron is lost. One electron can easily be lost to form positive ions. The ease with which it can be lost increases down the group because the electron is less tightly held in the atom and therefore reactivity increases down the group.

1. Seven electrons in the outer shell.

2. The atoms need to gain only one electron to achieve a full outer shell.

3. Chlorine molecules are made up of two atoms combined/bonded together, Cl_2.

4. Solid. The trend down the group is gas, liquid, solid.

5. A displacement reaction involves one Group VII element being reduced (gaining electrons) and one being oxidised (losing electrons).

6. They involve both oxidation and reduction.

Pages 188–189

1. Chlorine kills any bacteria that might be present in the water.

2. Iodine.

3. The non-stick surfaces on pans/frying pans.

4. **a)**

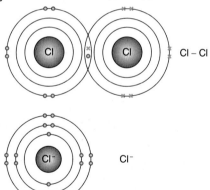

Cl – Cl

Cl^-

b) $2Cl^-(aq) \rightarrow Cl_2(g) + 2e^-$. The chloride ions lose electrons.

c) $2NaOH(aq) + Cl_2(g) \rightarrow NaCl(aq) + NaClO(aq) + H_2O(l)$

d) Chlorine is a more reactive halogen than bromine. Chlorine will displace bromine from a solution of bromide ions. (Chlorine will oxidise bromide ions to bromine.)

Observations: chlorine water is pale green. When this is added to a colourless solution of potassium bromide the resulting solution will turn orange due to the presence of bromine.

5. **a)** The reactivity of fluorine is due to its electronic structure 2,7. Fluorine needs to gain only one electron to form a fluoride ion. This is very easy because of its small size and large attractive force of the nucleus.

b) $F_2 + 2e^- \rightarrow 2F^-$

c) Both chlorine and iodine are less reactive than fluorine. Fluorine could only be displaced from fluoride ions by a more reactive halogen. As there are no halogens that are more reactive than fluorine, fluorine will not be displaced from fluoride ions.

Page 192

1. No. Copper is very unreactive – it is below hydrogen in the reactivity series.

2. The number indicates the oxidation state of the chromium.

3. **a)** $FeSO_4(aq) + 2NaOH(aq) \rightarrow Fe(OH)_2(s) + Na_2SO_4(aq)$

b) Green

Metals

Page 202

1. A ductile metal can be drawn into wires.

2. A malleable metal can be hammered into shape.

3. An alloy is a mixture of a metal with one or more other elements.

4. Cupronickel is used for making coins.

5. The element added in the alloy disrupts the rows of aluminium atoms making them less likely to slide over each other when under strain.

1. No. Copper is below hydrogen in the reactivity series.
2. $2K(s) + 2H_2O(l) \rightarrow 2KOH(aq) + H_2(g)$
3. No. Carbon is below magnesium in the reactivity series.
4. $Mg(s) + PbO(s) \rightarrow MgO(s) + Pb(s)$

1. Iron ore, coke and limestone.
2. Iron(III) oxide.
3. Carbon dioxide, carbon monoxide, nitrogen (from the air).
4. $2Fe_2O_3(s) + 3C(s) \rightarrow 4Fe(s) + 3CO_2(g)$
5. a) An alloy is a mixture of a metal and another element.
   b) The proportion of carbon is decreased by heating the blast furnace iron in oxygen.
   c) The blast furnace iron is brittle – steel is more flexible and more resistant to corrosion.
6. a) $2Al(s) + Fe_2O_3(s) \rightarrow 2Fe(s) + Al_2O_3(s)$
   b) Aluminium is higher in the reactivity series than iron, therefore it is more reactive. Aluminium is able to displace the less reactive iron from its oxide and so form iron and aluminium oxide.
   c) Any metal that is higher than iron in the reactivity series can be selected theoretically. The higher the metal in the series, the more reactive the metal and the more reactive the reaction will be. If the chosen metal is above aluminium, the reaction is more reactive. In practice this is not feasible.
   d) Aluminium is displacing iron in iron(III) oxide and becoming aluminium oxide by losing electrons. Iron(III) oxide is gaining electrons to become iron metal.

Redox is when oxidation and reduction occur. Aluminium is losing electrons (oxidation). Iron(III) oxide is gaining electrons (reduction).

7. a) Oxygen + water
   b) Chromium protects iron from oxygen and water/used because it is shiny – good decorative effect.
   c) Aluminium forms a thin layer of aluminium oxide, which acts as a protective layer – so it does not react with the air.

1. Air (oxygen) and water must be present.
2. The grease can be easily removed or wiped away.
3. a) Galvanising involves coating iron or steel with zinc.
   b) Because zinc is more reactive than iron, moist air will react with zinc in preference to the iron.

Air and water

1. Anhydrous means without water (water of crystallisation).
2. Cobalt(II) chloride will change from blue to pink.
3. a) The first filter is coarse gravel. The second filter is fine sand.
   b) Chlorine is used to kill bacteria.
4. a) Nitrogen is 78%.
   b) Carbon dioxide is 0.04%.
5. In the Haber process the temperature is 450 °C and the pressure is 200 atmospheres.

1. A major source of carbon monoxide is the incomplete combustion of fuels, such as in a car's engine.

2. a) Sulfur dioxide and nitrogen oxide(s) are gases that cause acid rain.

   b) Sulfur dioxide forms sulfuric acid; nitrogen oxide forms nitric acid.

   c) Environmental problems include: harming plants and fish in lakes, damaging buildings made of metal, marble or limestone.

3. a) $N_2(g) + O_2(g) \rightarrow 2NO(g)$

   b) The nitrogen monoxide is converted back into nitrogen and oxygen.

1. In a limited supply of air, carbon will form carbon monoxide.

2. a) copper(II) carbonate + sulfuric acid → copper(II) sulfate + carbon dioxide + water

   b) $CuCO_3(s) + H_2SO_4(aq) \rightarrow CuSO_4(aq) + CO_2(g) + H_2O(l)$

3. a) calcium carbonate → calcium oxide + carbon dioxide

   b) $CaCO_3(s) \rightarrow CaO(s) + CO_2(g)$

4. Rust is iron(III) oxide/hydrated iron(III) oxide.

5. Covering in grease, painting, plastic coating, coating with a metal will all stop air and water getting into contact with iron.

6. Galvanising involves coating iron with zinc.

7. Zinc is more reactive than iron. Air (oxygen) will therefore react with zinc in preference to iron.

Sulfur

1. A higher temperature is used to give a suitable rate of reaction.

2. The catalyst is vanadium(V) oxide.

3. Increasing the pressure would be uneconomical because the yield is already very high at 98%.

4. Sulfuric acid reacts with ammonia to produce ammonium sulfate:

$$2NH_3(aq) + H_2SO_4(aq) \rightarrow (NH_4)_2SO_4(aq)$$

SECTION 4 ORGANIC CHEMISTRY

Organic chemistry

1. The supplies of petroleum are limited – it takes millions of years for crude oil to be formed.

2. Natural gas or methane. It is trapped in pockets above the oil.

3. Short chain of carbon atoms.

4. Long chain of carbon atoms.

5. These fractions readily form a vapour.

1. Ethene is a member of the alkene homologous series.

2. The fractional distillation of crude oil produces a high proportion of long-chain hydrocarbons, which are not as useful as short-chain hydrocarbons. Cracking converts the long-chain hydrocarbons into more useful shorter chain hydrocarbons.

3. The conditions required for cracking oil fractions are a temperature of between 600 and 700 °C and a catalyst of silica or alumina.

Page 256

1. a) A compound that has no C=C double bonds.

b) A compound containing hydrogen atoms and carbon atoms only.

2. a) $C_{15}H_{32}$

b) Carbon dioxide and water.

Page 257

1. The fuel will burn with a yellow (rather than blue) flame.

2. Carbon and carbon monoxide.

3. It combines with haemoglobin to form carboxyhaemoglobin, which prevents the haemoglobin from combining with oxygen.

4. Wind, wave, solar and nuclear power are alternative ways of generating energy.

Page 259

1. It contains at least one C=C double bond.

2. The manufacture of polymers (polyethene).

Pages 260–261

1. a) Saturated compounds contain only covalent single bonds. Alkanes contain only carbon–carbon and carbon–hydrogen single bonds and are therefore saturated hydrocarbons. Alkenes contain a C=C double bond and are therefore unsaturated.

b) Alkane: C_6H_{14}, alkene C_6H_{12}. The position of the double bond can be between any pair of carbon atoms, but there should be one fewer hydrogen attached to each of the double-bonded carbons.

2. a) Fuels are substances that provide heat energy. Alkanes burn readily in air combining with oxygen to produce carbon dioxide and water vapour and large quantities of heat.

b) Incomplete combustion leads to the formation of carbon monoxide instead of carbon dioxide. It is a very poisonous gas and is particularly dangerous because it has no odour and causes drowsiness. Carbon monoxide is poisonous because it reacts with the haemoglobin in the blood, forming 'carboxyhaemoglobin'. The haemoglobin is no longer available to carry oxygen to the body and death results from oxygen starvation.

c) Short-chain hydrocarbons are more likely to form carbon dioxide and water as their main products because there is less carbon per molecule in these hydrocarbons to react with the available oxygen. Long-chain hydrocarbons often burn with a smoky flame and leave black carbon deposits because there is insufficient oxygen to form carbon dioxide, with the many carbons in the longer chains. Carbon monoxide is also formed.

Page 263

1. C_4H_9OH

2. It is a relatively 'clean' fuel and releases only carbon dioxide and water into the atmosphere. (It does not release sulfur dioxide and nitrogen oxides, as petrol does when it burns.)

3. A solvent is a liquid that dissolves other substances (solutes) to form solutions.

Page 264

1. Fermentation is the process in which ethanol is made from sugar, yeast and water.

2. The optimum temperature is in the range 25 to 30 °C.

3. The yeast contains enzymes, which increase the rate of the reaction.

4. The fractional distillation separates the ethanol from the water.

Page 269

1. The individual beads are like monomer molecules. The string of beads is like a polymer made by joining together many of these monomers.

2. Poly(ethene)/polythene is used to make plastic bags.

3. a)

b)

4. Poly(chloroethene) is an addition polymer.

Page 270

1. Nylon is made from two monomers and a small molecule is eliminated when the two monomers combine. An addition polymer has only one monomer.

2. To produce a polymer chain the monomers need to be able to form amide groups at both ends of the molecules.

Index

Notes

Notes

Notes

Notes

Notes

Notes

Notes

Notes

Notes

Notes

Notes

Notes

Notes

Notes

Notes

Notes